DELIVER US FROM EVOLUTION?

A Christian Biologist's In-Depth Look at the
Evidence Reveals a Surprising Harmony
Between Science and God

AARON R YILMAZ

To my wife, Melanie,
for her unconditional love
and unfailing support.
Thank you.

CONTENTS

CHAPTER ONE

INTRODUCTION

This is a book that nearly forced me to write it. The faith that encompasses my entire way of life is being unwittingly besieged from within its borders by Christians themselves, and attacked from without by a vocal minority of belligerent scientists, and I cannot stand idly by. The addled Christian empire is at war with itself and with culture at large. With the deluge of information begotten by the recent explosion of genetics, the case for evolution has never been more visceral and pressing. The flood of evidence demands a verdict, and the Christian faith now stands at a crossroads unlike any other in history. The decision to accept or reject evolution will have a profound impact on the faith itself and will significantly affect how the world sees faith. Either decision made will have permanent effects that will echo throughout centuries to come.

For quite awhile, I have been gestating the idea of a book that accurately and comprehensively encapsulates the "science vs. religion" debate. I have for some time pushed away this idea and devoted myself to other pursuits, but the time has come that I can no longer ignore what I believe is a calling upon my life. As a devoted Christian and biologist, I feel that I have a duty to help bridge the chasm between these two seemingly disparate juggernauts of the human experience.

While I am neither one who hears voices nor receives prophecy or visions, I feel that if there ever was a calling from God for my life, this book would be the most likely candidate for said purpose. Having been a nominal Christian, agnostic, devout Christian, creationist, Intelligent Design (ID) proponent, and theistic evolutionist at various times in my life, I believe I offer a unique perspective on this important topic. I am confident this book will challenge both Christians and non-Christians alike in a positive way, while also engaging hearts and minds.

But this raises the question: Is the science vs. religion controversy truly that big of an issue? Is there really a need for an entire book devoted to the topic? My answer to that question would be yes and no. I am not being facetious; rather, I am confessing that, at the core of the debate, there is a false dichotomy that forces one to choose between two worlds: the world of atheistic science, and the world of Christianity devoid of mainstream science. As we will see, this is a false dilemma, as this heated topic is much more complex than two cut-and-dried options. Accordingly, since both science and faith, when properly understood, have no quarrel with each other, ideally there *should* not be a need for such a book.

However, my affirmative response to the aforementioned question betrays the weight I feel this topic carries, particularly for our unique place in history. I can scarcely read YouTube comments, scientific articles, or listen to the radio without being inundated by abrasive and inflammatory voices at opposite ends of the spectrum, screeching about our origins. The shouting match is growing louder and has been since the publication of Charles Darwin's *Origin of Species* in 1859. Both sides are becoming more entrenched, and the debates are rapidly shifting from polite discourse to bombastic and polarizing condemnation of one side toward the other.

It is into this cage-match that I precariously enter my tiny book and my individual perspective. Though I am reticent to add my voice to the myriad of voices out there, I believe my grueling personal journey and exhaustive research into this topic will provide a unique angle on this debate and prove insightful to any audience interested in this issue. My hope is that this book will simultaneously encourage and challenge the believer, as well as help the agnostic and atheist understand the challenges evolution presents to the traditional Christian worldview.

My challenge to you is to keep an open mind while reading this book. I encourage you to do your own research and to check out all of my citations and references. Furthermore, I commend you for even picking up this book in the first place. It shows you have a genuine interest in finding truth no matter what the cost. Continue to have the courage to follow the evidence no matter where it leads. As a Christian, I am convinced that God is the embodiment of truth, and all truth points to God.

STATEMENT OF FAITH

I want to be completely up front with who I am. I am a fully devoted follower of Jesus Christ, who prays daily, reads the Bible daily, and attends church at least weekly. I have volunteered my time and money for my church, participated in small groups, and do daily devotionals with my wife. As if all that is not "uber Christian" enough, my wife and I even had a "purity covenant" while we were dating and were abstinent until marriage (which was no easy task, mind you). I am not a watered-down, liberal, progressive, or fake Christian. I hold firmly to Evangelical/Protestant theology and orthodoxy, and my personal relationship with Christ is the absolute center of my life and of everything I do. It feels a little awkward and forced to try and list my "Christian credentials," but I say none of this to beat my chest; I merely wish to establish myself as someone who can be trusted when it comes to exploring this kind of in-house topic. Unfortunately, some Christians have challenged my personal faith, or have assumed that I am not a serious Christian because of my views on science, and I often feel the need to have such a disclaimer.

By the same token, I am also a serious scientist who holds to mainstream scientific views. I hold six earned college degrees, including an M.S. in Biology and a B.S. in Biology (with honors). I have studied evolution at both the undergraduate and graduate levels and have also undertaken a massive amount of study of the topic at the personal level. I do not advocate any kind of novel or heterodox interpretation of science and hold to most all modern scientific theory. I hope I will not be prematurely judged or dismissed due to either of my views.

TRUTH AT ANY COST?

Literary giant C.S. Lewis once said, "If you look for truth, you may find comfort in the end; if you look for comfort you will not get either comfort or truth only soft soap and wishful thinking to begin, and in the end, despair."[1] This brings home the reality of what it means to be an honest seeker of truth. Truth always comes at a cost, as it has for all people throughout history. But for those willing to face the unknown and the uncomfortable, I believe there will always be a bounty and a blessing to be had.

For those who do not even believe in any objective truth, I would follow up with one question: Is it *true* that there is no truth? The contradiction readily becomes apparent, as the relativist saws off the limb on which he sits. It cannot be true that there is no truth, because that statement would be true, and thus there would be truth! More could be written on this subject, but suffice it to say that truth is the foundation from which we can investigate claims about the universe.

For Christians, God is the ultimate truth. That is, He is quite literally the embodiment of truth. For the believer, things that are true in this universe—meaning something that is in accordance with fact or reality—cannot contradict God, since He is the ultimate standard of truth. This is all to say that our starting point should be truth, for if God is who He says He is, following truth will inevitably lead to Him. Healthy religion has no fear of questioning.

The Bible commands us to pursue and uphold truth. Psalm 25:5 states, "Guide me in your truth and teach me, for you are God my savior, and my hope is in you all day long." Proverbs 12:19a tells us that "truthful lips endure forever," and within Isaiah 45:19 we find, "I, the LORD, speak the truth." Perhaps Jeremiah puts it best when he writes in 5:3a: "LORD, do not your eyes look for truth?" Lastly, Jesus himself made the claim, "I am the way and the *truth* and the life" (John 14:6a; emphasis added). Truth is apparently of great importance to God, and so should it be to us.

Some would argue our starting place should always be the Bible. But this begs the question: Why is the Bible true? The popular retort is usually, "Because the Bible says that the Bible is true." While I agree the Bible is the inspired Word of God and is true, this kind of logic is called "circular logic" or "arguing in a circle," as the premise of the argument is in need of proof just as much as the conclusion is. If we use the Bible to prove that the Bible is true, then by the same logic one could just as validly argue that the Qur'an is true because the Qur'an says so, or that the Vedas are true because the Vedas say so.

Therefore, we must start with *truth* and proceed from there. Indeed, I believe that philosophy, logic, history, and the inner witness of the Holy Spirit support the truth of God and the Bible, but these are truths that can be found external to the Bible, and which help us avoid arguing in a circle. Accordingly, truth is our foundation for everything, and rightly so. This may seem unorthodox and heretical to some, but if God is truth, and He is who He says He is, then truth will always point us to Him and His Word. Thus we should not fear it.

Challenging our worldview—our deepest held beliefs and convictions about how the world really is—is never easy. No one purposely holds false beliefs; if they did, they would discard those false beliefs in favor of true ones. Yet one cannot find a single person in the world who believes the exact same things as he himself does. It is almost certain that all of us harbor at least some false beliefs, and to think we have cornered the market on absolute truth is absurd in the highest degree. In light of this, we must be willing to assess evidence honestly and with an open mind. Instead of dogmatically asserting that we are right and others are wrong, we would do well to be willing to change our views if they are plainly shown to be patently false.

Often, Christians feel a great deal of anxiety when forced to examine claims or competing worldviews that appear to contradict a particular view of God or a certain interpretation of Scripture. We must remember, however, that if something we formerly believed to be false is shown to be true, God will not fall off His throne. When we investigate science and Scripture, we do not need to be worried that "something will jump out from under a rock and eat God; if it does we should worship that thing!" [2]

We need to embrace the incredible mental faculties of reason that God has granted for us. I would argue that embracing reason and searching for truth is actually good stewardship of the mind God has given us, and I would go so far as to say it is a God-given moral imperative. Our faith is not like a Jenga tower, whereby removal of a certain piece causes the whole structure to crumble. Perhaps it is best summed up by the following:

> For him [the Christian with rigid doctrine], faith isn't a trampoline; it's a wall of bricks. Each of the core doctrines for him is like an individual brick that stacks on top of the others. If you pull one out, the whole wall starts to crumble. It appears quite strong and rigid, but if you begin to rethink or discuss even one brick, the whole thing is in danger [. . .] one of the things that happens in 'brickworld': you spend a lot of time talking about how right you are. Which of course leads to how wrong everybody else is. Which then leads to defending the wall [doctrines] [. . .] you rarely defend a trampoline. You invite people to jump on it with you. [3]

Our faith should be like a trampoline. It is held by the springs of doctrine, but it flexes, bends, and moves as we attain a deeper knowledge and a more intimate understanding of God and His Word. I hope you are willing to take this journey of faith and discovery with me. I believe the end result will be a faith built on a firmer foundation, and an ability to "always be prepared to give an answer to everyone who asks you to give the reason for the hope that you have" (1 Peter 3:15, NIV). And lastly, I hope this journey will provide a surprising and deeply satisfying answer to the evolution and religion controversy.

PART I

THE NATURE OF SCIENCE AND SCRIPTURE

CHAPTER TWO

THE NATURE OF SCRIPTURE

The Multifaceted Jewel of Scripture

The ancient Hebrews held that Scripture was like a multifaceted jewel. It has many different facets and becomes beautiful in a new and exciting way when examined in another light. The Word of God never changes but reveals itself in new ways to us when we study it again and again. What believer has not had the experience of reading a portion of Scripture and not thought much of it, only to have that same passage come alive in a powerful way when re-read in a different season of life? There is a reason the Bible is called "the Living Word." As Christians, we believe the Word is active and vibrant, and those who persistently mine Scripture are rewarded extravagantly with wisdom and knowledge.

This dynamic nature of Scripture raises the question of exactly how we should approach the Bible. What is its intent? What is the time and place of the authors? What is the cultural context in which it should be understood? And perhaps most importantly, what can we or should we expect from the Bible? I believe that crucial to the debate at hand is a proper understanding of the nature of Scripture and the way it was put together. The Bible is the inspired Word of God, but it was neither hand-written by God, nor dictated by Him. God inspired people to write down their experiences with Him, and so they did. What we have as the Bible is then a collection of people's encounters with God, and recorded revelation from God.

Perhaps helpful here would be what Peter Enns calls the "Incarnational Analogy": Just as God allowed Himself to be humiliated by becoming a Human and by suffering an unjust death, God also humiliates Himself by allowing His Word to be a lesser reflection of His perfection; He allows Scripture to meet people where they are—in their culture, their place in time, and in their scientific understanding.

Lest anyone dispute that the Bible is not the inspired Word of God but rather the direct and dictated Word of God, let us consider the uniqueness of the 66 books of the Bible. Why is it that we can tell that a certain book of the Bible was written by one author rather than another? Why do the different books of the Bible use different languages (e.g., Greek, Hebrew) and different vocabularies? Why are the styles of books like Proverbs and Chronicles so different from one another? It is because people were vessels for the inspiration of God, but they were not empty vessels; God did not bypass their humanity. The way in which these people recorded their encounters with God bears the indelible stamp of their place in time, their culture, and their individual personalities.

By asserting this, I am in no way challenging the inerrancy of the Bible. Properly defined, I *do* believe the Bible is indeed the inerrant Word of God. At some point, however, we as mature Christians must grapple with the nature of Scripture itself. We must move beyond a one-dimensional understanding of the Word to an understanding that is true to the intent of the authors who wrote it, and place Scripture in its proper historical and cultural context.

John Walton illustrates this point masterfully in his book *"The Lost World of Genesis One."* He explains that in the Bible, the seat of emotion is often referred to as the "innards," or more specifically, the heart and the intestines.[1] When the earliest parts of the Bible were written some 2,600 years ago, these people truly believed emotion sprang from the abdominal organs; this was not a metaphor. When God communed with these ancient writers, He did not inform them that the seat of emotion is actually the brain rather than the innards. God is infinitely wise, and His reasons for not correcting the ancients' physiological knowledge can only be speculated upon. One may postulate that to revise the ancients' entire understanding of science was superfluous to the purpose and message God had for these people. God did not feel the need to update their scientific knowledge—perhaps because God felt no need to do so, or perhaps to do so would have bewildered them and made them suspicious of this God who knew nothing of their "correct" science.

Examining Genesis 1:6–8 presses the point further: "And God said, 'Let there be a firmament in the midst of the waters, and let it divide the waters from the waters.' And God made the firmament, and divided the waters which were under the firmament from the waters which were above the firmament: and it was so. And God called the firmament Heaven. And the evening and the morning were the second day" (KJV). Ancient Near East cosmology was one that pictured the sky as a solid dome. Furthermore, Genesis 7:11–12 adds: "In the six hundredth year of Noah's life, in the second month, on the seventeenth day of the month, on that day all the fountains of the great deep burst forth, and *the windows of the heavens were opened*. And rain fell upon the earth forty days and forty nights" (my emphasis added) (ESV). This again portrays the sky as a solid dome with water above it, and when "windows" open in the firmament, water pours down upon the earth.

Ancient cosmology also held that the earth was fixed, and that the sun and planets orbited around it, an idea termed "geocentrism." Verses such as Joshua 10:12–13 suggest this vividly: "Joshua said to the Lord in the presence of Israel: 'Sun, stand still over Gibeon, and you, moon, over the Valley of Aijalon.' So the sun stood still, and the moon stopped, till the nation avenged itself on its enemies, as it is written in the Book of Jashar. The sun stopped in the middle of the sky and delayed going down about a full day" (NIV). 1 Chronicles 16:30 adds: "The world is firmly established; it cannot be moved." Psalms refers to the unmovable earth four times (Psalms 19:6, 93:1, 96:10, and 104:5), with Psalm 93:1 concurring that, "[T]he world also is established, that it cannot be moved" (KJV). Lastly, Ecclesiastes 1:5 concludes: "The sun rises and the sun sets, and hurries back to where it rises."

Copernicus published his heliocentric theory in 1543, and Galileo later supported and defended this theory in the early 1600s. As those versed in history might recall, Galileo came into conflict with the Catholic Church over his heliocentric views, which rivaled what the Bible appeared to teach (i.e., geocentrism). Regarding Copernicus' views, the famed Martin Luther quipped:

> People gave ear to an upstart astrologer who strove to show that the earth revolves, not the heavens or the firmament, the sun and the moon. [. . .] This fool wishes to reverse the entire science of astronomy; but sacred Scripture [Joshua 10:13] tells us that Joshua commanded the sun to stand still, and not the earth.[2]

Martin Luther prematurely cast aside an idea that clashed with his own interpretation of Scripture. Instead of examining the evidence and following where reason led, he chose to buttress his prior conclusion and dismissed the theory that would shortly be proven true beyond a shadow of a doubt. While it is easy, in retrospect, to lampoon such a passionate defense of the geocentric theory, we must remember that none of us is immune to brushing off ideas or arguments that challenge the core of our belief system. As the Simon and Garfunkel song, "The Boxer," beautifully sums up: "A man hears what he wants to hear and he disregards the rest."

One may respond to the accusation of the Bible's apparent support of geocentrism by countering that the Bible is simply recording the story from man's point of view. The ancient authors simply recorded what they saw with their own eyes, which is what appears to be the sun moving across the sky. They recorded what they experienced to be true: that the earth does not appear to be moving under their feet. And so the counterargument goes that the Bible is neither endorsing geocentrism nor heliocentrism; it is merely recounting a story in human terms. I wholeheartedly agree, but for one, that already abandons a literalistic interpretation, and two, we have the benefit of indisputable proof that the earth does indeed revolve around the sun, not the sun around the earth.

For hundreds of years, people interpreted these Scriptures to mean what seems to be plainly stated—namely, that the earth is stationary. There was no reason to believe that the earth was not stationary, so this thinking predominated until the 1500s. When it was revealed that science had discovered something that appeared contrary to a literal reading of Scripture, many had the gut reaction of defending the traditional prevailing thought. The intention of this is presumably to protect the "inerrancy" of the Bible, as if heliocentric theory being proven true would mean the Bible contradicts the truth as revealed by science and thus becomes nothing more than a book of fancy.

Half a millennium later, Christianity is still standing. Copernicus' and Galileo's observations about the solar system did not "dethrone" God or cause Him to cease to exist. What sensible and mature Christians did when shown undeniable evidence was accept that heliocentrism was true and go back to Scripture to reinterpret the verses in question, in light of this newly revealed truth. Instead of dogmatically defending what the Bible "plainly says," or what we know "must be true," we should take caution not to read into the Bible what is *not* there. We must come to the Bible now as adults and deal with serious and challenging questions in an adult manner. When we are confronted with something that appears to "contradict" the Bible, perhaps we need to turn the jewel of Scripture to extract its truth in a new light, and ask God to grant us understanding of His revealed truth and how it relates to His Word.

Two Ships Passing in the Night

The philosopher Voltaire has been attributed with the saying, "Define your terms, and we shall be like two ships passing in the night." So, before we proceed, I should define what I mean by "creationism," "Intelligent Design (ID)," and "evolution." When I use the word "creationism," I use it in the strict sense to refer to the belief that the earth is about 6,000 years old (some allow for 10,000), and that animals and man were specially created and not the products of evolution. I use the term "Intelligent Design" to describe groups of Christians who believe the earth is up to 4.5 billion years old but still do not believe evolution is responsible for creating the diversity of life we see today. For the sake of simplicity, I lump Old Earth Creationism, gap, Day-age, and Progressive creationism into the ID category, since in general they all agree that the earth is older than 6,000 years but still reject wholesale evolution. When I refer to evolution, I am including any group that believes in an old earth and common descent of all creatures by way of evolutionary change. This includes non-theists as well as theistic evolutionists, evolutionary creationists, and other views that believe in evolution and also believe in a creator. In simplifying these groups and terms, I mean no disrespect or misrepresentation; I am merely attempting to streamline our discussion.

Admittedly, there exists a wide spectrum of beliefs, and I could not possibly hope to do all of them justice in such a book. For example, some ID proponents such as Michael Behe even believe in common ancestry of all species (including humans) but believe there were points throughout natural history where God supernaturally intervened. Similarly, I could claim to be a creationist in the sense that I do believe in a creator that is ultimately responsible for everything that exists; however, I reject that designation for myself, as it is commonly tied to belief in a 6,000-year-old earth and an anti-evolutionary stance. Likewise, I could claim to be an ID advocate, as I do believe there is an intelligent force guiding the creation of the universe and the process of evolution. Again, however, ID is commonly understood as denying the validity of macroevolution (large-scale evolution); thus, I also disavow this label.

The big point here is that when I refer to evolution, this certainly is *not* the view that there is no creator; evolution can, without a doubt, be in accordance with an all-powerful God.

Biblical Literalism

Apologist Dinesh D'Souza writes in his book, *What's so Great About Christianity*:

> One of the first literalists was the church father Origen, who read in Matthew 19:12 that there were some who had made themselves "eunuchs for the sake of the Kingdom of heaven." Taking the passage literally, Origen promptly castrated himself. I am not aware of any modern literalists who have put themselves under the knife in this way.[3]

Many have told me that the reason they reject evolution and/or an old earth is that they hold to a "literal view" of the Bible. Literalists believe Genesis can neither be allegory nor a God-inspired story colored by its author's place in time. Literalists generally hold the view of concordance as mentioned earlier. That is, things that are described as happening in the Bible must be found to be true today. For example, by adding up the genealogies in the Bible stretching all the way back to the first man, we find the date of Adam and Eve's creation to be roughly 6,000 years ago (interestingly, this conclusion was popularized less than 400 years ago by an Archbishop named James Ussher)[4]. Literalists maintain that this must be factually supported in the world around us—that humanity *must* have its origins 6,000 years ago, a snake *must* have audibly spoken to Eve, and a worldwide flood *must* have occurred roughly 4,500 years ago (hereafter referred to as the "Nochaic flood"). All because the Bible (according to their interpretation) says so. They believe these things not because of empirical evidence, but often in spite of it. Oddly enough, even though this concordist logic would necessitate a belief in biblical geocentrism, most concordists find a way to rationalize their way out of such a belief.

Such wooden Biblical literalism in its strictest sense is simply not possible. Allow me to explain. Jesus says in the Gospel of Mark:

> What shall we say the kingdom of God is like, or what parable

shall we use to describe it? It is like a mustard seed, *which is the smallest of all seeds on Earth.* Yet when planted, it grows and becomes the largest of all garden plants, with such big branches that the birds can perch in its shade. (Mark 4:30–32, NIV) (emphasis added).

Is the mustard seed truly the smallest seed? No. It is not even close. A mustard seed is indeed small—about 1/20th of an inch. But petunia seeds measure in at about 1/50th of an inch, begonia seeds at 1/100^{ths} of an inch, and incredibly, some orchid seeds are a nearly microscopic 1/300^{ths} of an inch long![5] These orchid seeds weigh so little that they disperse into the air like dust, hoping to land in a fertile spot within the canopies of the rain forest. But some may argue that Jesus was only referring to seeds known to his audience at that time (which already strays from a strict "literal" interpretation of the text). This also does not save the literalist option, as black orchids, which possess seeds much smaller than the mustard seed,[6] would have been found in that area during Jesus' time.

I want to be clear here: I am not attacking our Savior or doubting His message or words. I am simply observing that Jesus said the mustard seed is the smallest seed, even though it is not. My point is that while Jesus is God and has perfect knowledge of all things, He did not address people as though *they* had an exhaustive and correct scientific knowledge of everything. Jesus was not presenting a seed comparison study at a botany symposium; He was speaking to a group of laypeople who would have been familiar with mustard seeds and may have planted said seed and watched it grow.

Does the fact that the mustard seed is not the smallest seed diminish the power of this parable? Of course not! I have read this parable over and over, and its power and word-picture make my heart yearn for the Kingdom and inspire a sense of awe and reverence within me every time I read it. Just because I know the mustard seed is not the smallest seed does not mean I need to throw out the entire Bible, since it makes a "false" statement not supported by modern botanical science. Nor do I need to plug my ears and pretend the mustard seed *is* indeed the smallest seed, or come up with a theory that the mainstream botanists are merely anti-Christian scientists trying to destroy our faith. I also don't need to do a theological and pseudo-scientific contortionist act to try to explain away what is clearly said in the text.

I am not embarrassed by the Bible! I don't need to apologize for Jesus incorrectly identifying the smallest seed, and neither do you! We also don't need to twist and weave an ad-hoc explanation of how Jesus said something factually wrong but actually meant something factually right. We live in a very Western and legalistic culture, where everything must read like a legal contract, and if there is one mistake or vague meaning, we throw the baby out with the bathwater and imagine we are Emmanuel Kant committing these pieces of writing to the flames, since they contain nothing more than "sophistry and illusion."

Jesus used literary devices, just as writers still do today and did so back in the time of the ancient Israelites. Hyperbole, analogies, metaphors, and allegories are all devices that the Son of God used to teach us the truth—correct botany be darned! When you read the parable of the mustard seed, it is not diminished by its lack of scientific acumen. The point remains the same, and the parable holds just as much power to explain one of God's truths. Jesus, being fully omniscient God and man at the same time, chose to use the mustard seed metaphor because it was what his audience needed to hear; it was what they could relate to and easily understand.

Furthermore, John 3:26 states, "And they came to John and said to him, 'Rabbi, He who was with you beyond the Jordan, to whom you have testified—behold, He is baptizing, and *all* are coming to Him!'" (NKJV) (emphasis added). When it says *all*, are we to assume an ultra-literal interpretation and believe that truly every single person came to be baptized in the Jordan that day? Additionally, consider, "You blind guides! You strain out a gnat but swallow a camel" (Matt. 23:24, NIV). Are we really to believe that camel was the *soup de jour* of the Pharisees? And what about, "I am the true vine, and My Father is the vinedresser. Every branch in Me that does not bear fruit He takes away; and every branch that bears fruit He prunes, that it may bear more fruit" (John 15:1–3, NKJV). Should we read and believe what is literally written? Are we to believe that Jesus did in fact consist of plant material? Jesus did not say that He was like a vine, or similar to a vine; but that He *was* a vine (the true vine). I am not trying to be facetious, but I am challenging those who take the position that a "literal reading of the Bible" is the only possible reading.

I want to reiterate for those who may think I am attacking Jesus or doubting the inerrancy of the Bible that I am doing neither. I believe what we have as the modern Bible is trustworthy, accurate, and inerrant *in context*. I don't believe that Jesus was a green plant, nor do I believe that the mustard seed truly is the smallest seed in existence. An ultra-literal wooden reading of the Bible simply falls apart at the seams; it is unfeasible. I *do* believe that Jesus used hyperbole and metaphors to illustrate concepts, and that God's only Son had perfect knowledge of all things such as seed sizes. But, those details of scientific minutia were obviously of little importance to our Savior. For whatever reason, He felt that things such as accurate botanical knowledge were of little consequence to His message and mission.

The same reasoning applies to the Old testament. Recall how the internal organs were referred to as the seat of emotion (John Walton). We know now that the seat of the emotion is the brain, yet we don't throw out the Bible because of its "incorrect" scientific knowledge. Likewise, recall that the ancients believed the sky was in fact a solid dome covered by water (Genesis 1:6–8)—a fact we all know to be patently false. We have also discussed the myriad of passages suggesting that the earth does not move, and how this thought prevailed until the sixteenth century. Still, knowing all of this, we *insist* that the six days of creation must have happened exactly as written—with no evolution having taken place, despite the fact that we can honestly admit that other parts of Scripture include metaphors or hyperbole and are not meant to be taken literally. This "salad bar theology" is a dangerously slippery slope. When we pick and choose what is literal and what is metaphorical, based solely on our own preconceptions, desires, and personal worldview, we lose sight of the over-arching theme of the Bible and are prone to making costly mistakes.

Savvy readers may have spotted what appears to be a contradiction in what I have just written. I am admonishing others for picking and choosing what is literal in the Bible and what is metaphor, all the while I have been making the case that some parts are indeed literal and some parts metaphor, and we need to distinguish between them. So how should we decide upon what is metaphor and what is not? Well, at the risk of sounding clever, we should read the literal parts literally, and the metaphorical parts as metaphor. This is not just tautology but a recognition that some parts of the Bible are clearly presented as factual historical accounts (e.g., Gospels, Chronicles) and some parts are clearly of a different genre (e.g., Proverbs, Song of Solomon). And even within historical books of the Bible, we can allow for non-literalism (e.g., Jesus being the true vine) without sacrificing the inerrancy of the Bible or compromising its message.

Some books, however, are not so cut-and-dried. Should Genesis be categorized as a historical narrative or as poetry? Maybe a mix of different genres? This is the question we will delve into shortly. What you think you know about Genesis may surprise you.

A Literal Reading of the Creation Story? Which One?

How many times is "sin" mentioned in the creation story? In the story of Adam and Eve? The story of the fall of man? Many would be surprised to learn that sin is not explicitly mentioned once in the fall of man story (though it is implicitly). Sin is not mentioned by name until Genesis 4:7, in reference to Cain and Abel. Careful readers of Genesis will notice something that has puzzled believers for millennia: Genesis 1–2:3 appears to present one version of creation, whereas Genesis 2:4–25 seems to present a second, slightly different version. Hereafter, I will refer to the first creation account as Genesis 1, and the second account simply as Genesis 2. Genesis 1 is the account most of us are familiar with and is the battleground where most of the creation versus evolution controversy takes place.

In Genesis 1, creation takes place over a period of six days. As a quick Sunday School refresher, day one is light, day two is firmament, day three is dry land and plants, day four is "lights in the sky," day five is flying and swimming creatures (note how God says, "Let the *earth* bring forth living creatures"), day six is land animals and people (male and female), and finally the seventh day is when God rested. Alternatively, Genesis 2 suggests that all creation took place in one day.

> This is the history of the heavens and the earth when they were created, in the *day* that the Lord God made the earth and the heavens, before any plant of the field was in the earth and before any herb of the field had grown. For the Lord God had not caused it to rain on the earth and there was no man to till the ground; but a mist went up from the earth and watered the whole face of the ground (Genesis 2:4–6, NKJV). [Emphasis added].

According to Genesis 2, not only does creation occur all in one day, but the order of events is significantly different. In this account, man (Adam) is created, *then* the garden with trees and rivers is created (plant life); thirdly, land animals are created, and lastly, woman is created. This contrasts sharply with Genesis 1, in which the order of these events is plants (day three), sea and flying animals (day five), and then land animals along with male and female humans (day six). Furthermore, Genesis 1:20 seems to imply that the "waters" brought forth fowl (birds), whereas Genesis 2:19 says birds are formed out of the ground.

The overall structure of the two accounts is diverse as well. In Genesis 1, God is portrayed as a God who is transcendent over creation and is speaking, blessing, dividing, and naming. In the Genesis 2 account, God is portrayed in an anthropomorphic way and is described as being more active in creation—forming, breathing, building, planting, and putting Adam to sleep. Moreover, the Genesis 1 account portrays creation as "good" and humans as ones given dominion over creation. Genesis 2 casts man as a caretaker and servant and places prohibitions on what he can and cannot do (i.e., avoiding the tree of the knowledge of good and evil).

Even if we found a solution to explain away the differences in the two accounts (and many Christians have provided somewhat unsatisfying explanations that require a great deal of theological and semantical gymnastics), we are still left with some puzzling questions: How is light created on day one, but the sun and moon are not created until day four (Genesis 1:14–19)? How could there be day and night if the moon and sun did not yet exist? Better yet, how are plants created on day three, but the sun is not created until a full day later? And lest anyone think that the "framework" of Genesis meshes neatly with the fossil record (by providing an explanation of sequences of life forms appearing in the fossil record without invoking evolution), the fossil record suggests otherwise. Flowering plants (plants that bear fruit and seeds) show up in the fossil record well after the first birds, and land mammals are present before birds. This is in direct opposition to the order presented in Genesis 1.

The overall point I am trying to make here is that even if you wanted to hold to a 100% literal reading of Genesis, you would have to embrace a good deal of things that at least *on the surface* appear to stand in contrast to each other. When one tries to explain how Genesis 1 does not differ from Genesis 2, one is forced to read into the text things which simply are not there. Or, one must try and force an awkward harmony by providing a lengthy explanation of what the text "really means," or what would be a "better translation" of the original text.

Can we call a spade a spade? Let's be honest for a minute and admit that Genesis is not as clear-cut and straightforward as we would like it to be. It is not as simple as, "Well the Bible says it, so I believe it." If you are a thinking person, then you naturally have questions when you read the Bible. Let us push away from the kids' table for a second and join the adults. We must move from the "milk" to the "meat" and do the hard and uncomfortable work of reconciling the real world (God's revealed *truth*) with God's revealed *Word*. God is not afraid of our questions; He can handle them, and He is not threatened by them. If we truly believe that there is a God, and that He is the God of the Bible, then let us throw off the shackles of philosophical inhibition and ask the tough questions! The only reason we have to fear honestly and openly investigating the evidence for evolution is if we believe, in the darkest corner of our hearts, that there might not be a God, or that He would be "dethroned" if evolution were found to be true. As it turns out, God is not threatened by evolution, but we have been beguiled by extremists on both sides, who would have us choose between two narrow options, when in reality other possibilities exist.

God the Professor, the Bible the Textbook

Many have wondered why Genesis was not written in more explicit language. Out of the entire Bible, why leave only two condensed chapters to the creation of not only plants, animals, and man, but of the entire universe? Furthermore, if evolution is true, why did God not describe it in Genesis? Surely He could have said something along the lines of, "A very small animal first appeared—smaller than man can see [bacteria]; these were fruitful and multiplied, giving way to larger and more numerous kinds [different species], having changed form after many generations [evolution]." My example may be crude, but it makes the point that if Genesis is God-inspired, why is it so vague and seemingly counter to mainstream science?

One thing that bears repeating is that the Bible is different from many other religious books. For instance, the Qur'an of Islam is believed by Muslims to be the *direct* Word of God. Not just the *inspired* Word of God, but quite literally, word for word what God himself said (much the same as Christians view the Ten Commandments). On the contrary, the Bible is written by people who encountered God and were *inspired* by Him to write down His message. We must remember that people are not empty vessels; they have a language, culture, and personality, which all leave their mark on the Biblical writings, despite the fact that Scripture is God-inspired.

So why would God inspire someone to write Genesis the way it was written? It may be a situation where a careful balance had to be struck between the audience of that time, and audiences to come. The creation account in Genesis is written in a style that is neither fully satisfying to any generation scientifically, nor completely devoid of some scientific ideas believed throughout history. If Genesis were written down 2,600 years ago in a way that was up to snuff as far as modern science is concerned, it would have baffled almost anyone who read it up until about 150 years ago. Moreover, it would have been ridiculed as a book that was full of "erroneous" scientific beliefs. If you were an ancient Israelite, or a medieval artisan, or anyone living prior to the nineteenth century for that matter, it would have been laughable and lunacy in the highest degree to read of a 4.5-billion-year-old earth, abiogenesis, or common descent. Not only that, but our modern science would be all but unintelligible to previous generations. Accordingly, some might have rejected a book that was full of such "scientific inaccuracies." Likewise, had the Bible included scientific beliefs common during the Middle Ages, it would have been absurd to the ancients, and likewise nonsense to modern readers.

Genesis was written in a way that is relevant to all generations throughout history. It is the story of the one true God, who creates the universe *ex nihilo* (out of nothing). It is the story of a personal God who is responsible for everything that exists. Genesis aims not so much at exactitude and preciseness, as conveying the important message that there exists a God who cared enough to create us and everything in our world, and He is sovereign over all. This message was given to a nomadic and tribal Near Eastern people, and the Bible bears witness to this human element through its understanding of the natural world.

As pastor Steve Norman of Kensington Community Church has astutely pointed out[7], 1 Kings 5–8 gives an astounding amount of detail as to the building of the Temple of Solomon. The precise length of every wall, beam, and pillar is recorded in its entirety. The number of windows, columns, and canopies is listed explicitly. Every detail is so painstakingly and meticulously written down in obsessive detail, that it boggles the mind. Verse after verse, chapter after chapter, the story of the construction of the Temple of Solomon is so clear and unambiguous that it reads like the "methods" section of a scientific journal article (where the details of an experiment or observation are enumerated)!

Now, why would God provide such immaculate detail for the construction of a temple, but be so vague and brief regarding the construction of the universe? Perhaps it is because God never intended Genesis to be the finely detailed scientific blueprint of the universe so many want it to be. Creationists and Intelligent Design proponents would like to champion Genesis 1 as the "blueprint" and "construction details" of the universe and of life as we know it, but it is difficult to accept this premise when the account of the construction of *one* Temple is nearly twice the length of the entire creation narrative of the universe!

Would I, as well as many others, love to see the construction notes for the entire universe plainly spelled out in the Bible? You bet! But is scientific dogma the point of Genesis 1–2? No. The overarching theme of the Bible is that of a personal God who created the universe and sent His Son Jesus to bridge the gap between a fallen humanity, who is deeply loved, and a righteous God who longs for His people to have relationship with Him. Could scientific jargon and data possibly contribute anything meaningful to this all-important story?

I would like to close this subchapter with a passage from St. Augustine, a Christian theologian and philosopher who was born nearly 1,700 years ago. This prophetic passage was recorded in St. Augustine's *The Literal Meaning of Genesis* at least 1,400 years before Darwin, and at least 1,200 years before the Biblical age of the earth was in any serious scientific doubt. His words ring as true today as they did 400 years after Christ's resurrection, when they were written. St. Augustine may never have known how prophetic his words truly were.

> Usually, even a non-Christian knows something about the earth, the heavens, and the other elements of this world, about the motion and orbit of the stars and even their size and relative positions, about the predictable eclipses of the sun and moon, the cycles of the years and the seasons, about the kinds of animals, shrubs, stones, and so forth, and this knowledge he holds to as being certain from reason and experience. Now, it is a disgraceful and dangerous thing for an infidel [non-Christian] to hear a Christian, presumably giving the meaning of Holy Scripture [referring here to Genesis], talking non-sense on these topics; and we should take all means to prevent such an embarrassing situation, in which people show up vast ignorance in a Christian and laugh it to scorn. The shame is not so much that an ignorant individual is derided, but that people outside the household of the faith think our

sacred writers held such opinions, and, to the great loss of those for whose salvation we toil, the writers of our Scripture are criticized and rejected as unlearned men. If they find a Christian mistaken in a field which they themselves know well and hear him maintaining his foolish opinions about our books, how are they going to believe those books in matters concerning the resurrection of the dead, the hope of eternal life, and the kingdom of heaven, when they think their pages are full of falsehoods on facts which they themselves have learnt from experience and the light of reason? Reckless and incompetent expounders of holy Scripture bring untold trouble and sorrow on their wiser brethren when they are caught in one of their mischievous false opinions and are taken to task by those who are not bound by the authority of our sacred books. For then, to defend their utterly foolish and obviously untrue statements, they will try to call upon Holy Scripture for proof and even recite from memory many passages which they think support their position, although "they understand neither what they say nor the things about which they make assertion."[8]

What if the Roles Were Reversed?

I have often asked fellow Christians, "What if the roles were reversed?" That is, what if the Bible described both an old earth and species that changed markedly over time? Imagine you woke up one day in a parallel universe and found that Genesis had been written to conform to *our* modern-day mainstream scientific findings (old earth plus evolution). In this hypothetical parallel universe, also imagine that mainstream science was adamant that the universe was only 6,000 years old, and that life forms are now as they always had been, with no changes having taken place between species.

Now be honest: If Christians lived in this parallel universe, how hard would they be fighting *for* a biblically advocated 4.5-billion-year-old earth and common descent instead of *against* it as they do now? If the Bible described the universe as definitively being 13.8 billion years old, with all life originated from microbes, would they still be fighting tooth and nail for schools to be teaching the "evidence" of a 6,000-year-old earth and no evolution? I sincerely believe that Christians would not. They would be the champions and advocates of evolution and an old earth. What this scenario exposes within us is our true reasons for believing what we believe about evolution and the age of the earth— whichever way you answered.

A Fourth Member of the Trinity?

If you ask the average Christian on the street what their faith was founded on, what do you think they would say? I would be willing to bet that a large number of them—perhaps even the majority—would say their faith rests on the Bible—the "Word of God." If that question was posed to a first-century Christian, would he or she respond the same? Since the Bible canon was not even collected and approved until 397 A.D. at the Council of Carthage, I would say not. I would venture to guess that they would say their faith is founded on the resurrection of Jesus, and perhaps the inner witness of the Holy Spirit.

John Pavlovitz of Relevant Magazine presses the point further:

> The Bible has become for so many believers, a fourth addition to the Trinity; something to be worshiped, rather than something to help us seek the One worthy of worship. We've come to treat Scripture as the destination of our spiritual journey, rather than what it was for the earliest believers: essential reading material on the way to the Promised Land. [. . .] Many of us wield the Bible like an oversized power tool that we couldn't be bothered to consult the manual for.[9]

The Bible, for some, has arguably become an end unto itself.

I was recently unfortunate enough to come across a YouTube video of controversial televangelist Mike Murdock singing his "Love song to the Holy Spirit." In this video, he walks around on stage kissing and caressing his Bible, revealing to the crowd that he "sleeps with" the particular Bible on which he was presently slobbering. With a smirk, he asks the crowd to kiss and pet their Bibles along with him, as he repeats "stroke it again" several times in a slow baritone voice. I'm not sure if this is heretical, just plain creepy, or both. Don't misunderstand me—I dearly love and treasure the Holy Scripture. I spend time in the Word every single day, and it has been fundamental in transforming my life and has been a boon to my walk with God. But do some of us commit the same error as the religious before us?

Recall in the Gospels the people with whom Jesus mainly came into conflict: the Pharisees. These men had an incredible knowledge of the Scriptures—so much so that it is commonly held that many of them had the first five books of Moses memorized, if not all thirty-nine Old Testament books. However impressive that may be, Jesus said to them, "You search the Scriptures, for in them you think you have eternal life; and these are they which testify of Me. But you are not willing to come to Me that you may have life" (John 5:39–40; NKJV). As the saying goes, they missed heaven by eighteen inches—the distance from their heads to their hearts. They knew God's Scriptures, but did they know *Him*? The Pharisees are portrayed in the Gospels as constantly peppering Jesus with legalistic Scripture riddles, relentlessly badgering Him in an attempt to one-up Him with Scripture. They couldn't see the forest for the trees, and though they never missed a word of the law, they missed God in the flesh right in front of them.

What is my point? There is a very real danger of making the Bible into an idol by elevating it to the status of God. When we deify the Bible, it becomes a rigid and inflexible ideologue that engenders pitched battles of the creation–evolution type. While the Bible is indispensable and vital to our walk with Christ, it is not the sole element upon which we base our entire faith. Indeed, "All Scripture is God-breathed and useful for teaching, rebuking, correcting, and training in righteousness" (2 Timothy 3:16; NIV); however, when the Scripture supersedes relationship with Him, we limit the ability of God to speak into our lives, and the ability of the Holy Spirit to reveal God's truth. It is at that point we begin to drift and wither.

God in Our Image?

Author Anne Lamott once wrote, "You can safely assume that you've created God in your own image when it turns out that God hates all the same people you do."[10] I would extend this philosophy to include a God that hates all the same ideologies that one hates. No one is immune to making God out to be something He never asked to be. It is our fallen human nature that seeks to reinforce our own ambitions by enlisting God in our battles.

This becomes readily apparent when one considers how many differing "images" Jesus ostensibly has in today's culture. To some, Jesus is a self-help guru—essentially a "good moral teacher." Many TV evangelists champion Him as a get-rich-quick scheme. Some hold He is a peace-loving, nonviolent hippie. Others hold that He was a judgmental Savior, listing the types of people who would not inherit the Kingdom, and warning many of the gnashing of teeth and wailing in Gehenna (hell) that would befall sinners. Still others charge He was a rogue rabbi that never claimed to be God, but whose message was nonetheless hijacked.

I do not subscribe to any of these one-dimensional beliefs. However, it demonstrates how people can shape God into what they want Him to be, instead of what He truly is. When we deprive God of the ability to work in the universe in the way He chooses, when we dictate to our Lord exactly how He designed the cosmos, and when we adamantly claim to have the unequivocal truth on the specifics of creation, we make God in our image. Instead of respecting the enigmatic nature of Genesis and the inscrutability of God, we foolishly make the claim that we have the market on truth cornered—that we know, without a doubt, what Genesis *really* means.

I will be the first to admit I don't have all the answers. Genesis is as much an enduring mystery to me as it is (or should be) to even the literalist. What I do know is that one way or another, God is responsible for everything present in the universe today, and I hope at least this is something upon which all Christians can agree. God designed all the laws of this universe in a way that would ultimately birth planets and bring forth life and eventually humanity. Is it so inconceivable to think that God could have designed the principles of natural selection before the foundations of the world, knowing full well that the result after billions of years would be creatures worthy of possessing a soul? Just because something is not a supernatural act does not mean that God cannot be involved, or that God is not to be credited.

Some may reject this understanding, holding it to be too much like deism (i.e., God wound up the clock and let it run on its own). Creationism and ID, however, also are guilty of the same flaw. Since we don't see any new animal "forms" popping up today, can we assume that God created everything at once 6,000 years ago and then went on hiatus? It would seem that God "wound up the clock" 6,000 years ago and then let it run. Intelligent Design is fraught with even more difficulties, as it suggests God as one who dips His hand in every now and then to bring about the first microbial life, to bring about new forms during the Cambrian explosion, and to finally create humans after 4.55 billion years of earth, while He was doing . . . what exactly? According to Intelligent Design advocates, God tinkers with animal life every once in a few hundred million years or so, for reasons never made explicitly clear.

The reason many may hold to a strict belief in special creation, at least as far as humans are concerned, may stem from Genesis 1:26: "Let us make mankind in our image, in our likeness" (NIV). Many take this to mean that our physical form is that of God's, but is this even possible? God is not a "material" being—at least not in the sense that we are. Yes, Jesus was God in bodily human form, but He was present from before the beginning of the world (hinted at by the "us" in "let *us* make mankind in our image"). If the universe had not even been created yet, would not God and Jesus *have* to be immaterial beings? It is not like an episode of *Star Trek*, in which one can jump in the Starship Enterprise and go find God in a distant corner of the galaxy. God is omnipresent, yet He is immaterial.

We are made in the image of God because we are beings deemed worthy by Him of possessing a soul. We are made in His image because we are capable of relationship with the Creator of the universe. Likewise, we have intellectual, rational, and ethical capacities greater than that of any other species. The things that "set us apart" are not physical things but rather spiritual and immaterial things. Therefore, being made in His image does not refer to our shell of flesh and blood but instead to our immaterial likeness and capacity for communion with the Father, Son, and Holy Spirit.

Ad Ignorantiam

As Christians, we are often tempted to seek material "proof" for God in the unknown or the unexplained. The faithful once championed phenomena such as trees bearing fruit and children being knit together in their mother's womb as mysteries that could only be explained by invoking the Lord's direct involvement. Such unexplained enigmas provided the raw material for the Christians' refutation of materialist explanations of the world. Over time, the arguments have become more sophisticated, but the premise is still the same. From Paley's watch to

Michael Behe's flagellular motor, there is ever present a desire for the faithful to "prove" God's involvement in the universe.

But let us ponder for a moment what happens to that "proof" for God once the unexplained becomes explained? Science has shown us comprehensive and exhaustive information regarding the blooming of flowers, the development of an unborn child, and the intricate processes of the smallest cells. What now becomes of the argument that these previously unsolved mysteries "prove" or "suggest" evidence of God? I can't help but feel that we do untold damage to our own faith and the faith of those around us when we hinge our belief in God on such unexplained natural phenomena. Once the unexplainable becomes explained (and if history is any guide, this will almost inevitably occur), then the argument for God is obliterated, and creationists are forced to retreat to another piece of unexplained science, where they hope to find intellectual refuge, if only for awhile.

Kenneth Miller of Brown University elucidates this idea masterfully in his book *Finding Darwin's God.* Miller states, "If a *lack* of scientific explanation is proof of God's existence, the counterlogic is unimpeachable: a successful scientific explanation is an argument *against* God."[11] As Christians, when we proclaim the unexplained or difficult to explain as "proof" or "evidence" of God, we do so at our own peril, and we set ourselves and other believers up for a potential crisis of faith. We imprudently set up the pins and polish the lanes, and then the unanticipated bowling ball of scientific progress promptly annihilates our just-so story. We instead need to be judicious and responsible when making such grand claims, so as not to precariously place our faith on the dangerous precipice of the currently unexplained. Making such a "God of the gaps" argument is irresponsible at best and disastrous at worst. From a Nazi concentration camp, theologian and martyr Dietrich Bonhoeffer wrote,

> How wrong it is to use God as a stop-gap for the incompleteness of our knowledge. If in fact the frontiers of knowledge are being pushed further and further back (and that is bound to be the case), then God is being pushed back with them, and is therefore continually in retreat. We are to find God in what we know, not in what we don't know.[12]

CHAPTER THREE

WHAT SCIENCE CAN AND CAN'T SAY AND DOES AND DOESN'T SAY

The Limitations of Science

An important question to ask before embarking on a philosophical and theological journey such as the one we are about to take regards the limitations of knowledge. Specifically in this discussion, we must ask: "What are the limitations of science?" There is scarcely a person who has not heard something along the lines of, "I don't believe in God because there isn't any evidence for God" or "I trust science because it can be proven and the supernatural cannot." The list of declarations goes on and on, although ironically, I would argue that there *are* very good arguments and evidences that show God's existence to be more rational than His nonexistence. In any case, is science the only way to gain knowledge about the universe?

A colleague once told me, "I only believe things that can be scientifically proven," and I quickly turned the tables by asking, "Well, then why do you believe *that*, since *that* cannot be scientifically proven? Your method of investigating truth is built on a construct that you *believe*, despite an absence of scientific proof for your philosophy, so by your own philosophy you shouldn't believe your own philosophy because it cannot be scientifically proven." My acquaintance then proceeded to stare at me, head tilted like a dog staring at a blaring television. If one claims that "it's only true if you can prove it scientifically," then he is making a statement that cannot be proven scientifically. In what way could one prove scientifically that all claims must be proven scientifically? Such self-refuting materialistic claims are definitely not science and are at best hillbilly philosophy. Furthermore, things like mathematics cannot be proven scientifically, as science presupposes mathematics. Similarly, the reality of the past cannot be proven, as we could have been dropped into our bodies five minutes ago with pre-programmed memories, and we would never be able to tell the difference. We also cannot prove that other people have consciousness, as they could just be soulless biological robots that perfectly mimic a conscious being. *Everyone* believes things that cannot be proven, despite any metaphysical posturing and pseudo-intellectual rhetoric. In truth, for many materialists, belief is like being at a salad bar, picking and choosing beliefs that are convenient or comfortable, but this is not science.

Science studies things that are subject to the scientific method. That is, science asks a question about something, makes a hypothesis regarding that question, devises an experiment or way of testing that hypothesis, analyzes the results, and draws conclusions from the data. Science answers questions based on empirical evidence, which means evidence acquired by observation or experimentation. Questions such as, "What happens when we die?" or "What makes something objectively right or wrong?" are questions that science cannot answer in any meaningful way. Such questions lie in the realm of philosophy, ethics, and theology.

Furthermore, absence of evidence does not mean evidence of absence. That is, even though there is no indisputable scientific evidence for God, a lack of evidence is not "proof" that there is no God. Not having scientific evidence for something does not count as evidence against its existence and does not mean that thing does not exist.

For now, I want to address what I see as the true problem in the war between science and Christianity. This dispute is central to the entire debate and cuts to the heart of the conflict. What I am referencing is teleology versus dysteleology. Or in plain terms, purpose versus no purpose. As Christians, we believe that every human being has a God-given purpose, as evidenced by numerous passages including Psalm 138:8: "The Lord will fulfill His purpose for me." Furthermore, we believe that ultimately *everything* has purpose; either God causes it or allows it.

How then could evolution, which is seemingly unguided and purposeless, be compatible in any sense with Biblical Christianity? The solution is found by recalling the limitations of science. Purpose is outside the realm of science. That is to say, science cannot detect purpose and therefore can neither prove nor *disprove* the existence of purpose in the universe, throughout evolutionary history, or anywhere else. Think about these questions for a moment: How exactly would science detect purpose? Can the scientific method be applied to the question of purpose? What experiment could be designed to furnish empirical evidence for or against purpose?

To illustrate my point, consider FM waves. FM waves surround us at all times, yet we can't perceive them by human capacities alone. They are invisible, tasteless, odorless, noiseless (by themselves at least), and immaterial. If I were to ask you if there were any FM waves in close proximity to you, you would probably respond truthfully that there are no *discernible* FM waves present. But what if I turned on a nearby radio? It would manifestly show that there *are* FM waves present. You are just not set up to detect FM waves, even though they exist and are all around you. In the same way, science detects no *discernible* purpose because it is not set up to detect purpose; you need the "tuner" of philosophy, logic, theology, and faith to credibly answer those questions.

Philosopher William Lane Craig likens science to a metal detector. A metal detector is great for finding metallic objects, but that is all it is set up to find; it will not find wood, stone, water, or organic material. Therefore, it would be patently foolish to assume that since all a metal detector ever detects is metal, then the only thing that exists is metal. However, many materialistic scientists want to employ this same flawed reasoning when it comes to "the big questions." Since science, by definition, cannot be used to "detect" purpose, some scientists simply conclude that there is no purpose. But this is like scanning a patch of your backyard with a metal detector and concluding that there is no soil, grass, earthworms, or rocks. Non-metal detection lies outside the domain of metal detectors; you must use other means to ascertain the existence or nonexistence of nonmetals. In the same way, purpose lies outside the scope of science, but this certainly does not mean that it does not exist, despite the fact that some scientists would have you believe otherwise.

Purpose, just like questions of morality and life after death, lies out of the reach of science's grasp. Individual *scientists* may purport to have answers to questions of purpose, but here they speak not out of scientific expertise, but out of their own metaphysical and philosophical beliefs. Evolution is *seemingly* unguided and without purpose. Don't miss this apparently minor distinction, as this is an enormously important point. Even though evolution may *seem* devoid of purpose, this is only because science cannot validly speak to issues of purpose; that is the territory of faith, philosophy, and theology. Therefore, we as Christians believe *sola fide* (by faith alone) that there *is* purpose to things such as the universe, our individual lives, and even evolution. We don't accept this based on proof, if only for the simple fact that purpose can neither be proven nor disproven by science; purpose is a matter of *faith*.

Even if evolution were completely random (and it is not; mutations are random, but natural selection is nonrandom), that would still not rule out the possibility of purpose for randomly evolved creatures. For instance, the placement of the stars in the sky is random, but they have been ascribed purpose by travelers, who have used them as a navigational aid for millennia. If God gives purpose to someone or something, then it has purpose. Period.

Furthermore, we as Christians seem to be comfortable with the idea of randomness in human history, but not with the idea of randomness in natural history. As a teenager, I once was almost blinded by a blast of acid to my eyes while I was working. My contacts dissolved instantly, and my eyes burned with some of the most intense pain I had ever experienced. The emergency room doctor said that had I not been wearing my contacts, I would have surely been blinded. Now it's *possible* that I *could* have not worn my contacts that day, as I sometimes did, and I would have been blinded. But thankfully, I *happened* to have worn them that day, and so I still have my sight. Human history is full of choices, random events, and happenstances. Why is natural history any different?

Another objection that is often thrown around by creationists regarding the limitations of science is that of "historical" or "origin" science versus "operational," "observational," or "experimental" science.[1] The premise of this argument is that the theory of evolution is based on "historical science;" thus, its conclusions are inferior to those of "experimental science," since the former cannot be repeated and verified in a laboratory. However, not all science depends upon carefully controlled laboratory experiments. Cosmology, astronomy, astrophysics, geology, paleontology, and archaeology are all examples of "historical" sciences that do not use experimental methodologies but provide equally valid results based on empirically verifiable data. Archaeologists cannot go back in time, and astronomers can't bring red dwarf stars into their laboratories, but both disciplines have made incredible progress in understanding our universe through observation and comparison of data. Furthermore, evolution is not only a historical science but also an experimental science. As further chapters will reveal, there are plenty of real-time laboratory observations of evolution in action, such as experiments with bacteria, insects, and other organisms with short generation times.

These word games creationists play are merely a smoke screen, as anyone who has watched an episode of CSI or Forensic Files knows full well. In a forensic science investigation, does "historical science" offer no help of any kind? When a detective encounters a dead body, is he to shrug his shoulders and head off to the nearest doughnut depot? After all, no one was there to witness the murder, so what could really be known scientifically? Of course we do know that science can answer questions about past events. Science is based on empirical evidence and is not temporally biased.

Furthermore, this artificial distinction between historical and experimental science is one found almost exclusively in the creationism/ID realm. No branch of science makes any such differentiation. Science is based on the scientific method and empirical evidence, whether studying past or present. You either have data or you do not, and the patterns in said data either support a hypothesis, or they do not. This manufactured distinction between "historical" and "observational" science is little more than semantics and distraction.

Splitting the Horns of the Dilemma

Perhaps the greatest logical fallacy presented by both ends of the creation-evolution spectrum is that of the false dilemma, or either-or fallacy. What I mean by this is that materialistic and atheistic scientists love to bait the populace with the idea that if evolution were true, there could be no God. He would be out of a job! The humanistic scientist tells us that evolution in fact provides a substitute for God. After all, if the universe created itself, and humans evolved unguided from random mutations, why bother with a God? Incredibly, many creationist and Intelligent Design proponents have agreed with this claim! Creationists argue that if evolution were true, it would show that Scripture could not be trusted, and thus our belief in God would be destroyed, or at least severely diminished. Creationists also tell us that if the God of the Bible is who He says He is, then this conviction demands belief in six-day special creation (or at least an old earth with no evolution having taken place).

What this all gets distilled down to is a false dichotomy presented by both sides. Essentially, it is either creationism and God, *or* evolution and atheism. In this false dilemma, atheists and creationists alike try to force us to choose between two options and inevitably lead us to believe that those are the only two options available.

Evolution critic Phillip E. Johnson emphatically states,

> [Science] has become identified with a philosophy known as materialism or scientific naturalism. This philosophy insists that nature is all there is, or at least the only thing about which we can have any knowledge. It follows that nature had to do its own creating, and that the means of creation must not have included any role for God.[2]

Lee Strobel, author of the "Case for" series, reiterates this logical fallacy multiple times in his book, *The Case for a Creator*:

> If the origin of life can be explained solely through natural processes, then God was out of a job! After all, there was no need for a deity if living organisms could emerge by themselves out of the primordial soup and then develop naturally over the eons into more and more complex creatures.[3]

Strobel continues his attack:

> Personally, however, I couldn't understand how the Darwinism I was taught left any meaningful role for God. I was told that the evolutionary process was by definition undirected—and to me, that automatically ruled out a supernatural deity who was pulling the strings behind the scene.[4]

And he has said that "you don't need God if you've got *The Origin of Species*,"[5] and "In which direction—toward Darwin or God—is the current arrow of science now pointing?"[6]

In his book *Systematic Theology*, Princeton theologian Charles Hodge concurs with Strobel by saying, "First, it shocks the common sense of unsophisticated men to be told that the whale and the humming-bird, man and the mosquito, are derived from the same source [. . .] the system is thoroughly atheistic, and therefore cannot possibly stand."[7] Apologists Ron Brooks and Norman Geisler concur that "the theory of evolution is now posited as fact. Who is right? The Bible or Science?"[8] Geisler reiterates this in another book: "Both, of course, cannot be right. If one is right, the other is wrong."[9]

Many atheistic scientists appear to agree wholeheartedly. Celebrated biologist E. O. Wilson concludes in his book *On Human Nature:* "If humankind evolved by Darwinian natural selection [then] genetic chance and environmental necessity, not God, made the species."[10] Finally, none other than infamous anti-theist Richard Dawkins remarks, "The more you understand the significance of evolution, the more you are pushed away from an agnostic position towards atheism."[11]

The gauntlet has been thrown down, and the line in the sand has been drawn. Both atheists and creationists implore us to choose one side or the other; you can have God or Darwin, but not both. This is fallacious reasoning, as these statements that it is either "God or evolution" imply that there are only two choices, when in reality, more options exist. In fact, a myriad of options exists, including theistic evolution, evolutionary creationism, or any number of middle ground choices. The point here is that the false dilemma is presented in a way to make you think that God and evolution are mutually exclusive, and that you must choose between only one of two possible options.

Why do we only hear the extreme voices on one end or the other that try to force us to choose? Because pitched battles make for good media ratings, book sales, and sound bytes. As humans, we seem to love a good fight. And so it goes—the fanatics on both ends of the spectrum polarize the public more and more and divide Christianity more and more. No one wants to talk about the middle ground in the debate, because frankly it isn't as sexy as entrenched screaming and mud-slinging from fanatics (on either side). Reasonable and sensible middle ground voices seem to get drowned out in the din of this vitriolic shouting match.

So can there really be a middle ground? Is there truly a third, fourth, or even more options than what we are led to believe? A 2009 Pew Research Center poll found that 22% of the general public believed in evolution guided by a supreme being, with Young Earth Creationism garnering 31%, and belief in evolution due to natural processes coming in at 32%.[12] While 22% is less than a quarter of the public, it certainly demonstrates that this demographic is severely underrepresented and minimized when it comes to the origins debate. Furthermore, a 2014 Gallup poll found that among those who attended church weekly, 24% believed in God-guided evolution. For those who attended church weekly or at least monthly, support rose to 39%, and for those who seldom or never attend church, support was at 32%.[13] Most impressive of all is the recent data from 2015, which showed that of those who attended religious worship services at least weekly, a whopping 46% agreed with the statement, "Humans evolved over time" (whether guided by God or natural processes)[14] God-guided evolution is not the majority held belief in almost any study, and that is not the case I am trying to make. Although creationism and ID seem to garner more support, this research still illustrates the point that there is a sizable proportion of the populace who rejects the premise that they must choose either God or evolution. Browsing comments on YouTube, online science articles, or scanning through book titles, one would never know that there exists a middle ground shared by so many faithful.

Christians' support for evolution goes even further, as the McLean vs. Arkansas court case illustrates. During this 1981–82 case, which opposed the teaching of "creation science," twelve of the twenty-three plaintiffs arguing *against* creationism were religious clergy. These diverse clergy represented Methodist, Episcopal, African Methodist Episcopal, Catholic, Southern Baptist, and Presbyterian groups among others.[14] At least 27 religious organizations have issued statements supporting the teaching of evolution in school, including the Affiliation of Christian Geologists, the Center for Theology and Natural Science, and the United Methodist Church to name a few.[16]

Furthermore, the "Clergy Letter Project," which collects signatures and maintains statements regarding support for the teaching of evolution, has garnered 13,220 signatures from Christian clergy as of May 29, 2016.[17] The statement itself reads:

> *The Clergy Letter - from American Christian Clergy – An Open Letter Concerning Religion and Science.* Within the community of Christian believers there are areas of dispute and disagreement, including the proper way to interpret Holy Scripture. While virtually all Christians take the Bible seriously and hold it to be authoritative in matters of faith and practice, the overwhelming majority do not read the Bible literally, as they would a science textbook. Many of the beloved stories found in the Bible—the Creation, Adam and Eve, Noah and the ark—convey timeless truths about God, human beings, and the proper relationship between Creator and creation expressed in the only form capable of transmitting these truths from generation to generation. Religious truth is of a different order from scientific truth. Its purpose is not to convey

scientific information but to transform hearts.

We the undersigned, Christian clergy from many different traditions, believe that the timeless truths of the Bible and the discoveries of modern science may comfortably coexist. We believe that the theory of evolution is a foundational scientific truth, one that has stood up to rigorous scrutiny and upon which much of human knowledge and achievement rests. To reject this truth or to treat it as "one theory among others" is to deliberately embrace scientific ignorance and transmit such ignorance to our children. We believe that among God's good gifts are human minds capable of critical thought and that the failure to fully employ this gift is a rejection of the will of our Creator. To argue that God's loving plan of salvation for humanity precludes the full employment of the God-given faculty of reason is to attempt to limit God, an act of hubris. We urge school board members to preserve the integrity of the science curriculum by affirming the teaching of the theory of evolution as a core component of human knowledge. We ask that science remain science and that religion remain religion, two very different, but complementary, forms of truth.[18]

Many perceptive readers may have been shouting at me this whole time, chiding me for attempting to use an *ad populum* argument (i.e., "so many people believe it, it must be true"). But I am in no way arguing that since so many Christians believe in evolution, it must necessarily be true and thus this is the correct option. I am instead trying to drive home the point that there *are* more than just the God/creationism or evolution/atheism choices. A large minority of Christians lives in the middle ground, believing in a sovereign Creator God, but also leaving open the possibility that He may have used laws that He set up (such as natural selection) to bring about life on Earth. The middle ground is real, and it is a growing force to be reckoned with.

Life After Darwin: My Personal Story of Crisis

When I was sixteen, I started to ask the "big questions" and began to investigate religion in general and Christianity in particular. It was also around this time that I had begun attending a local church and had started reading the Bible for the first time. As part of my investigation into the claims of Christianity, I purchased several apologetics books, including Lee Strobel's *The Case for a Creator* and *The Case for Christ*, and Norman Geisler's *I Don't Have Enough Faith to be an Atheist*, among others. I was initially very impressed with such books, and as an excited new believer, I wholeheartedly trusted Lee Strobel's "investigation" and "objective inquiry," giving no second thoughts to whether creationist authors such as Jonathan Wells or Lee Strobel might be misrepresenting the truth. Several of my Intelligent Design books were built on the premise that if evolution is true, then there is no God, or at least no God worth following (e.g., *The Case for a Creator*). Likewise, many of these same authors contended that if the God of the Bible is who He says He is, then the logical extension of that belief demands a belief in Creationism or Intelligent Design. I wholeheartedly believed the false dichotomy proposed by my apologetics books and by my favorite Christian talk show hosts, and for some time I became a vociferous defender of ID, and a critic of evolutionary theory.

When I entered college, I began to study the biological sciences. I held on to my ID ideals and even informally debated fellow students who were curious about my faith and how I viewed science. In my senior year at Oakland University, I enrolled in a 300-level evolutionary biology course. I had hopes of using this evolution class to in fact disprove evolution and gain evidence against the theory. I wanted to use my extensive knowledge of ID and my passion to defend "the Biblical truth" (as presented by creationists and ID advocates) to disprove evolution by infiltrating the ranks and exposing the secrets. Things quickly shifted, however, and I faced a life-changing dilemma.

Though I had hopes of exposing and disproving evolution, I found this class challenged many misconceptions I had been told regarding the theory. As I studied more and more about evolutionary theory, I began to realize, through careful research on both sides, that creationist and ID arguments were regrettably filled with sizable holes, and that evolutionary theory and the claims of science had been severely distorted and misrepresented by all my favorite apologetics authors. I increasingly found it difficult to buttress my convictions regarding ID. By performing my *own* research into the theory of evolution, I realized that my "case" for creationism and ID was a house of cards built on a foundation of straw men and mined quotes.

At this point, I suffered quite a bit of cognitive dissonance to say the least. I had been a follower of Jesus for seven years, had been baptized and married by my church and had committed my life to following Jesus Christ. Now everything I thought I knew was falling apart. I poured back over my ID books and materials and spent late hours exhaustively researching rebuttals to what I was coming to realize was an airtight theory. I was torn between wanting to continue to follow God and wanting to be intellectually fulfilled and follow where the evidence had led. I was still under the power of the false dichotomy perpetuated by those such as Strobel, Phillip E. Johnson, and Geisler (as well as vocal materialists such as Dawkins, Dennet, Hitchens, and Coyne) and believed that I had to choose; either it was God and ID, or it was evolution and atheism. Perhaps even more significant to me was the terrifying thought that if all the apologists were so wrong about evolution, were they wrong about Jesus too?

For months I prayed earnestly for a reprieve from my crumbling worldview. I spent many a night discussing with my wife the conflicting feelings I had regarding my biblical worldview and my newfound scientific knowledge. I was having a crisis of faith, and I dearly wanted to hold on to both God *and* his revealed truth as discovered by science. I thought this was impossible, however, as both the creationist and Intelligent Design advocates whose works had been crucial to my coming to faith, along with many prominent atheists, argued that evolution leaves no room for God and that there is no middle ground in the debate.

Flipping through the television one night, disillusioned and disheartened, I stumbled across Dinesh D'Souza participating in a debate entitled, "Science Disproves God?" D'Souza proceeded to explain how things like the afterlife, beauty, morality, God, and purpose are outside the scope of science, as they are not subject to the scientific method; thus, there is no real conflict between science and faith—only the illusion of such. I was thrilled by this possible resolution to my shattered reality and proceeded to read D'Souza's book, *What's So Great about Christianity*, along with other books such as *Finding Darwin's God*, *The Evolution of Adam*, *The Lost World of Genesis One*, and *The Language of God*.

As I learned more about this "other" option that had never been known to me before, I breathed a sigh of relief and relished in my freedom to investigate God's working in the world through science. I devoted myself to more research on evolution and faith, taking a graduate evolution course (in addition to my undergraduate evolution course) and eventually ending up with a Bachelor of Science in Biology (with honors), and a Master of Science in Biology.

I can honestly tell you that I feel my faith has been strengthened during this journey. Instead of my faith being built on the "evidence" of Creationism and ID, my faith is now built on *nothing* but Jesus Christ. Despite the prediction of Strobel (and many materialists), my acceptance of evolution did not propel me toward atheism or make me an enemy of the faith. On the contrary, I feel that my faith has renewed energy and vibrancy, and that I have a more grand and awesome view of God and His hand in the universe.

I consider it my primary purpose in life to spread the news of the gospel and to defend the truth of Christianity. To me, evolution is superfluous to the gospel, except when I perceive a misunderstanding of the theory or when its misuse may disenfranchise current Christians or become a barrier to faith for nonbelievers. I say this because I, myself, nearly lost my faith when I could no longer defend ID and became convinced, through exhaustive research, of the validity of Darwinian evolution. At that time in my life, many Christians' lack of acceptance, or more specifically, lack of willingness to engage in honest and unbiased discussion of evolution disillusioned me and made me question everything that had been coupled to ID arguments (e.g., validity of the Bible, historical resurrection, historical Jesus, existence of God).

Through much prayer and the writings of many Christians who see no conflict between evolution and God (e.g., Kenneth Miller, Peter Enns, John Walton, Francis Collins), I have retained my belief and in fact feel more firm and convicted in my faith in Jesus and the Christian message. Nothing "jumped out from under a rock and ate God" when I accepted evolution, and I found, as C.S. Lewis predicted, "truth and comfort." I have not solved all the questions like the historical Adam and Nochaic flood, nor do I expect I ever will. But I hope now to minister to those in science and academia who reject Christianity based on the presupposition that Christianity and evolution are mutually exclusive, and I hope to encourage those in the faith who are struggling with the same cognitive dissonance I experienced when my worldview was eviscerated.

What Science Doesn't Want You to Know

There were one hundred of them—biologists, chemists, zoologists, physicists, anthropologists, molecular and cell biologists, bioengineers, organic chemists, geologists, astrophysicists, and other scientists. Their doctorates came from such prestigious universities as Cambridge, Stanford, Cornell, Yale, Rutgers, Chicago, Princeton, Purdue, Duke, Michigan, Syracuse, Temple, and Berkeley. They included professors from Yale Graduate School, the Massachusetts Institute of Technology, Tulane, Rice, Emory, George Mason, Lehigh, and the Universities of California, Washington, Texas, Florida, North Carolina, Wisconsin, Ohio, Colorado, Nebraska, Missouri, Iowa, Georgia, New Mexico, Utah, Pennsylvania, and elsewhere.

Among them was the director of the Center for Computational Quantum Chemistry and scientists at the Plasma Physics Lab at Princeton, the National Museum of Natural History at the Smithsonian Institute, the Los Alamos National Laboratory, and the Lawrence Livermore Laboratories.

And they wanted the world to know one thing: they are skeptical [. . .] these professors, laboratory researchers, and other scientists published a two-page advertisement in a national magazine under the banner: "A Scientific Dissent from Darwinism."[19]

This proclamation from Lee Strobel grows even more exciting when one considers how many additional signatures have been added to this "petition against evolution." From 2001, when the original statement was issued, until 2016, the list has astoundingly swelled to over 800 names.[20] Upon further inspection, however, this triumphant decree shows some troubling signs of suppressed information. A quick look at the expertise fields of the signatories reveals that many come from nonbiological fields, such as meteorology, aviation, mechanical engineering, and computer science. In fact, of the 105 original "scientists" who signed the petition, fewer than one fifth of them were biologists. And of that twenty percent, few were found to have the expertise necessary to meaningfully contribute to the discussion on natural selection's role in evolution.[21]

The news gets worse when we consider the resulting counter-petition that was created. In 2005, *A Scientific Support for Darwinism* petition was created, gathering 7,733 signatures within just *four days!*[22] In contrast, the petition against evolution has gathered hardly more than 800 signatures in fifteen years!

But all of this raises the question whether evolution truly is a "theory in crisis," as creationists and ID proponents portray it to be. Jonathan Wells asserts, for instance, that "the case for Darwinian evolution is bankrupt [. . .] twenty or thirty years from now people will look back in amazement and say, 'How could anyone have believed this?'"[23] Peter Kreeft and Ronald Tacelli corroborate this assumption by disclosing, "The theory is indeed in scientific trouble. Perhaps it can be salvaged."[24] Another publication charges:

> Most scientists still accept some version of the theory of evolution, but a growing number of scientists have become dissatisfied as they learn more facts about the complexity of life [. . .] Paleontologists generally state that the fossil record does not support Darwin's theory [. . .] The Cambrian Explosion does not support Darwin's theory.[25]

I could spend a dozen pages trotting out similar quotes from creationist and ID publications, but suffice to say creationists and ID proponents believe by and large that evolution is a "theory in crisis."

The public has also picked up on this notion of evolution as a "theory in crisis." A 2015 Pew Research Center poll asked those who attend religious worship services weekly or more if they thought scientists agree or disagree that "humans evolved over time." Incredibly, 39% believed that scientists generally do not agree that humans have evolved over time. When this same question was posed to white evangelicals, the percentage skyrocketed to 49%![26]

But what does the evidence say about scientific support for the theory of evolution? Do a good number of scientists actually support creationism/ID? A 2009 Pew Research Center poll found that "nearly all scientists (97%) say humans and other living things have evolved over time."[27] The most recent Pew Research Center poll from 2015 showed that 99% of working PhD and research scientists agreed that "humans have evolved over time."[28] Even the most generous polls that allow for all types of scientists from such diverse fields as psychology, business administration, and computer science (i.e., not necessarily qualified to give an informed opinion on this subject matter) place the belief that "God created man pretty much in his present form at one time within the last 10,000 years" at an unremarkable 5%.

Perhaps more interestingly, however, is that the same poll found that a full 40% of scientists believe that "man has developed over millions of years from less advanced forms of life, but God guided this process, including man's creation."[29] Echoing this sentiment, a 1996 poll revealed that 40% of scientists profess belief in a personal God.[30] A more recent 2009 Pew Research poll surveyed members of the American Association for the Advancement of Science and found that 51% believe in God or a higher power.[31]

Many prestigious organizations, such as the National Academy of Sciences, have issued statements supporting the validity of evolutionary theory while disavowing creationism and Intelligent Design.[32] Somewhat recently, thirty-eight Nobel Peace Prize laureates issued strong criticisms against Intelligent Design as well, as summed up in a 2005 statement by the group of signatories.[33] Perhaps more impressive are the seventy-two United States Nobel Peace Prize Winners who signed an *amicus curiae* (unsolicited legal opinion) urging lawmakers in Louisiana to reject the teaching of creationism in schools. This brief was also signed by seven different scientific societies as well as seventeen distinguished state academies of science.[34]

Discerning readers may think they know where I am going with this, which is to make an *ad verecundiam* argument (appeal to authority). But that is not where I am headed. Am I saying that since the overwhelming majority of scientists believe something, that it must be settled scientific fact—end of discussion? Of course not. Up until the 1950s, many scientists believed in the Steady State theory, which says that the universe had no beginning but simply always was, whereas now the theory has no support in the scientific community and is considered obsolete, having been replaced by the "Big Bang theory."[35] Sensible readers at this point should be asking, "If the scientific majority was recently wrong on the Steady State, then couldn't they be wrong on evolution?" This seems highly unlikely given that over the past 150 years, the theory of evolution has been validated and strengthened time and time again by experiment and observation. The recent explosion in genetic technology over the past thirty years has only served to further cement evolution as a gold standard, making this an all but unassailable theory.

The point I am trying to make is twofold. First, scientists' support for evolution is in no way "waning" or "in crisis." Evolution has been gaining support since Darwin published *Origin of Species* in 1859 and has never enjoyed a higher level of support than it has at present. Scientists are neither beginning to doubt evolution, nor are they even becoming dissatisfied. Despite claims from creationist and ID advocates, evolution enjoys almost unanimous scientific support.

Second, why do we believe that scientists who have devoted their lives to the study of biology, have labored through years of schooling and training, and have become experts in their field, are less trustworthy on the subject of evolution than Christian talk show hosts? Should we really believe that 99% of scientists are flat-out wrong about evolution? Remember that according to one of the polls above, 40% of scientists believe in "God-guided" evolution, and another poll shows 51% believe in God or a higher power, so it would be difficult to support a claim that all scientists are atheists or pure materialists, forced to accept evolution as the only possible answer.

It astounds me that we trust Christian talk show hosts, such as Hank Haanegraf or Bob Dutko, on matters concerning the validity of modern scientific theory, despite the fact that neither of them is trained in the sciences and both possess only a high-school level education (at least from what I could find). Now, I am not making the argument that if you do not have a college degree or are not trained in the sciences, you cannot make valid and intelligent arguments about evolutionary theory. Indeed, I've listened to and read both aforementioned men (whom I respect and consider brothers in the faith), and they appear very learned and intelligent regarding some nonscience issues. However, it does make one wonder how 99% of scientists with PhD's and Master's degrees can be wrong concerning issues of modern scientific theory, but a handful of apologists, pastors, and radio talk show hosts can be right.

Furthermore, I would caution anyone who takes stock in creation and ID "scientists" to carefully consider their qualifications. Many creationist and ID scientists and proponents, whose books I have read, have degrees in Law (e.g., Phillip E. Johnson, Lee Strobel), Engineering, Medicine, or religious areas. Why do we trust that pastors, lawyers, and talk show hosts know more about science than scientists? As much as I trust my pastor, I wouldn't ask him to fly the plane I'm about to board; I'd rather trust a pilot when it comes to issues of aviation. Similarly, when I'm sick, I'd rather go to my family physician than call the "Bible Answer Man" for help.

The problem is exactly what St. Augustine identified in his passage quoted in chapter two. When we ask pastors, apologists, radio show hosts, and evangelists to double as science "experts," we do a great disservice to the faith and potentially do irreparable harm to those who are not yet part of our faith. Evolution is an extremely complex theory, with very nuanced underpinnings and principles. To know anything substantial about evolution, one must know a vast deal of biology in the first place. In fact, the reason I believe evolution has remarkably lower acceptance rates among the general public than among scientists is that the theory is counterintuitive and quite difficult to fully comprehend, and it is easily misunderstood. Bear in mind, however, that an argument cannot be invalidated based on the grounds that it "just doesn't make sense" or "just doesn't seem possible to me." This "fallacy of personal revelation" is inadmissible in determining whether or not evolution is valid. For instance, science tells us that the desk at which I currently sit is mostly comprised of empty space (as minuscule electrons and nuclei are exceedingly distant from one another). Yet, it appears to me an impenetrable solid, fully capable of holding my laptop, with no sign of any space or gaps. Therefore, at times we must rely on our logic over our senses when attempting to ascertain truth about the natural world.

I want to reiterate that this is not to say that nonscientists cannot know anything about evolution—they can—but as one trained in the sciences, it becomes readily apparent to me that most pastors, apologists, and talk show hosts are *way* out of their depth when it comes to the nuts and bolts of science. I don't fault them for not knowing the labyrinthine technicalities of science, because they are not trained to be scientists but rather theologians, and their expertise lies in a vastly different hemisphere. So considering this, how is it that these nonscientists know science so much better than scientists? It is a grievous calamity that so many pontificate about subject matter of which they have only a cursory understanding, and in doing so confuse many Christians and create unnecessary barriers for many agnostics and atheists.

White Coat Conspiracy

Some have charged that mainstream science is inherently biased and that creationists and ID proponents are barred from participation therein. I have scarcely read a creationist or ID book without coming across claims of "suppressed information" or "bias" in the scientific community. Many who are against evolution make modern science out to be nothing short of a full-blown conspiracy, with scientists circling the wagons to protect their own, afraid of the truth and validity of creationism and ID and desperate not to let the public know that their theory is compromised and supremely dubious. But is this truly the case?

Is there a white coat conspiracy unfolding before our eyes?

Having read a great deal of literature on both "sides," when it comes to suppressed information, I would argue that it is ironically the creationists and ID proponents who tend to in fact suppress a great deal of information. I need only reference the aforementioned figures on scientific support of evolution to make my point. No creationist or ID book I have ever read has reported that 95–99% of scientists support evolution. On the contrary, nearly every such book has been predicting the demise of Darwin and has struggled to convince readers that a large minority of scientists (if not the majority) are skeptical of evolution. One could make the argument that such an author who knowingly deceives his Christian readers may be bearing false witness and in doing so gives himself to great peril.

But I digress. To claim that science is blacklisting any view contrary to the reigning paradigm betrays a lack of understanding of the scientific process. One foundation upon which science is built is that of scientists publishing rebuttals to others scientists' hypotheses. The way science is further defined and purged of inaccuracies is precisely through the process of challenging prevailing thought. If you were able to show that the theory of evolution was dead wrong—why, you would be more famous than Einstein! You would be on the cover of TIME magazine, PBS would create documentaries about you, and the scientific world would be fawning over you. You see, in truth, scientists strive to disprove dominant theories in hopes of gaining status, tenure, grant money, and scientific fame.

If anyone doubts the validity of this claim, consider the story of the demise of the Steady State theory already described. In short, scientists Arno Penzias and Robert Wilson were using a large "horn antenna" at Bell Labs from 1964–1965 in an attempt to map signals emanating from the Milky Way. To their surprise, they discovered a static noise which would come to be known as the "Cosmic Microwave Background Radiation." Essentially, this was the "noise" left over from the Big Bang, which marked the beginning of the universe. This discovery absolutely turned the scientific world on its ear and immediately usurped the much loved "Steady State theory." This discovery, for which Arno Penzias and Robert Wilson would win a Nobel Prize in 1978, was heralded as "the greatest discovery of the 20th century."[36]

Don't take this lightly. This had profound implications on modern science and even scientists' own personal beliefs. Remember that the Steady State theory essentially said that the universe had always existed; it was never created, nor did it have a beginning. Now logically, if the universe had always existed and was never created, there is no need for a creator. Thus, one could be an "intellectually fulfilled atheist" by accepting the Steady State theory. But the Big Bang theory that replaced it posits that the universe is *not* infinite. Therefore, it had a beginning and *was* created and by logic essentially demands a creator. So if the "conspiracy theory" is that godless, materialistic, atheistic scientists must prop up any theory that minimizes God's role and upholds atheism, and they must ignore theories that point to a creator, then how did atheism's most important piece of dogma become crushed under the weight of the quickly embraced theory of the Big Bang—the theory that reveals there was a beginning and a creation of the universe? If it is true that scientists are all in cahoots with one other in trying to "keep God out of science," then how did the *one* theory that provided the most compelling argument for atheism become so readily dislodged from "dogmatic" science and become so effortlessly replaced with the theory that seems to provide a scientific corroboration of Genesis 1:1, "In the beginning"?

The most reasonable solution is simply that there is no conspiracy. If you have data to back up your conclusions, you can get published in mainstream science. The problem is that creationism and ID have nothing scientific to publish. For something to be science, it must be subject to the scientific method. This means that you must have a hypothesis that is falsifiable and hopefully makes predictions (evolution does both). How do you go about testing the hypothesis that God created creatures out of nothing? Can a theory that says such a thing be falsified? Creationism and ID are religious beliefs and thus have no merit in arguments of science. But some will retort, "We should look for the best explanation of the evidence, and the best explanation is Intelligent Design." However, for one to conclude that God is responsible for some act of creation or biology, one would have to exhaust all other naturalistic possibilities which would take an infinite amount of time, given that there are infinite other possibilities besides Intelligent Design.

Could evolution be replaced as the dominant theory describing change, adaptation, and diversity of life? Actually, yes, it could be. Is that likely? Highly unlikely. Mountains of supporting evidence have been built confirming the theory's validity, and where evolution makes testable and falsifiable predictions, it has passed with flying colors. Hypothetically, even if the current theory of evolution by natural selection were to be disproved, that would not mean that there is no common descent or macroevolution of species. The fossil and geological records indisputably show that species undergo large-scale changes over time. Snakes lose limbs, reptiles gain feathers, and species split to become new ones. Species changing significantly over geological time is an observable fact that is not in any doubt; evolution is merely the theory that describes the mechanism by which this happened. And even theoretically, if evolution were replaced by another theory, it would be replaced by another naturalistic scientific theory, not ID or creationism.

Additionally, some may be astonished and surprised when I admit that scientists and creationists both *do* look at the same evidence and come to different conclusions. This tag line has been trumpeted from the tops of creationist strongholds for decades, and the argument presumably has origins deeper still. However, there is a prior assumption here that there is more than one way to reasonably interpret the evidence, with the "underdog" hypothesis (creationism) deserving as much credibility as the dominant one. This is akin to looking at the evidence regarding the U.S. moon landing in 1969 and reaching the conclusion that it must have been faked in a warehouse in Los Angeles. Does the evidence *really* demand such an odd claim? Should the moon landing conspiracy hold as much or even more weight than the well-supported conclusion that we really did land on the moon?

Could one be justified in looking at the evidence for heliocentrism and reaching the conclusion that *geocentrism* is actually true? After all, it is the same evidence, just a different conclusion. Imagine that a murder suspect is found with a bloody knife and the victim's DNA all over him, his footprints and fingerprints are all over the crime scene, and witnesses to the crime positively identify him as the perpetrator. Sure, someone could look at the evidence and come to a "different" conclusion of innocence, but would it be a valid conclusion? When 99% of scientists look at the evidence and reach a conclusion of evolution, it is hard to argue that there is any other valid alternative explanation.

Furthermore, many creationists and ID proponents assert that scientists find what they want or expect to find and are blinded by their *a priori* commitments. This allegation rings hollow, however. Many early geologists from the 1600s until the mid-1800s expected to find evidence of a worldwide flood and special creation; however, their findings regarding fossils and geological strata actually helped to make the case for an old earth and evolution. As a result, by the late 1800s, an old earth and evolution were already widely accepted, and many geologists who had set out to prove the validity of a worldwide flood had abandoned these beliefs or significantly scaled them back. Adam Sedgwick and William Buckland were two such 19th century scientists who typify this sentiment.[37]

One could also make the counterargument that creationists are just as motivated to find what they are looking for and thus find it. Therefore, if one sees a cave painting, one might believe that one of the shapes is in fact a depiction of a dinosaur, supporting the premise that dinosaurs lived with humans (which ironically would not invalidate evolution but admittedly would fundamentally change our understanding of it). The bottom line is that no one is immune to seeing what he wants to see, or to finding "evidence" to support what he wants to believe. However, in science, one is *trained* to be objective. Of course everyone has preconceptions and assumptions about the world, and I am not arguing that scientists never have biases, but to argue that scientists cannot do objective science is an *appeal to motive* fallacy, which in essence says you can't trust what scientists say because they either want or do not want something to be true. Additionally, keep in mind that science is not done in secret lairs, or behind curtains. Science is carried out in the public arena, where experts duke it out by publishing studies and data that oppose or affirm prevailing theories.

What's more, creationists and ID proponents have many platforms and outlets already in place, from which they can share their ideas. When creationists publish books, express their views on the radio and on TV, and lecture in churches, it is difficult to argue that they are being silenced. The only circumstance where creationists and Intelligent Design advocates are prevented from publishing in scientific journals and textbooks are when they espouse something not backed by empirical evidence, wherein lies the problem.

Creationism and ID are wholly built on negative arguments. That is to say, the respective views consist mainly of, "How do you explain this?" or "What about [insert obscure piece of 'evidence']?" Creationism and ID are solely based on trying to explain away evidence. Creationists and Intelligent Design advocates have no arguments or theories of their own that rely on data or empirical evidence. By and large, neither makes testable claims that are falsifiable or that make predictions (and where they do make falsifiable predictions, they are always falsified). The only theories and arguments that either camp produces are those based on *faith*, such as belief in six-day creation, special creation, appearance of age, supernatural design, and other concepts based on certain interpretations of Scripture. In summation, the main difference between science and creationism/ID is the following: Science says, "Here is a set of facts. What conclusions can be drawn from it?" Creationists and Intelligent Design advocates say, "Here is our conclusion. What facts can we find to support it?"

Nothing encapsulates this truth better than a statement from creationist Ken Ham, founder of *Answers in Genesis* and of the "Creation Museum" in Kentucky. In the much publicized 2014 debate between "Bill Nye the Science Guy" and Ken Ham, which I encourage you to watch if you haven't already, Ham's answer to one particular question is quite revealing. When asked, "What, if anything, would ever change your mind [about creationism]?" Ken Ham responded in a very roundabout way that nothing would ever change his mind:

> Well the answer to that question is, I'm a Christian. And as a Christian, *I can't prove it to you*, but God has definitely shown me very clearly through his Word and shown himself in the person of Jesus Christ. *The Bible is the Word of God. I admit that that's where I start from.* I can challenge people that you can go and test that, and you can make predictions based on that; you can check the prophecies in the Bible, you can check the statements in Genesis, you can check that, and I did a little bit of that tonight, but *I can't ultimately prove that to you*. All I can do is to say to someone, "Look, if the Bible really is what it claims to be, if it really is the Word of God and that's what it claims, then check it out." The Bible says if you come to God believing that He is, He will reveal himself to you and you will know; as Christians, we can say we know. And so, as far as the Word of God is concerned, *no one's ever going to convince me* that the Word of God is not true.[38] (emphasis added).

Ken Ham's response makes clear two things. First, he starts with the Bible as the conclusion and then finds what "evidence" he can to support his interpretation of Genesis. Second, *nothing* would convince Ken Ham that evolution and an old earth are true. Some of you may think I am twisting his words, but I am merely distilling the essence of his comment; look carefully at what he said above. When asked if he would ever change his mind, Ham states in many words the following:

1. The Bible says the earth is 6,000 years old [in his interpretation].
2. "The Bible is the Word of God."
3. "No one's ever going to convince me that the Word of God is not true."

By logical extension, he is stating in an ambiguous and circular way that nothing would change his view on a 6,000-year-old earth, which would preclude evolution. Furthermore, on his website, *Answers in Genesis*, the statement of faith affirms that "by definition, no apparent, perceived or claimed evidence in any field, including history and chronology, can be valid if it contradicts the scriptural record."[39]

Now to be clear, I want to restate that I *do* believe the Bible is the Word of God. But is this the place to start when one asks a scientific question? If, for instance, we want to know physiologically where our emotions originate, and we start with the Word of God, we would arrive at the answer that the heart, sometimes described as the bowels or organs, is the seat of emotion (e.g., "For the mouth speaks what the heart is full of" Luke 6:45, NIV). Some of us may think this is merely poetic language, but as John Walton, author of *The Lost World of Genesis One* and professor of Old Testament studies at Wheaton College states, "In the ancient world this was not metaphor, but physiology."[40] Or suppose we start with the Bible when addressing the earlier question, "Which is the smallest of all the seeds?" By using the Bible as a "science textbook," we would arrive at the incorrect answer of the mustard seed.

My point here is two-fold. The first point is the refrain of this book: The Bible was not meant to be relied upon as a treatise on modern science. Thinking that the point of the Bible is about the accurate sizes of seeds, the physical location of emotion, or the scientific underpinnings of biological complexity completely misses the point. This is a categorical mistake; we are trying to force out of the text clues about *scientific* origins, when the text is more concerned about our *spiritual* origins and who we are in light of God. The intended purpose of Genesis bears repeating: God is all-powerful and sovereign, and He is ultimately responsible in one way or another for everything present in the universe. He created man in His image (spiritually, not physically) and desired for man to have a relationship with Him. It is a story of a God who loves us and desires for us to know Him. This is far more satisfying and profound than a scientific treatise.

My second point is that it makes no *logical* sense to start with the Bible to "prove" something. For starters, beginning with the Bible or using it as a starting point for an argument immediately alienates non-Christians, who are the ones we should ultimately be concerned about reaching with God's truth! For example, why would an atheist trust what the Bible has to say, when he or she doesn't even believe in God *or* His Word? When engaging that atheist, shouldn't we start with objective truth, which will ultimately lead to God and the Bible? Furthermore, someone from a different faith could argue that a discussion should start from *their* holy scriptures, and their logic would have just as much (or as little) force. A Hindu might say, "We should start with the Bhagavad-ghita." A Muslim could just as easily say, "We should start with the Qur'an."

One may retort, "Well, we should start with the Bible because the Bible is true." But why is the Bible true? Because the Bible says that the Bible is true? As previously discussed, this is an embarrassing circular argument. I want to repeat, I *do* believe that the Bible is true and is the Word of God. However, we should be careful that we do not damage our witness by using faulty logic that shows us to be uninformed on issues over which we purport to have authority.

So then, where do we start if not with the Bible? Here I have good news, as I believe that when we start with truth, we end up at the Bible and the person of Jesus Christ, as *all* truth is God's truth. He is the *embodiment* of truth. If the God of the Bible is who He says He is, as revealed through His Word, then by definition, nothing that is true in this universe can contradict him. As I stated earlier, we don't have to be afraid of starting with the truth—God *is* truth!

Methodological Naturalism

When we start with the truth, we (even as Christians) are engaging in what's called "methodological naturalism," sometimes referred to as "procedural naturalism" or "methodological atheism." While this term may initially appear impious, there is nothing antireligious about it. Dinesh D'Souza apprehends this idea best when he writes:

This [methodological naturalism] means that scientists go about their official business by presuming that we live in a natural, material world. Within this domain, miracles are forbidden, not because they cannot happen, but because science is the search for natural explanations. So, too, the mind and the soul must be studied materially, not because they are purely material phenomena, but because it is the job of science to examine only the material effects of immaterial things.[41]

Note that this method of science does not exclude God or the supernatural; it merely seeks a scientific explanation instead of *assuming* something was a miraculous act of God.

A particular phenomenon or event could very well be the supernatural work of God. However, to presume a supernatural cause eliminates any further inquiry into the matter. When we chalk an event up to "God must have done it," we deprive ourselves of opportunities for learning and exploration. Curiosity is extinguished, and we are no better for it. For this, among other reasons, we employ methodological atheism. This is not an affront to faith; on the contrary, it merely seeks to understand the material explanation of things.

Even the most orthodox, devout, doctrinal Christians engage in this practice daily. When we lose our keys, we do not assume they ascended to the throne at the right hand of God. Rather, we backtrack our steps, we search high and low, and we question others in our home as to their potential whereabouts. When a lamp is found demolished and lying adjacent to a soccer ball in the living room, do we designate this occurrence as a divine judgement and close the case? Or do we assume a material explanation involving an illicit indoor soccer game between siblings? Granted these scenarios are vastly different from the questions surrounding our origins, they serve to underscore the fact that methodological naturalism is practiced to some degree by all, and that this method is not antagonistic toward faith.

Furthermore, even if an event were found to have a material explanation, does this rule out the possibility that God's hand was intimately involved? Does God *only* work through violating the laws of nature? Can He not use the laws of nature He designed to accomplish His purposes? Could He not have providentially ordered the world so as to bring about life through a natural unfolding of what He had sovereignly decreed? Again, science is neither set up to detect purpose nor God's hand in events. These questions are outside of the parameters of science, meaning that we must employ different methods of gaining such knowledge (e.g., faith, theology, philosophy). We must remember that when we jump to proclaim the inexplicable and currently unexplained as miraculous, we jeopardize our Christian witness when a material explanation may ultimately be found. Then, for many, our argument *for* God becomes an argument *against* Him.

"Just a Theory"

I recurrently encounter pronouncements that "evolution is *only* a theory." Unfortunately, the potency of the word "theory" has been undermined by its usage in everyday language. "I have a theory about where all my lost pens go" is much different from legitimate scientific theory. A scientific theory is defined as "a coherent group of propositions formulated to explain a group of facts or phenomena in the natural world and repeatedly observed through experiment or observations."[42] Perhaps more simply put, the National Academy of Sciences defines a theory as "a comprehensive explanation of some aspect of nature that is supported by a vast body of evidence."[43] In other words, theories are borne out of the crucible of volumes of peer-reviewed research, typically subjected to rigorous scrutiny and critical evaluation from the scientific community for years before tentative acceptance, and they are never just conjured up out of thin air.

If one doubts the validity of the "theory" of evolution based on it *only* being a theory, one must be willing to cast doubt on other robust theories as well. The theory of gravity is *only* a theory, as is the germ theory, which postulates that small microbes may cause disease. The already discussed heliocentric theory, which states that we revolve around the sun, is but a lowly theory, too. Atomic theory is just a theory, but it sure seems to work well for creating weapons that can level cities. Cell theory states that we are composed of small living cells, but perhaps this too is a "theory in crisis." I am loath to be so sardonic; however, too few are aware of the true significance of the scientific usage of the word "theory."

Fallible Fallacy

Creationists have charged that the conclusions regarding evolution are not trustworthy, having originated from a "fallible" mind. Ken Ham writes, "Should we unite around man's fallible word OR unite around God's infallible word?"[44] Similarly, many creationists have hijacked philosopher Alvin Plantinga's "evolutionary argument against naturalism" and used it out of context to make it appear as though this argument invalidates the conclusion of any kind of evolution, due to man's "fallible mind." Plantinga writes, "If our minds arose from lesser animals via natural processes, then our minds may be fallible. Then the conclusions that we come up with are subject to doubt, including the conclusion of evolution itself"[45] It is important to note that Plantinga states in the introduction to the essay that he is *not* attacking evolution, or anything in that neighborhood" but instead philosophical naturalism (i.e., there are no supernatural entities). He states that he sees no problems with *theism* and modern evolutionary theory but here speaks about the self-defeating conjunction of *naturalism* and evolution (and I wholeheartedly agree with him). But for the sake of argument, let's consider this "fallible mind" line of thought in the way that creationists misuse it (and not how Plantinga intended it to be used). Doesn't it beg the question of how the fallible mind knows that the preceding arguments are true, if the mind is fallible? Can a fallible mind be trusted to know whether it itself is fallible or not? Furthermore, how can equally fallible minds argue *for* creationism and ID? Would their arguments not be equally null and void, having derived from the same fallible mind of man? How can fallible minds know for sure that the Bible is the infallible Word of God? Again, this line of thought is of the self-defeating type, which ends up convicting *itself* rather than the adversary.

Along the same lines, I have been rebuked by fellow Christians with verses such as, "Let no man deceive himself. If any man among you seemeth to be wise in this world, let him become a fool, that he may be wise. For the wisdom of this world is foolishness with God" (1 Cor. 3:18–19 KJV). But does this apply to arguing the validity of a scientific theory? Or is this a verse that is being contorted into a catch-all verse that should read, "I can't refute your arguments; therefore, the Bible says you must be wrong." Read in context, this verse is referring to the "foolishness" of the resurrection. Christ crucified and risen is certainly as foolish to the world today as it was then. We see this in the "wisdom" of our culture that tells us to "be true to ourselves" and "be happy" above all else. This is the same "wisdom" that affirms that all religions are the same, and that Christ was merely a wise teacher. I find it hard to believe that this verse is a denunciation of science. Was the first-rate physician Luke (of Gospel of Luke fame) foolish in the eyes of God because of his scientific wisdom?

You Weren't There!

The indictment is sometimes made by creationists and Intelligent Design advocates that "*you* weren't there! How do *you* know?" This refrain has been popularized by those such as Ken Ham (who used this line during his debate with Bill Nye), and by those who insist that science can't possibly know for sure what happened in the distant past, because . . . well, no one was there to observe what happened! This not only flounders as a piece of logic and argumentation, but more importantly, it is bad theology. When Ken Ham uses this escape hatch approach, he effectively saws off the branch on which he is sitting.

Think about this critically for a moment. Ken Ham also believes that Jesus lived 2,000 years ago, was crucified, and was resurrected. But how does he know? Was he there? Ken Ham believes that the Bible records actual historical events. But was he there? How about John the Baptist? The Virgin birth? Jesus' miracles? You weren't there, I wasn't there, and Ken Ham undoubtedly was not there. This seemingly robust retort of "you weren't there" utterly collapses when we scrutinize it rationally. We can't just apply this logic when and where it seems convenient. When we employ this rationale on arguments against evolution and an old earth, it simultaneously invalidates all historical claims that we Christians hold dear. This tactic is nothing more than a smoke screen—one that intends to distract the mediocre and placate the simple.

And even if no one was there, does that mean *nothing* can possibly be known about the unobserved past? As already noted, the past leaves traces that carry into the future. Fossils, geological strata, and elemental compositions of rocks all leave clues as to the history of our planet. Much like the TV show "CSI," we can learn a great deal about what happened even if you or I "weren't there." Also remember this: None of us was there to witness the claims of creationist and ID proponents. None of us observed the animals boarding Noah's ark. None of us observed God create Adam out of the dust of the earth. I am not saying that these events could not have occurred; I am merely illustrating that "you weren't there" applies just as much to Old Earth Evolutionists as it does to Young Earth Creationists. It is a double-edged sword that cuts both ways. The difference, I would argue, is that in regards to claims about evolution, science has a rich treasure trove of data woven into a coherent, testable, and falsifiable theory that can make predictions (and succeeds where it does).

CHAPTER FOUR

THE BEGETTER OF ALL EVILS?

The Dangerous Idea

Darwin's theory of evolution has been termed his "dangerous idea." But is there a more "dangerous idea" hiding in plain sight? I submit to you that creationism and Intelligent Design are in fact the "dangerous ideas," not evolution. I sincerely believe that these Christian movements are borne out of good intentions, with Christian's espousing these views earnestly convinced that the Bible must be "defended" against this attack on faith by materialistic, atheistic scientists. I have debated, talked with, and broken bread with those who hold to these views, and I have always and will always consider them brothers and sisters in Christ. However, many do not understand what great peril they put fellow Christians in when they advocate these anti-evolution views. They also do not realize how this destroys their credibility with the non-Christian world, or how it hamstrings their attempts to bring the lost back to the fold.

The first reason creationism and ID are dangerous is that they have the potential to set Christians up for failure. A close friend of mine told me he recently talked about evolution to a youth group at his church. Knowing his college major was not in the sciences, my curiosity was piqued. "Well, what did you tell them?" I asked with unease. He responded nonchalantly, "Eh, I told them that they [scientists] have a couple pieces of supposed 'evidence,' but it's really nothing to worry about. There's no truth to it [evolution]." I felt a sinking feeling inside me, knowing that when those kids reach high school, they will be confronted with the irrefutable evidence for evolution. What I hope they do *not* do at that point is throw the baby out with the bathwater, thinking, *"If the church lied to me about evolution, were they lying about the resurrection?"*

We must remember that Christianity is always just *one* generation away from dying out. Think about that seriously for a moment. If this current generation were to leave the faith, Christianity would become extinct in a matter of mere decades. This may sound like alarmist rhetoric, but most Christians are acutely aware that many young people are going away to college and leaving God behind. This current generation is the most science literate generation ever, and they have all the resources to investigate the claims of science quite literally in their pocket. Do we really want to set them up for failure? Do we really want them to believe that they must check their brains at the entrance to their classroom and practice the "three monkeys" style of college learning to remain a Christian? They *will* learn the truth about evolution, and if we catechize them with the "false dilemma" of "God or science," they *may* have a crisis of faith they may not be able to reconcile, and they may abandon God if forced to choose one or the other.

The second prong of the dangerous creationism/ID idea deals with the fact that it disenfranchises current Christians. When apologists and others assert that we are required to choose between evolution and God, they marginalize the large minority (22%–46%, according to polls; see chapter four) of Christians who find no rivalry between the two. I tell you truthfully that I have lost friends over this debate and have been castigated and derided as a "liberal" or "watered-down" Christian by others. When I voiced my concerns about this topic in my own faith community, I was met with warmth by some but was not well received by all. Though my faith is burgeoning, and I feel connected to God more than ever, there is still a part of me that feels alienated and estranged from my fellow Christians, due to the hostility and shunning I have occasionally experienced.

When I expressed these sentiments to a well-known Christian author whom I respect a great deal, I received this advice:

Aaron, you're in a fairly common predicament, which I know doesn't make it any less painful or difficult for you. Trust me, I've been there. The reason you're feeling alone is because in a sense . . . well, you *are* alone, at least in your current faith community. You and others like you are on the leading edge of a paradigm shift; the downside of this is that in your own community you begin to feel less comfortable and even less at home. For better or for worse, you'll never be able to go back to older ways of thinking, or return to when things were more comfortable.

It is regrettable that those who embrace viewpoints other than creationism/ID are often disparaged as apostates instead of brothers and sisters in Christ.

Proverbs 6:16–19 warns us, "There are six things that the LORD strongly dislikes, seven that are an abomination to him: haughty eyes, a lying tongue, and hands that shed innocent blood, a heart that devises wicked plans, feet that make haste to run to evil, a false witness who breathes out lies, and *one who sows discord among brothers*" (emphasis added). Although in a somewhat different context, Paul seems to echo this sentiment in the New Testament:

> Now I plead with you, brethren, by the name of our Lord Jesus Christ, that you all speak the same thing, and that there be no divisions among you, but that you be perfectly joined together in the same mind and in the same judgment. For it has been declared to me concerning you, my brethren, by Chloe's household, that there are contentions among you (1 Cor. 1:10–11 NKJV).

Some core doctrines are worth fighting over: Jesus' divinity, the Resurrection, the Holy Trinity, and The Virgin Birth are such battles worthy of our allegiance. But is evolution really the hill on which we want to die? Should we not choose our battles a little more judiciously? As our Lord said, "Every kingdom divided against itself is brought to desolation, and every city or house divided against itself will not stand" (Matt. 12:25 NKJV).

My final point is that creationism and ID create unnecessary barriers to faith for those investigating Christianity. I have had a very close atheist friend tell me point blank that he "cannot believe in a faith that conjectures that 'the ark [Noah's] must have carried *baby* dinosaurs on board, since adult dinosaurs certainly would not have all fit.'" Now, I didn't make that up. That declaration was actually made on a popular metro-Detroit Christian radio talk show, which I also heard with my own ears. This same talk show went on to proclaim that Marco Polo saw living dinosaurs in China as recently as 700 years ago!

Correspondingly, this particular talk show regularly features Kent Hovind, founder of the now defunct "Dinosaur Adventure Museum" whose entrance sign read:

> We believe that the Bible is literally true and scientifically accurate. God made this world in six literal 24-hour days about 6,000 years ago. Dinosaurs were just big reptiles that lived with Adam and Eve. Noah took them on the ark (probably babies!) People killed most of them after the flood (they called them dragons in those days). There could still be a few small ones still alive today (like Loch Ness).

I had a hard time believing these preposterous claims had truly been posted on the entrance sign, so I actually confirmed it via email with a family member of Hovind's. Hovind's website also postulates that T-Rex was a vegetarian before the Fall, as were all animals in his assessment.[1]

Sadly, they are not the only ones who propagate such embarrassing beliefs. Creationist Carl Baugh raises the bar for absurdity in his interview with the Dallas Observer, as the article states,

> This past year he's traveled to Papua New Guinea in search of 'living pterodactyls.' Baugh says these giant prehistoric flying reptiles have been spotted by locals for years. In the three trips he's made to the country, he's seen evidence of them—scratch marks, feet and tail imprints, even their 'glow.' Pterodactyls apparently glow at will, like giant fireflies.[2]

As Christians, we are throwing ourselves on this sharp object over and over again! Who in his right mind, being an atheist or agnostic, is going to sign up for a faith that thinks Marco Polo discovered *dinosaurs*! Who could possibly take us seriously when we are busy looking for pterodactyls and the Loch Ness monster in order to prove the Bible is true? As Christians, we are at times our own worst enemy. When we conjure up such preposterous claims, we make ourselves look like daft conspiracy theorists rather than normal and rational people seeking God. Elvis sightings, Bigfoot encounters, and alien abductions seem mundane compared to outlandish propositions of medieval dinosaurs. When we say such things, how will anyone take us seriously regarding the historical Resurrection of Jesus? We advance these asinine arguments, unfortunately, much to the detriment of the Gospel.

Some may think I am making a straw man, and that I am cherry-picking fringe beliefs in order to take a cheap shot at creationism, and that these views don't represent most Christians but are merely a caricature. However, the secular world sees anyone who denies evolution —whether ID or progressive creationism—in the same light as these extreme creationists. Whether it's believing that dinosaurs still exist or that humans and chimpanzees do not share a common ancestor, the unbelieving world we are so eager to reach sees this denial of very solid and accepted mainstream science as a deal-breaker when considering Christianity. As a result, when we try to gain "converts" by using creationism and ID, we either turn them off entirely, or if we are successful somehow, we set them up for future failure when they inevitably discover the half truths and whole lies told by these advocates. If people think we've got it so wrong when it comes to basic science, how will we convince them of the truth of the Gospel?

The takeaway point is that creationism and ID are things to which we do *not* want to hitch our wagon. This is the "geocentrism" of our time that we would do best to abandon and let fade into oblivion. When we package the historicity of Jesus, the authenticity of the Bible, and the truth of God together with creationism/ID, we graffiti a beautiful masterpiece. When one discovers the forgery of creationism, one is inclined to repudiate all the other arguments tied to the creationism/ID argument (e.g., historical resurrection, validity of the Bible). It is like learning that your doctor still practices bloodletting; it would make you skeptical of *all* his medical advice, fair or not. The Bible, the person of Jesus, the love of God, and the conviction of the Holy Spirit are enough to bring people to faith; we only get in the way when we add unnecessary and unbiblical accouterments.

Darwin Made Me Do It

Evolution has been blamed for everything ranging from the Third Reich to Lee Strobel's voracious loins. Strobel unabashedly blames Charles Darwin for his uncontrollable and rampant libido that resulted in the indulgence of his carnal cravings during his hedonistic adolescence before converting to Christianity, quipping, " [After embracing evolution] I felt unleashed [. . .] to pursue pleasure at all costs. The sexual revolution of the '60s and '70s was starting to dawn, and I was liberated to indulge as much as I wanted."[3] Some Christians have likewise blamed evolution for increasing crime rates and contributing to an overall moral decline in society.[4] Ken Ham gives his nod of agreement in writing, "His [Hitler's] treatment of Jews may be attributed, at least in part, to his belief in evolution."[5] But is evolution really the begetter of these evils?

The validity of a theory cannot be determined by examining the positive or negative effects that theory has had on society. Even if evolution were responsible for raising crime rates (a claim that has no evidence whatsoever to support it, and even *if* the two were correlated, this would not necessarily mean one caused the other), this would have no bearing on whether or not the theory holds any water. A theory's legitimacy is based on its merits, not what effects the application or misapplication of that theory has on society. Furthermore, science is descriptive, not prescriptive, meaning it cannot tell us what ought to be or ought not to be. Science, by definition, can have nothing meaningful to say on issues of morality and ethics, as these lie outside the domain of testing, observation, and empirical evidence.

Multiple branches of science have been involved in crimes against humanity, loss of human life, and suffering in general. Should we blame the field of physics and nuclear science for the nearly quarter million Japanese killed by the atomic bomb drops during WWII? Should the "fruits" of nuclear theory cause us to consider banning its teaching? Should we teach an alternative to chemistry? After all, chemists devised treacherous contrivances used to commit genocide during the Nazi regime. Chemistry made possible killing a significant proportion of the eleven million Holocaust victims by lethal gas poisoning. Evolution is either true or not based on its data and utility as a theory. Evolution should not be condemned merely on grounds of its misappropriation.

Similarly, claims that "if you teach people that they are animals, they will behave like animals" are neither persuasive nor compelling reasons to disavow the theory of evolution. Biologically, we *are* part of the animal kingdom. We share much of the same organic machinery, biochemistry, and anatomy that all animals do. What sets us apart as humans is our *soul*. As Christians, we believe that we are indwelt with an eternal God-given soul, which gives us the capacity for relationship with God and provides us with ethical and rational qualities that no other animal possesses; we are God-"breathed" and unique among animals.

And in any case, why would we suddenly act as anything but human when confronted with the theory of evolution? Would a student, upon learning the theory, start to act like a hamster or a dung beetle rather than a human? We act like "animals" because we are fallen people living in a fallen world. Jeremiah 17:9 tells us, "The heart is deceitful above all things and beyond cure. Who can understand it?" (NIV). Matthew 15:19 concurs with, "For out of the heart come evil thoughts— murder, adultery, sexual immorality, theft, false testimony, slander." The evil is within us. The cure is not to ban the teaching of evolution; rather, the cure is to become a new creation in Christ and receive the Holy Spirit. This is the doctrine the world desperately needs, not the farce of creationism and ID.

Have You Read Both Sides?

When I engage creationists and Intelligent Design advocates in verbal jousting matches, I am often rebuffed with the refrain, "Well, have you ever looked at or read the *other* side's arguments?" They are occasionally surprised when I respond, "Actually, yes! And I still do!" Many don't know that I "cut my teeth" on creationist and ID publications. I was a creationist/ID advocate long before I embraced evolution. In fact, I informally debated against those who believed in evolution and was actually quite good at it! For years and years, all I ever read and explored was creationist/ID material. I voraciously read creationist/ID websites to learn all the responses I possibly could to the "claims of evolution." I devoured books by creationist and ID "scientists" and was first in line to see movies such as *Expelled: No Intelligence Allowed*. Like a sponge, I absorbed the content of YouTube videos that rebuked evolution, and I listened to my favorite Christian radio show hosts discredit evolution, much to my satisfaction. In fact, I *still* read creationist/ID material almost daily.

However, the question gets interesting when I toss the proverbial football back to the inquisitor. "Have you ever cracked an evolution textbook?" I sometimes ask. While *very* few have responded that they have, most sheepishly hem and haw, looking to move the conversation elsewhere out of embarrassment because they know they have not. I'll be the first one to admit I never seriously examined the claims of evolution until my junior year of college. All my previous "research" had been done through the tendentious lens of apologists and ID/creationist authors. I trusted that these fine Christian folks would give me an unbiased and objective summary of the evidence. This most certainly was not the case. The combination of my naivete and intellectual laziness led to a worldview built on toothpicks and quicksand.

One thing I learned during my scientific training is that you *always* do your *own* homework. As the old science saying goes, "In God we trust, in all others show us the data!" Don't trust me, Lee Strobel, Richard Dawkins, or anyone else to do your homework for you. When you seriously investigate a claim about the universe, always try to identify the *source* of the information, and audit all of the references provided when possible, and if none are provided, this could certainly be a red flag. When you see a superscript number at the end or in the middle of a sentence in this book (called an endnote), you can turn to the back of the book in the corresponding "Notes" section and evaluate my sources for yourself. The vast majority of my reference material for claims comes from peer-reviewed (refereed) scientific journals written by professionals in their field of study, and the rest of the sources are largely reputable university websites or trustworthy scientific publications. I tried very hard to use mostly free to view journal articles that can be accessed by anyone at "scholar.google.com." While investigating this topic on your own, be very wary of anything cited from online sources (save for online peer-reviewed journals or credible university sites), especially from a personal webpage, blog, Wikipedia, or group that is forcefully pushing a certain worldview. In other words, use the mind God gave you to boldly ferret out the truth. Can we come to a truly trustworthy conclusion on anything, having analyzed only one side of the issue?

And herein lies the problem. We don't investigate the other side, because we are dogmatic, apathetic, or afraid of what we might find. I know I was. I didn't *want* evolution to be true. I tried everything I could to convince myself that it was all a hoax. Try as I might to prop up and reinforce my creationist/ID beliefs, they toppled under the weight of the full spectrum of carefully examined evidence. Sometimes I still make believe that evolution isn't true, and that I can go back to having a simplistic, one-dimensional understanding of Holy Scripture. I don't say this to be terse; this is a candid admission I'm making to you. It is confounding and perplexing to deal with newfound questions such as the historical Adam and Eve, the Nochaic flood, and the intention of Genesis. Evolution may very well raise more questions about the Bible than it answers. However, like Plato's allegory of the cave, I cannot go back to my life in the dark cave now that I have seen the light of the outside world. I have viewed things as they truly are, and I cannot go back to intellectual darkness.

Evolution Leads to Atheism

Many have hinted heavily, if not outright stated as fact, that belief in evolution will necessarily lead to atheism—or worse yet—to a liberal, watered-down version of nominal Christianity. Creation Ministries International bemoans that "there is a common pattern in many apostates—exposure to evolution."[6] Lee Strobel affirms this notion, publicizing the charge that evolution "propelled" him "towards atheism" during his school days. He goes on to state, "My disbelief flowered after discovering that Darwinism displaces the need for a deity."[7] Geisler and Brooks add their two cents to this conclusion, asserting, "The Bible's view on origins of the universe, first life, and new life forms, have caused many to falter in their acceptance of the Scriptures as truth."[8] I could easily spend the next dozen or so pages dredging up creationist and ID'er quotes (see subchapter "Splitting the Horns of the Dilemma" for more examples), but suffice to say that many Christians believe acceptance of evolution inevitably leads to atheism.

Not surprisingly, many atheists agree wholeheartedly. Richard Dawkins writes that "Darwin made it possible to be an intellectually fulfilled atheist."[9] Cornell biologist William Provine similarly boasts that "evolution is the greatest engine of atheism."[10] What is clear is that many prominent atheists, as well as many ardent creationist/Intelligent Design advocates, subscribe to the notion that belief in evolution leads to disbelief in God.

But can a biological theory truly be held responsible for spawning so many religious dissidents? Or is it more likely that our flawed human nature implores us to rationalize our actions? Where Dawkins and Provine wanted to find fodder for their antireligious beliefs, they found it. Where Lee Strobel wanted to find "license to thrill," he found it. And out of the very same well, where I want to find appreciation and wonder for God, *I* find it. As broken people, we have a tendency toward confirmation bias. That is, we interpret things, search for things, and remember things in a way that supports our own beliefs and desires. All the while, we dismiss what doesn't fit into our own personal agenda.

A good atheist friend of mine told me a story about rationalization that has stuck with me to this day. It is about two twin brothers with an alcoholic father. One brother becomes an alcoholic and gives the explanation that he is an alcoholic because his father was an alcoholic. The other brother never touches a drop and gives the explanation that he never drinks because his father was an alcoholic. Have we not at one time or another looked into the clouds and seen what we wanted to see? As Christians, we should know that people will twist anything to suit their inclinations. Have we not all experienced someone who twists Scripture to support what he or she desires? There are those who hijack the faith as well as those who hijack science. The only difference between the two is the means; the ends are the same.

Moreover, I am living proof not only that evolution does not lead to atheism, but that embracing God's revealed truth can lead to a more fulfilling and deeper relationship with Him. The only thing that ever steered me toward atheism, ironically, was the false dichotomy largely perpetuated by creationists and Intelligent Design advocates. In my crisis of faith, I began to consider that they were right; since I believed in evolution, I must give up my faith. And so the creationists create a self-fulfilling prophecy! Evolution is not driving Christians toward atheism; it is the false dichotomy that the creationist/ID propaganda machine constantly screeches through its megaphone that is driving many toward atheism! Also, recall the aforementioned statistics showing that 22%–46% of church-going Christians believe in evolution. If evolution is like kryptonite to biblical faith, why are almost a quarter to nearly half of regular church attenders who believe in evolution still attending?

The Noble Lie?

I have been asked before if we Christians should continue to prop up creationism and ID, even if they are neither scientific nor accurate. In other words, should we perpetuate the "noble lie?" Evolution and an old earth can be a bitter pill to swallow, and indeed I have seen my brothers and sisters struggle with cognitive dissonance after their worldview was disemboweled by the facts and evidence for evolution. Is evolution too much for Christians to handle? Will they walk away from the faith, being disillusioned and confused by this apparent capitulation and kowtowing toward modern science? Maybe the Christian masses are best left with a simplistic and literal understanding of Scripture; after all, can they *really* be trusted to discern the truth by themselves?

I would respond that a lie is a lie, and it is *never* noble. I reject the hypothesis that Christians are intellectually weak and unable to handle the concept of God utilizing evolution to accomplish His ends. Ironically, the church was at one time the center of intellectual and scientific thought in the Western world, not on the fringes as it is today. Why don't we take God's science and revealed truth back? Let's be champions of truth in *all* areas. For those who may falter based on their inability to reconcile the Bible and science, recall the parable of the sower, which I have paraphrased: 'If we have been sown in good soil, we will produce a bountiful crop; if we have been sown on rocky ground, we will have no root in ourselves and quickly fall away' (Matt. 13:20–23).

If our faith is founded on creationism, Intelligent Design, or even evolution alone, our faith will falter. If our faith is founded on Jesus Christ, we will *never* be disappointed. It is with great imprudence and recklessness that we base our faith on man-made constructs such as Young Earth, Day-age, Gap, and Progressive Creationism, or Intelligent Design and Theistic Evolution. While I believe in evolution completely, It is not the basis of my faith in God, Jesus, or the Bible. If evolution, being shown to be 100% true to you, would cause you to lose your faith, perhaps you built your house on the sand of "proof-seeking."

What creationism and ID *appear* to offer is material "proof" that God is real and that the Bible can be trusted. If the earth was found to be only 6,000 years old, it would seem to very strongly support the idea that Genesis is a literal and historical narrative and would leave us little choice but to conclude that the Bible is truly the Word of God. If it could somehow be shown that the first microbe was a miracle, or that the Cambrian explosion was an act of God, or that DNA is a coding language directly dictated by God, every knee would bow and every tongue would confess! We all desperately want proof of God. We seek after a "sign," just like the "wicked and adulterous generation" we have always been (Matt. 16:4).

But we will never have proof of our faith. We can research the historicity of Jesus and the Bible. We can learn Thomas Aquinas' and St. Anselm's proofs for the existence of God. In other words, we can wrap the rope of reason around our waists and back toward the abyss of the unknown, but when we reach the edge of the chasm, the rope will be stretched taught. We must choose to either make a leap of faith—or not. Some choose not to leap, and in the end, all abstentions will be counted as "no's." For those who take the leap of faith, there is an unimaginable reward stretching from here into eternity, greater than the mind can fathom. But it is always a leap of faith, not a leap of proof. As the old hymn goes,

> My hope is built on nothing less
> Than Jesus' blood and righteousness.
> I dare not trust the sweetest frame,
> But wholly lean on Jesus' name.

Paul substantiates this doctrine when he writes, "And if Christ has not been raised, your faith is futile; you are still in your sins" (1 Cor. 15:17 NIV). Now, I am not referring to fideism. There is enough evidence from logic, philosophy, history, and the inner witness of the Holy Spirit to make a reasonable leap of faith; however, there is not undeniable proof that would negate our free will and coerce us into believing. When we seek Him instead of proof, we will never be let down.

Darwin for Sale

When it comes to the evolution vs. creation issue, I often get the feeling fellow Christians feel as if I am trying to "sell" them something. When I debate my brothers and sisters, I see the suspicion in their eyes, and their sense of mistrust is often palpable. I am often obliged to remind them that I am not an evolution infomercial; I am not a salesman for Darwin. I gain nothing if you decide to abandon creationism and adopt evolutionary theory. This book—admittedly in support of evolution—is being sold close to cost, and I also am using my own money to distribute this book free of charge. One of the main reasons I wrote this book is to reach my friends and colleagues who are struggling with this issue. The original "book" was to be nothing more than a pamphlet printed from my own computer. This is my ministry. I don't profit off of you or anyone accepting the theory of evolution. As stated previously, God is the center of my life. Glorifying Him, obeying Him, and spreading the gospel is my primary mission in life, not proclaiming the gospel of "Darwinism." I am only involved in this debate because I strongly feel that this area is destroying Christianity from the inside out. Anti-evolution and antiscience sentiments are malignant pathoses we must excise in order to shift our focus back to the Gospel.

Why Christians Hate Evolution

It is no secret that there is a quite vocal minority of scientists who are intensely devoted to a materialistic worldview—a philosophical view that maintains matter is the only thing that exists. There is no room for the supernatural or divine in this worldview; there is neither soul nor spirit. Although science cannot by its own definition speak with any authority on whether or not God exists, materialists expeditiously discard this fact and habitually wield science as a club with which to abuse Christians. Chief iconoclast Richard Dawkins screeches:

> Mock them [the religious]! Ridicule them! In public! Don't fall for the convention that we're all too polite to talk about religion. Religion is not off the table. Religion is not off limits. Religion makes specific claims about the universe which need to be substantiated and need to be challenged and if necessary need to be ridiculed with contempt.[11]

Physicist Steven Weinberg less frothily opines:

> I think the world needs to wake up from its long nightmare of religious belief, and anything that we scientists can do to weaken the hold of religion should be done and may in fact be our greatest contribution to civilization.[12]

Geneticist Richard Lewontin is quite candid as well when he confesses openly:

> Our willingness to accept scientific claims that are against common sense is the key to an understanding of the real struggle between science and the supernatural. We take the side of science *in spite* of the patent absurdity of some of its constructs, *in spite* of its failure to fulfill many of its extravagant promises of health and life, in spite of the tolerance of the scientific community for unsubstantiated just-so stories, because we have a prior

commitment, a commitment to materialism. It is not that the methods and institutions of science somehow compel us to accept a material explanation of the phenomenal world, but, on the contrary, that we are forced by our *a priori* adherence to material causes to create an apparatus of investigation and a set of concepts that produce material explanations, no matter how counter-intuitive, no matter how mystifying to the uninitiated. Moreover, that materialism is absolute, for we cannot allow a Divine Foot in the door.[13]

I could fill volumes with antireligious quotes from prominent scientists, but at the risk of beating the proverbial horse to death, I'll make my point instead: Scientists such as Richard Dawkins, Christopher Hitchens, Samuel Harris, Daniel Dennet, and Jerry Coyne have made a name for themselves by using science to assault faith. It is clear that these men attempt to hijack science and misuse it to extol their epistles of atheism. And scientists wonder why acceptance of belief in creationism has increased in the past decade![14] When anti-theists make such caustic and polarizing remarks, the theist's gut reaction is to repudiate the aggressor by attacking the science from which the atheist purports to derive his conclusion. Instead of striking at the scientist's metaphysical arguments, we engage the wrong enemy and unwisely besiege science. Scientists who desecrate religion are a vociferous minority, but they do so with such vitriol that they leave a bad taste for science in anyone's mouth.

When scientists speak about nonscience issues, their arguments carry about as much weight as when pastors talk about evolution. When prominent atheists espouse their views on God, faith and the supernatural, they do so out of their own metaphysical beliefs, *not* the convictions of science. This thinly veiled attempt to smear people of faith is nothing more than anti-theists commandeering science, claiming it says things it doesn't and declaring it proves things it doesn't. Atheistic scientists may allege that science disproves faith, but science *cannot* do anything of the sort. Science deals with the natural world and is based on the scientific method and empirical evidence. Things like faith, morality, beauty, and the afterlife are fields that science couldn't touch even it if wanted to.

The real enemy, however, is materialism, not science. Materialism is the narrow-minded charlatan masquerading as the "free thinker" or "rational intellectual." Materialists refuse to consider any kind of knowledge outside of scientific knowledge. Period. While some promulgate this view as being "enlightened" or "logical," it is nothing of the sort; it is intellectual suicide in the strictest sense. Closing off vast realms of knowledge to the mind is neither noble nor reasonable. While Christians are unreasonably excoriated by atheists for being "bigoted," materialists are in fact the ones bigoted in their militant adherence to their insular worldview of materialism. Dinesh D'Souza astutely writes:

> By contrast [to the materialist], the theist is much more open-minded and reasonable. The theist does not deny the validity of scientific reasoning. On the contrary, the theist is constantly reasoning in this way in work and life. The theist is entirely willing to acknowledge material and natural causes for events, but he also admits the possibility of other types of knowledge.[15]

Physicist John Polkinghorne illustrates this point marvelously by giving the example of a kettle of boiling water. One could ask a scientist, "Why is that water boiling?" and he or she would answer in terms of molecules and temperatures. But there is a second explanation: The water is boiling because I want to have a cup of tea. This second explanation is a perfectly valid description of reality, yet it is ignored or avoided by the scientific account.[16]

Though atheistic scientists can be quite forceful and bitter in their lambasting of religion, that does not necessarily mean they are mistaken when it comes to their scientific views. Difficult as it may be, we must not confuse what scientists themselves say for what science itself says. Though a handful of evolutionary biologists may be thoroughly acrimonious, we must remember that the theory of evolution rises or falls on the merits of its data and utility as a theory. Disliking someone's metaphysics is not grounds for dismissing his science.

PART II

THE EVIDENCE FOR AN OLD EARTH

CHAPTER FIVE

YOUNG EARTH BY THE NUMBERS

Young Earth Creationism most commonly holds that the earth is only 6,000 years old. Some allow for up to 10,000 years, however, but what "young-earthers" all have in common is that they utterly reject the notion that the universe is billions of years old.[1] This position stems from firm adherence to a literal interpretation of Genesis—that is to say the six, twenty-four hour days of creation. Through their interpretation of biblical genealogies, YECs date creation no earlier than 8,000 B.C. Another important date in YEC is the Nochaic flood of Genesis 6–9, which YECs consider to be a worldwide flood that occurred approximately 4,500 years ago.[2]

At the risk of sounding pretentious, it must be stated that the hypothesis of the 6,000-year-old earth enjoys no mainstream scientific support and is found only in religious circles. As previously noted, polls indicate that 95%–99% of scientists believe in evolution that could not have taken place in 6,000 years. Furthermore, the InterAcademy Panel on International Issues, which consists of sixty-eight international and national science academies, issued a statement in 2006 affirming the scientific consensus of a 4.5-billion-year-old earth and an 11- to 15-billion-year-old universe.[3]

The belief in a 6,000-year-old earth was all but abandoned by mainstream science by the middle of the 19th century and is unlikely to ever be resuscitated. Yet surprisingly, 39% of the general American public agrees with the statement, "God created the universe, the earth, the sun, moon, stars, plants, animals, and the first two people within the past 10,000 years," according to a 2009 poll.[4] The same poll also reveals that 60% of Americans agree with the statement, "There was a flood within the past 10,000 years that covered all of the earth and was responsible for most of the rock layers and fossils that are seen across the world."[5]

One of the many problems surrounding YEC is that it invalidates many diverse fields of science, such as chemistry, genetics, paleontology, biology, astronomy, biochemistry, molecular biology, physics, geology, cosmology, astrophysics, geophysics, and anthropology, to name a few. These fields all are united in their support of an old earth and of evolution. All of these fields contribute a small piece of the puzzle that creates the "box top" picture of an old earth rife with evolution. Are we to believe that these diverse disciplines comprised of scientists from around the world, spanning the last several hundred years are all colluding together to deceive the public? How can the same science that delivers us airplanes, smartphones, and electricity be so wrong when it comes to the age of the earth and evolution?

It's an Old World After All

Until now, only the theological, philosophical, and psychological aspects of the creation–evolution controversy have been covered. Admittedly, I have thus far been presupposing evolution and an old earth to be true without yet demonstrating any evidence for that view. Accordingly, I would now like to get down to brass tacks and examine the actual evidence for an old earth in order to set the stage for discussing evolution. The evidence for both is a deluge of information, much of which, to be quite honest, can be quite tedious and monotonous. Therefore, I will here present the evidence I feel makes the most powerful case for the true age of the earth, though there are many more examples than the few I have chosen.

CHAPTER SIX

SENIOR ORGANISMS

Bristling at the Conclusion

If the YEC premise is that a global flood covered the earth 4,300–4,500 years ago, then any presently living organism shown to be older than 4,500 years of age would effectively dismantle this belief (I am not doubting a historical Noah or a regional flood, only a *worldwide* flood). Incredibly, there are many organisms that fit this bill. One bristlecone pine (*Pinus longaeva*) residing in the White Mountains of California was studied in 2012 and found to be an astounding 5,062 years old.[1] This tree amazingly is still alive and has two deceased companions, "Methuselah" and "Prometheus," which rank in at 4,845 and 4,844 years old respectively.[2,3] Prometheus is, unfortunately, recently deceased, having been cut down in 1964 as part of a graduate student's research.[4]

These trees were measured by crossdating, a widely recognized and legitimate dendrochronological technique that matches up narrow and wide ring patterns between core samples from not only the same tree but also different trees from various locations.[5] This process acts as a built-in cross-check to accurately ascertain the age of a tree with a great degree of certainty.[6]

For the uninitiated, dendrochronology is an entire sub-branch (pun intended) of science that deals solely with tree-ring dating. These scientists analyze growth ring patterns in trees in order to pin down a date in history when the tree was felled or had germinated. While YECs often express doubt about carbon dating, which I will address at the end of this chapter, the ages of the three aforementioned trees were ascertained by studying their rings, *not* by radiometric dating.

Some YECs insist that tree-ring counts cannot be trusted, attributing their suspicion to "false rings." While this phenomenon of an occasional false ring can occur, missing rings can also happen, leading a ring count to cause a tree to actually appear *younger* than it truly is. Additionally, false rings easily stand out to trained dendrochronologists.[7] What's more, recall that the three trees in question were also crossdated, which ensures each individual tree ring is assigned its exact year of formation.[8] Furthermore, scientists have used crossdating techniques to create an unbroken record of tree rings from live and dead trees that extends back 13,900 years.[9] This is much older than the alleged 4,500 year date of the Nochaic flood, the 6,000 year date of creation, and even the generous 10,000 year creation date.

On somewhat of a side-note, I heard a Detroit area Christian radio talk show host (the same one mentioned throughout the book) defend a young earth by casting doubt on trees claimed to be older than 4,500 years:

> C'mon folks—think about it for a second. How could they possibly date those trees? How do they know they're older than 4,500 years? They don't, 'cause they would have to cut 'em down to find out! They don't know how old these trees are. They're just guessing in order to support their evolutionist views!

I kid you not, I nearly drove my truck off the road because I was so stunned and horrified by what I heard emanating from my radio.

There is no need to cut down the tree! The main tool of dendrochronologists is the increment borer. It is a "T"-shaped instrument that bears a striking similarity to an old-fashioned auger or drill (not the Three Stooges kind—older than that). The difference is, the increment borer is hollow like a straw, and as it drills deeper into the tree, it preserves a pencil-thin elongated plug of the tree for ring study, thereby eliminating the need to cut down the tree. And as stated above, a 4,844-year-old tree *was* cut down and definitively aged as older than 4,500 years.[10] Thus, this radio-show host fulfills St. Augustine's prophecy that "people show up vast ignorance in a Christian and laugh it to scorn."[11]

The takeaway point here is that there are confirmed organisms (some still living) older than the proposed 2,500 B.C. date of the Nochaic flood. It would be very difficult indeed to imagine that these bristlecone pines could possibly have survived after having been completely submerged for a year. As one who has studied plant physiology at the graduate level, I can tell you with certainty that they would have died within weeks, if not less.[12] The question for YECs is this: How is there a *living* 5,062-year-old tree if a year-long worldwide flood took place 4,500 years ago? The conclusion is inescapable, as the most cogent solution is that there simply was not a worldwide flood 4,500 years ago.

Old Tjikko

Norway Spruce (*Picea abies*) trees may only be several years old when they grace your living room at Christmastime, but one such tree in Sweden is an astounding 9,550 years old.[13,14] This individual, named "Old Tjikko," is the oldest living individual tree in the world. For those suspicious of ring-counting (albeit there is no good reason to doubt such practice), it will be comforting to know that this tree's age was determined by carbon-14 dating. The visible trunk of the tree is only a few centuries old; however, Norway Spruces employ vegetative cloning, whereby the individual trunk dies but the root remains alive and subsequently sprouts a new trunk. Trees such as these also perform "layering," a process where a branch touches the ground and there creates new roots. Hence, it may be more accurate to say that the root system is 9,550 years old and still very much alive. Furthermore, there is a cluster of nearly two dozen other Norway Spruce trees in the same location, all of which date to over 8,000 years old.[15] In any case, this 9,550-year-old tree is older than YECs believe the whole universe is.

Huon Pine

The Huon Pine (*Lagarostrobos franklinii*) of Australia's Mount Read is another clonal tree that has individual trees ranging anywhere from 2,000 to 3,000 years old. However, since this also colony reproduces vegetatively, the age of its root system has been approximated to be 10,000 years old.[16,17] It bears reiterating that this is the same living organism that has been alive from 10,000 years ago to this very day. If Noah's flood was worldwide and occurred 4,500 years ago, this plant certainly would not be alive today. Likewise, this 10,000-year-old plant started life 4,000 years before creation was alleged to have taken place in 4,004 B.C.

Box Huckleberry

This humble shrub was nearly exterminated by the most recent ice age but managed to hang on. Box Huckleberry (*Gaylussacia brachycera*) is a relative of the familiar blueberry and other huckleberries and inhabits the east-central United States. By measuring this shrub's rate of growth, scientists estimate that a particular colony in Pennsylvania may be as old as 13,000 years.[18,19,20,21] However, doubts have recently been raised about this age, as the biome in that area 13,000 years ago would have been a boreal forest that would be somewhat cold and inhospitable to the box huckleberry. More conservative estimates, therefore, place the colony's age at around 8,000 years, based on its rate of growth.[22] In any case, this organism is significantly older than the 6,000 year creation date.

Eucalyptus Recurva

Another botanical wonder from Down Under is the "Ice Age Gum" or "Mongarlowe Mallee" (*Eucalyptus Recurva*). Only five individuals of this species remain alive today, making this an exceedingly rare and interesting plant. Their growth spreads horizontally at an observed rate of 2 millimeters per year, with the largest plant spanning 26 meters from its center. Using this growth rate, scientists have estimated this individual to be an impressive 13,000 years old.[23]

King Clone

Deep in the Mojave Desert of the American Southwest resides a lowly clump of unassuming creosote bushes (*Larrea tridentata*) dubbed "King Clone." This ancient plant clocks in at a mind-blowing 11,700 years old and still ticking. This organism provides perhaps one of the most convincing evidences against a young earth, as the bush's age has been derived from both ring studies *and* carbon-14 dating. What lends this age determination robust credibility is that the two different methods yield the same age.[24,25] Which is more reasonable and logical to believe— that both the ring and carbon dating methods are wrong and that this bush is *not* 11,700 years old? Or that this still thriving bush is much older than the supposed date of creation, because the earth is in fact much older than 6,000 years?

Palmer's Oaks

The Jurupa mountains of California contain yet another elderly specimen. Tucked away on a mountainside is a grove of the clonal Palmer's Oak (*Quercus palmeri*), which has been growing there for the past 13,000 years.[26] This tree was dated not by carbon dating but by ring counts,[27] providing yet another supreme example of a living organism more than twice as old as a 6,000-year-old earth.

King's Lomatia

This interesting plant lives in the exotic jungles of Tasmania, where only one lone colony remains in the wild. All King's lomatia (*Lomatia tasmanica*) are genetically identical, making this sole survivor of the species very unique indeed. This species is sterile, as it is genetically triploid, meaning it has three copies of each chromosome instead of its normal two. This genetic abnormality renders the plant unable to reproduce except by "cloning" itself vegetatively. This means that when a branch of this plant hits the ground, it begins to grow new roots and creates a new plant that is 100% genetically identical to the "parent" plant.

All this becomes more relevant when one examines fossilized leaves of this plant found nearby. The fossilized leaves are indistinguishable from those of the current plant, as are its cells and overall structure, a strong indication that this fossilized plant also possessed the same triploidy condition that uniquely affects leaf characteristics. This would indicate that this fossilized plant would also not have been able to reproduce except vegetatively, meaning that the fossilized plant is almost certainly the exact same plant we have today! Using carbon-14 dating, this plant is conservatively estimated to be a mind-boggling 43,600 years of age. Estimates do, however, range as high as 135,000 years.[28]

Ancient Seagrass

In an area of the Mediterranean Sea, between Spain and Cypress, lies an enormous meadow of seagrass (*Posidonia oceanica*) that spans nearly ten miles and weighs over 6,000 tons. Forty of these enormous meadows exist, covering an area of 2,000 miles. Based on the colonies' rate of spread, these asexual clonal plants were found to be between 80,000 and 200,000 years of age.[29] Even the lower estimate of these colonies' ages are over ten times older than the YEC believes the entire universe to be.

CHAPTER SEVEN

ANCIENT NATURAL PHENOMENA

Ancient Coral

The Eniwetok Atoll (part of the Marshall Islands) is perhaps best known for hosting post-WWII nuclear bomb tests, but this coral reef atoll holds other tantalizing secrets as well. The reef is perched atop an extinct volcano and is nearly a mile thick (approximately 4,530–4,610 feet).[1,2] This is not flood deposition material as some YECs have tried to argue; Eniwetok instead is bonafide grown-in-place coral.[3] Corals are marine animals that secrete calcium carbonate (lime) to form hardened skeletons. This creates the foundation of the reef, as corals are constantly depositing calcium carbonate, and new corals subsequently grow on top of this. At best, the species of coral that provide a platform for new growth can grow no faster than 0.5–1.0 inch per year.[4,5,6]

Creationists will note that branching corals may grow up to 125mm per year; however, since these corals are built like the branches of a tree, they do not build reefs at rates anywhere close to those of non-branching corals.[7] Additionally, branching corals have a similar mass compared to dense corals, but the difference in growth rate is due to how mass is allocated. In other words, dense and branching corals may grow at the same rate when the *overall* growth rate is taken into account, but branching corals grow thin branching structures more quickly, whereas dense corals grow more evenly and slowly throughout their entire structure, though both are adding roughly the same amount of mass in the same span of time. Furthermore, branching corals are subject to wave action and other such forces that break and wear branches.[8] In any case, even if we were to assume optimum conditions for growth in reef-building corals and also assume the uppermost limit of growth rate for the reef's entire history, we still arrive at a very conservative 54,300 years before present. Even if the corals were growing twice as fast in the past (for which there is no evidence), this still would render the corals over 27,000 years old. Even five times its present growth rate would yield an age of 10,800 years.

And the picture gets even worse for a young earth, as these overly optimistic growth rates do not take into account weathering and erosion that have been shown to have taken place at Eniwetok, nor do they take into account the established fact that reefs as a whole grow markedly slower than the individual corals that comprise the reef.[9] Also a matter of consideration is the long periods of time during which the ancient reef stood above water, preventing reef growth completely and even at times allowing trees to grow on the reef.[10] Considering these factors, a very generous and idealistic growth rate would be about one centimeter (0.394 inches) per year.[11,12] Using this more legitimate growth rate, scientists have placed the minimum age of the Eniwetok atoll reef at 138,000 years.[13] Even a twenty-fold increase of this modest growth rate (for which there is no evidence) would still yield an age of 6,900 years.

Furthermore, devout Christian Geologist Daniel Wonderly places the reef's age at a minimum of 176,000 years, based on a carefully determined growth rate of 8mm per year.[14] Wonderly adds, "Thus the total length of time required for forming the 4,610 foot reef deposit of Eniwetok was undoubtedly many times 176,000 years."[15] Is it really reasonable to believe that this coral was growing over twenty times faster in the past, then it suddenly slowed down by more than twenty times when people began studying it? Or is it more likely that the earth really is indeed older than 6,000 years?

Clear as Ice

Perhaps nothing is more troubling to YECs than ice cores. In areas where temperature does not typically rise above freezing, a phenomenon termed "ice layering" occurs. This phenomenon is readily observed in ice sheets and glaciers, where annual differences in irradiation and temperature result in distinct layers of ice from one year to the next. The result is a series of alternating light and dark ice layers, similar to the tree rings previously mentioned. These layers are easy to read, and since one layer is accumulated each year, they give an accurate minimum age of the earth.[16] Scientists can use a coring bit to drill down into the ice sheets or glaciers, which produces a very long, thin plug of ice that allows them to look at the layers and count the years that have passed (Figure 7.1). Contrary to creationist claims, these samples are taken from static and stable parts of the glacier or ice sheet not subject to the periodic thawing, freezing, and precipitation that would give the false impression of many years,.[17]

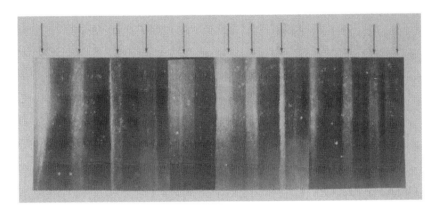

Figure 7.1 A short section of the GISP2 ice core from a depth of 1,855 meters shows alternating light (summer) and dark (winter) layers. The arrows indicate eleven annual summer layers. From: NOAA

Utilization of this dating method on one Antarctic ice sheet yielded an impressive 700,000 years.[18] Other studies have found even older ice in east Antarctica, where the European Project for Ice Coring in Antarctica (EPICA) found a core sample obtained from a site dubbed "Dome C" to be 800,000 years old.[19,20,21] An overabundance of evidence also exists for the age of the Vostok ice core from Antarctica, which has been dated to 420,000 years before present.[22,23] Although YECs may counter with unsubstantiated claims of "false layers" (strangely similar to the "false tree ring" claims) and of WWII planes buried under hundreds of ice layers (in actuality, the plane landed on a warmer coast and on an active glacier; additionally an ice core sample was never taken), definitive proof exists for the reliability of the ice core dating method.[24] Since dates of some volcanic eruptions are known for certain through human-recorded history (e.g., the eruption of Mount Vesuvius in AD 79, which destroyed Pompeii), we can look back that many years in the ice layer record and see if we find any ash that corresponds to that date. And guess what? Ash deposits from multiple volcanic events mesh neatly with the annual layer count derived from the ice cores.[25,26,27]

In order for a YEC to preserve belief in a 6,000-year-old earth, he or she would have to believe that ice layers in the past were somehow laid down at a rate over 70 times their present rate! Furthermore, YECs would have to believe that this 7,000% increase in ice layer accumulation miraculously stopped just before volcanoes began to erupt and deposit ash during years that match up perfectly with the ice layer record of history. The simpler solution, of course, is that the earth is much older than 6,000 years, as clearly evidenced by multiple ice cores.

Dark Side of the Moon

For eons, mankind has contemplated the moon. This enigmatic orb holds just as much fascination for us today as it did for our earliest ancestors, albeit for some today, this interest is only in regards to settling the question of the age of the earth. It is oft cited by YECs that there should be anywhere from 100–2,000 feet of dust (technically termed "lunar soil") on the moon if the earth truly were 4.54 billion years old, and that it was feared by NASA that astronauts would plummet into mires of dust upon landing on the moon in 1969.[28,29] In actuality, however, there was no fear that astronauts would sink into moondust. Surveyor I had already landed on the moon in 1966 and dispelled any fears of such a fate, and even one year earlier scientists had largely dismissed this concern, due to observed optical properties on the moon's surface.[30]

Furthermore, creationists' expectations of bottomless fathoms of moondust were based on an obsolete calculation made nearly six decades ago. It is universally agreed that the 1960 paper upon which this creationist claim is founded was based on flawed methodology and is void for any scientific use.[31,32] In the more than half a century since this questionable paper was published, many other technologically advanced techniques have ascertained rates of dust accumulation. Satellite penetration, zodiacal light refraction, Antarctic ice cores, seafloor sediments, atmospheric dust measurements, and photo recordings of light streaks made by meteors entering the atmosphere have all since obtained cosmic dust deposition rates orders of magnitude smaller than the antiquated 1960 measurement.[33,34]

Multiple methods and many different scientists have placed rates of cosmic dust deposition from 1.6x10^9 gm/year to 1.7x10^11 gm/year.[35,36,36,38] This averages out to roughly 2x10^-9 grams/cm^2/per year, as postulated by geophysicist J. S. Dohnanyi.[39] In plain English, this means the moon accumulates two nanograms of dust (one nanogram is one thousandth of a millionth of a gram) over every square centimeter of its surface on an annual basis. At this rate, the moon would have accumulated nearly two inches of dust over 4.5 billion years. And what did the astronauts find when they landed on the moon? An average of two inches of dust—an amount consistent with a 4.5-billion-year-old moon.[40,41]

To believe that the moon is 6,000 years old, you would have to dream up a past lunar dust deposition rate 500,000 times faster than the current rate! And of course this would also commit one to believing that this accelerated rate of moondust deposition ceased sometime before the 1970s, when we determined current rates of deposition. Why would moondust accumulate 500,000 times faster in the past, only to slow down when we began studying it?

Even some creationists now disown the "moon dust proves young earth" line of defense. Below the headline "Moon-Dust Argument No Longer Useful," Young Earth Creationist website *Answers in Genesis* laments that "the moon-dust argument was easy to understand and explain. Nevertheless, it has been found to be an invalid argument for creationists."[42] Other creationists have also derided the moon dust argument, like the *Institute for Creation Research*, which writes the following in their *Creation Ex-Nihilo Technical Journal*:

> Calculations show that the amount of meteoritic dust in the surface dust layer, and that which trace element analyses have shown to be in the regolith, is consistent with the current meteoritic dust influx rate operating over the evolutionists' timescale [. . .] the moon dust argument, using uniformitarian assumptions to argue against an old age for the moon and the solar system, should for the present not be used by creationists.[43]

The amount of dust present on the moon and the corresponding rate of dust deposition provide powerful evidence that the moon is in fact billions of years old. This may be a bitter pill to swallow, but even Young Earth Creationists have had to admit defeat on this one.

Wishing Upon a Star

When you look up in the night sky, do you ever think about how long and how far the light from those stars has been traveling to reach you? Well, with a pair of binoculars, one can see stars that are 10 million light years away. Buy an amateur telescope at your local department store, and you can peer at quasars looming 2 billion light years away. Even your naked eye can spot the Andromeda galaxy, which is located 2.6 million light years away from Earth.[44]

Light moves very fast (186,000 miles per second), and at earth speeds, this only translates to minuscule fractions of a second when looking at earth objects. However, when you watch the sun rise in the morning, you are actually looking at light that left the sun a full eight minutes prior; it takes light that long to traverse the 93 million miles from the sun to the earth. Similarly, when you gaze at a star a million light years away, it has taken the light that long to reach you. The star itself may no longer even exist, but its light travels onward throughout the universe.

Herein lies the troubling problem for Young Earth Creationism. If the earth were created only 6,000 years ago, why are we seeing stars that are *farther* than 6,000 light years away? This would seem to be the trump card that would put to rest any Old Earth critics, for it seems exceedingly absurd that a universe created 6,000 years ago would have light beams that have been cruising through space for millions of years. How is this not the death knell for a young earth? How does a 6,000-year-old earth have light that has been traveling through space for millions, if not billions of years? Ever-present with negative arguments ready in the holster, YECs have cooked up a few flimsy rebuttals.

One creationist response is that the stars really are not hundreds of thousands, millions, or billions of light years away. They are actually only 6,000 or fewer light years away. I sincerely hope at this point that you are as underwhelmed as I am. Several independent methods have calculated the distance of celestial bodies as far as 13 billion light years away![45] Could the technology and science that works so well for space shuttles and smartphones really mistake 13,000,000,000 light years for 6,000?

Another hypothesis is that the speed of light was somehow faster in the past, yet at some point before we were able to measure its speed, it slowed down to its present rate. For the speed of light to have changed enough to give the impression of an old earth, it would have had to be more than a million times faster than it is currently. Is this reasonable to assume? There is no evidence whatsoever for a million-fold increase in light speed. Furthermore, recall from your high-school days the famous Einstein equation "E=mc^2." Without boring anyone to death, this equation necessitates that if you were to increase the speed of light ("c" in the equation), you would have a corresponding increase in energy ("E" in the equation). Now, if "c" were increased enough in the past to give the impression of a 13.8-billion-year-old universe that is really only 6,000 years old, the amount of energy that would have been released would have been more than enough for the sun to completely vaporize the earth.[46] Or, if we were to increase "c" but leave "E" constant, we would have had so little gravity in Adam's day that he, along with our atmosphere, would have floated off into space due to insufficient gravitational attraction.[47]

Perhaps the most intellectually vapid and disturbing argument is the "appearance of age" response. This line of reasoning posits that 6,000 years ago God created everything to appear as though it had been made 13.8 billion years ago. The rationale is that if God could make Adam as a fully formed man, He could also make the universe with light beams already in place, giving the universe an "appearance of age."

One of many monkey wrenches that can be thrown into this flawed apology is the 1987A supernova. This exploding star was observed 170,000 light years away in 1987, which means the actual supernova event had taken place 170,000 years prior, and it took the light beams that long to travel to our lenses.[48] But according to the appearance of age argument, the universe was created 6,000 years ago with light beams already in place, so this star explosion 170,000 years ago would never have taken place. Instead, 6,000 years ago, God must have created a light beam that He knew would hit our telescopes in 1987, and which would appear to show an exploding star that in reality never even actually existed.

Why would God engage in such elaborate deception and trickery? If the universe really is only 6,000 years old, why has God placed so many clues that would deliberately mislead 95%–99% of scientists into believing that the earth is billions of years old and that evolution is true? Did God create deceitful supernova light rays, false ice cores, fraudulent bristlecone pines, bogus coral reefs, and phony amounts of moon dust? Is a God that deceitful even worthy of following?

The idea of a God that deceptive is perverse and unbiblical. Reason and inspired Word tells us that He is *not* a deceiver, and we can take solace in the fact that "the heavens declare the glory of God; the skies proclaim the work of his hands" (Psalm 19:1; NIV). The magnificently ancient universe is nothing to be ashamed of. On the contrary, the cosmos are more elaborate and elegant than any "appearance of age" argument would lead one to believe, and in my opinion, more awe-inspiring and worthy of praise.

Stalactites

Stalactites are the mineral formations readily seen hanging from the ceilings of caves. Superficially similar in appearance to icicles, some stalactites, such as those harbored in the Jeita Grotto of Lebanon, can reach an impressive twenty-seven feet in length.[49] This becomes even more impressive when we consider the growth rate of these structures. Moore and his co-researchers place the average stalactite growth rate at 0.1mm/year,[50] as do Short and his collaborators.[51] Harmon and others sampled forty-three locations on eleven stalactites from four sites across North America. They found that the growth rate varied from 0.0005mm/year to 0.1mm/year, with an average growth rate of 0.0139 mm/year.[52] At the very uppermost growth rate, this translates to less than half an inch of growth per hundred years (0.39 inches). Doing a quick back-of-the-envelope calculation reveals that a twenty-seven foot stalactite would have taken *at least* 83,076 years to attain such a size, even with the most optimistic average growth rate. Even if the stalactite growth rate had been eight times faster in the past, this would still deliver an age of more than 10,000 years. Furthermore, radiometric dating has confidently determined several stalactites to be over 190,000 years old.[53]

Some creationists will retort that stalactites growing on concrete can grow an inch or more per year. And indeed, dripping pipes or precipitation on concrete can create formations that outwardly resemble cave stalactites. Unfortunately, the similarity ends there, as the chemistry and environment of these concrete stalactites are vastly different from those that occur naturally in caves. Concrete and caves are both comprised of limestone; however, the carbon dioxide in concrete has been largely removed during heating, unlike in caves. As a result, water and concrete form calcium hydroxide, which is a hundredfold more soluble than the calcite of caves. When this concrete-borne aqueous calcium hydroxide hits the air, it imbibes copious amounts of carbon dioxide, which gets turned into calcium carbonate and thus forms stalactites.[54] Before anyone falls asleep, I'll state it plainly: This is an unnatural circumstance which bears little if any resemblance to actual cave stalactites. For those who still doubt that there is any difference between cave stalactites and concrete ones, scientists Moore and Sullivan point out in their book *Speleology: The Study of Caves*:

> In 1925, a concrete bridge was constructed inside Postojna Cave, Yugoslavia, and adjacent to it an artificial tunnel was opened. By 1956, tubular stalactites 45 centimeters long were growing from the bridge, while stalactites of the same age in the tunnel were less than 1 centimeter long.[55]

Numerous stalactites are undoubtedly older than 6,000 years. This is evidenced by both known stalactite growth rates and radiometric dating. Both methods provide dates much older than 6,000 years by at least one order of magnitude. Any attempt to dismiss stalactites as "young" inevitably involves special pleading and unreasonable assumptions. These problems become even greater for YECs when one considers that the caves must have been present before the stalactites and that the caves undoubtedly took a substantial amount of time to form as well.

Varves

Varves are similar in construction to tree rings and ice cores in that they have annual layers that provide perhaps the most persuasive evidence for an old earth. Varves consist of thin layers of sediment that accumulate from annual fluctuations in organic matter and river flow. Depending on the time of year and the amount of water flow, either an organically rich, dark fine silt will be deposited on the lake bottom or an inorganically-dominated coarse, light-colored sediment will be. These light–coarse deposits and dark–fine deposits occur once a year respectively, so one light and dark band together in the varve record represents one year of lake sedimentation (Figure 7.2).[56,57,58,59] Scientists can thus count these varves and determine how many years have passed since its formation.

The Green River formation in Colorado, Utah, and Wyoming contains perhaps one of the most impressive varves in terms of antiquity. This formation has an average of 6.5 million varve pairs, representing 6.5 million years of sediment deposition.[60] However, this is a calculated average, as pair estimates range from five million[61,62,63] to eight million.[64,65] Furthermore, one particular area of the formation contains an astounding twenty million varves.[66] However, five million is the minimum number of varves in any place in the formation that is agreed upon by all sources, so this is the number that will be used for this discussion.

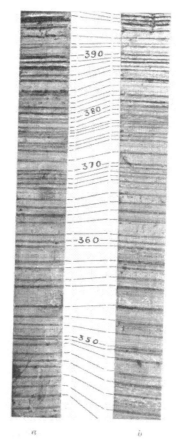

Figure 7.2 Varve sample with annual light and dark layers.

From: Sauramo, Matti. Studies on the Quaternary varve sediments in southern Finland. No. 60. Valtioneuvoston Kirjapaino, 1923.

If five million annual light–dark rings are recorded, it stands to reason that this geological formation is at least five million years old. However, YECs argue that storms may create "false" layers in the varve record (similar to the "false" tree ring and ice core claims of YECs). Assuming that storms *could* create false varve layers, how many storms would have had to occur to make a 6,000-year-old formation appear five million years old? Answer: 893 storms every year from creation up until European colonization of that area around the year 1600. This would mean there would have to be at least two storms (2.44) every single day of the year for 5,600 years straight in order to create five million varve layers. And again, this would also mean the storms suddenly stopped right as the Europeans arrived. This argument is spurious at best and deceitful at worst. At two storms or more per day, there would have been *no* such sedimentation whatsoever like we find in the Green River formation! Neither a catastrophic flood, mega-storm, nor thousands of smaller storms could create such fine alternating layers since these laminae (layers) are *only* created from settled out sediments in *still* water.[67]

Is it more reasonable to believe that almost 900 storms a year occurred in this location over the past 5,600 years and laid down nice, neat alternating organically rich–dark and inorganic–light layers, or that the five million annual layers really do represent the passage of five million years? And why would these perpetual storms cease just before the Europeans came on the scene? Nowhere close to 900 storms a year have been recorded in that area since man has been keeping track. Is it more reasonable to believe a catastrophic flood deposited up to 20,000,000 alternating layers all at once even though the layers are of a type that could only have been formed by *still* water,[68] or that the 20,000,000 million annual layers represent 20,000,000 years?

Creationists' only retreat is in believing the fossil record of this formation vindicates their disbelief of an old earth. Indeed, this formation contains some of the most incredible and well-preserved fossils in existence. Creationists point to fossilized fish passing through multiple annual layers and conclude that these fossils could not have formed over multiple years, since ostensibly they would have rotted away or been scavenged.

However, deep and cold waters, such as those found on the bottom of lakes that create such varves, are perfectly capable of preserving organisms for inordinate lengths of time. Such cold waters may be anoxic (oxygen poor), disallowing the bacteria that promote decay to inhabit those realms.[69,70] These cold, anoxic areas are also unlikely to harbor scavengers, and additionally may contain poisonous compounds, such as hydrogen sulfide, which would further inhibit scavenging and decay.[71] Also, lake bottoms do not always undergo seasonal mixing and aeration, leading to bottom waters that have significantly increased amounts of salt. This may aid in preservation by essentially "pickling" the deceased organism.[72]

Furthermore, fossilized adult and nestling birds have been found alongside their tracks, eggs, nests, and coprolite (feces) together in the same layer of the Green River formation.[73,74] If these varves were accumulating at over two layers per day (or all at once), how did these birds have time to make a nest, lay eggs, hatch the eggs, eat, and poop all in one layer? All this activity would take weeks at the least and flatly contradicts the hypothesis of many varves per day or a catastrophic upheaval creating many varves at once.

Additionally, the Green River formation varve record coincides neatly with records of sunspots and variations in Earth's orbit, providing a built-in cross-check that demonstrates that the varve layers are indeed annual.[75,76] And finally, parts of this formation have also been radiometrically dated to around 50 million years old.[77,78,79] And Green River is not the only lake with a conclusive varve record. Lake Suigetsu in Japan has 40,000 varve layers that have been cross-checked with C-14 dating that agrees superbly on its age.[80] Lake Baikal in Siberia also has five million varve layers that have been radiometrically dated to five million years old.[81] The Salido, Castile, and Bell Canyon formations in New Mexico and West Texas also contain 260,000 varve couplets.[82] Taking into account this overwhelming deluge of strong evidence, varves may be considered the quintessential "checkmate" in the argument against a young earth.

Catchin' My Drift?

Have you ever noticed how the continents fit together like a jigsaw puzzle? South America and Africa, for instance, seem to fit each other remarkably well. Why is this so? The answer is that at one time the continents were gathered together into a supercontinent dubbed "Pangaea." Over the last 175 million years, this supercontinent has been drifting apart into today's configuration of landmasses via a process termed "plate tectonics." This theory is built on the fact that there are eight major plates (along with some smaller plates) on the surface of the planet that are moving across the globe. Sea-floor spreading causes two plates to move apart from each other as rising magma creates new oceanic crust. Two plates may also collide and over time create mountains, or one plate may move under the other and into Earth's mantle in an act termed "subduction." Lastly, plates may slide past each other at transform boundaries, causing the occasional earthquake (San Andreas fault in California is perhaps the most familiar example).

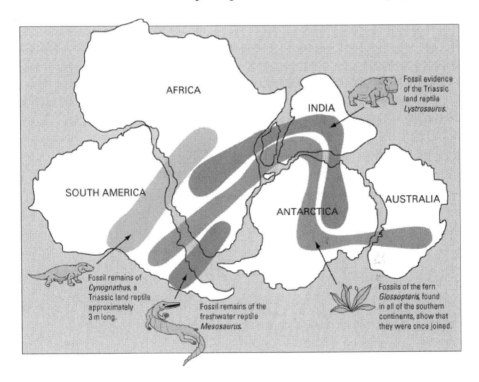

Figure 7.3 The distribution of fossils across continents supports other lines of evidence that strongly indicate the existence of Pangaea. From: USGS

Plate tectonics makes sense of the fact that the specific types of rocks found on the West Coast of Africa are nearly identical to those on the East Coast of South America, and the plants of South Africa and Southern South America are strikingly similar to one another.[83] Furthermore, the concept of plate tectonics explains why China and

North America share similar plant species such as catalpa, witchhazel, and ginseng among many others.[84] The same holds true for the similarity between the Appalachian mountains and the mountain ranges of Greenland and other parts of the UK as far as structure and rock type. Patterns of fossil deposition across continents also strongly supports the idea that the continents were once joined together (Figure 7.3).

So what does all of this have to do with the age of the earth? Well, the shortest distance between North America and mainland Europe is about 2,800 miles. Add to this the fact that the Mid-Atlantic Ridge is pushing the North American plate away from the Eurasian plate at the known and confirmed rate of 2.5cm/year (almost one inch).[85,86,87,88] If North America and Europe are moving away from each other at almost one inch per year, and they are currently at least 2800 miles (177,408,000 inches) apart, the conclusion is obvious: at least 177,000,000 years must have passed since the two were joined together.

Despite a lack of any empirical evidence or scientific data, creationists have a pet theory of "catastrophic plate tectonics," whereby in the past 6,000 years plates raced across the globe at many orders of magnitude greater than they do today. But is this realistic? If we double the current rate of continental drift (although there is no evidence that the plates have moved significantly faster in the past), we end up at 89 million years before present. If we increase the rate by ten, we still end up at 18 million years. Increase by a hundredfold and we get 1.8 million years. Even if the rate of drift were 10,000 times faster in the past, the result would still be almost 18,000 years. If drift occurred 28,000 times faster in the past, the earth would still be older than 6,000 years! In order to shoehorn a young earth belief into the reality of continental drift, you would have to swallow the whopper that the plates moved at over 30,000 times their present-day rate, but inexplicably slowed down before the 20th century, when we started to measure them.

Geomagnetic Reversal

Everyone has known since childhood where the South Pole lies, admittedly if only for reasons relating to Christmas gifts. However, the South Pole has not always been the "south" pole. Earth's magnetic poles flip their polarity—magnetic north becomes magnetic south and vice versa—roughly every 50,000 to 800,000 years (some have been shorter and some longer than these figures), with an average of about 200,000–300,000 years.[89,90,91] This means if you had a compass 800,000 years ago (the last time the polarity reversed), your compass needle would point toward what we call the South Pole instead of the North Pole.

This information becomes more relevant when we consider the seafloor previously discussed. Recall that seafloor spreading creates new rock material that pushes the adjacent plates farther away from each other. Furthermore, when this lava hardens and cools, it locks in and records the orientation of Earth's magnetic field at that time.[92] What scientists discovered roughly half a century ago when they ran a magnetometer (a device that measures magnetization and direction of magnetic field) over the seafloor, was that the seafloor was magnetically "striped" with alternating bands of north–south polarity starting from the Mid-Atlantic Ridge outwards (Figure 7.4).[93,94] These magnetic stripes on the ocean floor mean that each time the rock is measured as going from north polarity to south polarity or vice versa, from one band of rock to another, this documents a reversal of Earth's magnetic poles. In total, 171 of these polarity reversals have been geologically documented.[95,96]

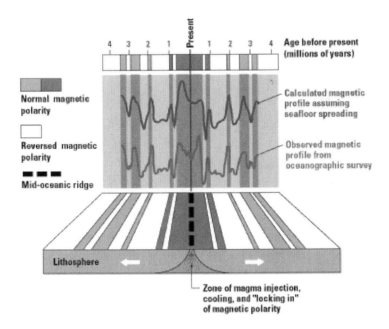

Figure 7.4 Geomagnetic reversal is revealed by the alternating "stripes" of normal and reversed polarity found on the ocean floor. From: USGS

Simple math will reveal that if these reversals occur on average every 200,000 years and there are 171 documented reversals, then this would place the minimum age of the earth at 34,200,000 years old. Even if we assume the lowest value of 50,000 years per reversal, we still end up with 8.5 million years. In order to defend a 6,000-year-old earth, one would have to believe that these 171 magnetic reversals took place roughly every 23 years on average, rather then every 200,000 years. Again, this would also include a belief that the poles reversed every 23 years since creation then suddenly stopped reversing 2,200 years ago (when the first compass was invented) and have not reversed in the two millennia since.

A definite pattern emerges when one studies Young Earth Creationism. Many of the young earth arguments involve incredibly faster rates of natural processes that curiously stopped right before we started studying them. Moon dust deposited faster, light traveled faster, coral grew faster, stalactites grew faster, continents drifted faster, radioactive decay was faster, and magnetic reversals were faster in the past, but somehow they shifted to their current rates at or before the moment we commenced studying them.

Doesn't this strike anyone as awfully convenient? Should we accept the premise that many natural processes were faster in the past, despite a complete and total lack of evidence to that effect? Should we also believe that these accelerated rates of phenomena slammed on the brakes just as we began investigating them? To be quite honest, all of the young earth "evidences" and arguments I have ever researched, evaluated, and analyzed ended up being nothing but pseudoscience and conjecture. Once you scratch at a young earth argument, the paint flakes and chips off pretty easily. I am not intending to be rude or disparaging to my fellow brothers and sisters in Christ, but sometimes we have to call a spade a spade and speak the truth in love.

A very well-traveled YEC argument regarding geomagnetism involves the earth's magnetic field decaying exponentially since the first recorded measurements in the mid-nineteenth century (although in actuality, Earth's magnetic field has been decreasing *linearly* since 1850, but not *exponentially*). According to this YEC argument, if Earth's magnetic field is currently decaying exponentially, then one can extrapolate backwards into the past and arrive at the conclusion that Earth's magnetic field would have been impossibly high more than 20,000 years ago. Therefore, the earth must be young.

Unfortunately, this hypothesis suffers from a great deal of suppressed evidence. First, Earth's magnetic field reverses periodically, which entails intervening spans of decaying and increasing magnetic fields especially surrounding reversal events. Second, Earth's magnetic field varies in intensity, so on a scale of hundreds or thousands of years, we would expect to see increases and decreases in magnetic field strength, and this would not be unusual in the slightest.[97] Interesting how YECs typically deny steady and unchanging rates, except in a case like this, where it would favor them. YECs want to claim a steady exponential decay since the beginning of time for this magnetic decay claim, yet they want a highly variable and accelerated rate for all other phenomena!

The Dating Game: Radiometric Dating

Did you know that the bananas you eat are radioactive? Bananas contain 40K (potassium-40), a radioactive isotope found in nature.[98] This is not cause for alarm, however, unless you hold that the planet is less than 10,000 years old. While the amount of 40K in a banana is not a health risk, it may be a psychological risk to those who deny the great age of the earth.

40K is an isotope, which is to say that it is a "species" of potassium with a different amount of neutrons in its nucleus than other kinds of potassium such as 39K (the most abundant type on Earth). 40K is unstable, which means it undergoes a process called radioactive decay. When 40K decays, it decays into a different element called 40Ar (argon-40). Now, the time that it takes half of a specific amount of 40K to decay into 40Ar is called its half-life, which for 40K is 1.28 billion years.[99,100] This means that if you have an initial quantity of 40K, after 1.28 billion years you will have half the original amount of 40K and the other half will have turned into its daughter nuclide 40Ar, then in 2.56 billion years you would have one quarter of your original 40K and the other three-quarters will be 40Ar, and so on.

As you can imagine, this is a huge boon to scientists trying to ascertain the age of the earth. If you know the current ratio of parent and daughter isotopes in a rock, the decay rate of the parent radioisotope, and the initial ratio of isotopes in a rock, you can determine the age of that rock using a very simple formula ($t = 1/(\text{decay rate})\ln(D/P+1)$—this is somewhat simplified, but I'll spare you the math.[101]

This may seem problematic, as it would appear difficult to know the exact starting ratio of 40K–40Ar in ancient rocks, but volcanic material is excellent for this purpose. Argon is a rare gas, which escapes easily from a volcanic rock in the formation process. However, once the rock has hardened and cooled, the 40K is essentially "locked" inside, leaving the 40K–40Ar ratio untouched. Time and again, rocks dated with this method conclusively support the scientific consensus that the earth is orders of magnitude older than 6,000 years.[102,103,104,105]

Additionally, 40K is not the only game in town. Other radioactive isotopes such as samarium-147, rubidium-87, thorium-232, uranium-238, uranium-235, uranium-234, lutetium-176, and carbon-14 are commonly used in radiometric dating.[106,107,108] Do any of these dating methods provide support for a 6,000-year-old earth? The answer is an unequivocal "no."

In western Australia, hundreds of zircon crystals have been found that yield dates of 4.4 billion years. These crystals also hint at the proposition that there were low temperatures and liquid water on the earth at that time (conditions necessary for life).[109] The Amitsoq gneisses in Greenland were analyzed using *five* different radiometric dating methods, which all gave an approximate age of 3.6 billion years, with a range of error less than 1% between the different methods.[110,111] Rocks from northwestern Canada have been dated to four billion years.[112] Also, moon rocks collected by astronauts have been dated to 4.46 billion years, and in addition many asteroids in our solar system have been dated at 4.56 billion years.[113] And the list goes on and on. The bottom line is this: Every single radiometric dating method used provides dates of the earth at much older than 6,000 years. The radiometric data all support the idea of an earth approximately 4.54 billion years old.[114,115,116]

Additionally, as Kenneth Miller points out in his book, *Finding Darwin's God*, out of thirty-four naturally occurring radioactive isotopes with a half-life greater than one million years, we only find twenty-three of those still present. And when we look at which radioactive isotopes are currently present or not, a definite pattern emerges: Any found today are either still being produced or have half-lives longer than 80,000,000 years.[117] What does this mean? Well, for one, Earth had a beginning, and two, the earth is much, much older than 80 million years. Remember that a half-life is the time it takes for half of the original amount of a radioactive isotope to decay into another element. Those elements with a half-life of less than 80 million years have in Kenneth Miller's words, "decayed themselves out of existence," since it would take about one billion years for these shorter-lived isotopes to decay beyond detectable levels.[118] Wouldn't a young earth still have all of those young radioactive isotopes around? One would expect so.

Despite this robust compilation of evidence, some will protest that radiometric dating is prone to error. YECs often contend that we don't know that rocks are closed systems, and isotopes may move in and out of a sample. Initially, they assert that we don't know how much of the daughter isotope was already present in a rock when it formed, thus the estimate of a sample's age may be skewed.

Luckily for these critics, uranium-lead dating has a built in cross-check that allows for closure of a rock system to be tested; this is done by use of a condordia diagram. This fortuitous feature of nature arises from the fact that two different types of uranium isotopes (235U and 238U) decay into two different isotopes of lead (207Pb and 206Pb, respectively). When these two isotopes of uranium occur together in the same sample, the ratio of 207Pb/235U against 206Pb/238U can be plotted to see if they lie on a concordia line. If the rock has remained a closed system, it will fall on this line and thus is accurate and reliable in regards to radiometric dating.[119]

As if this wasn't enough proof to validate the precision and exactness of radiometric dating, recall that Lake Suigetsu in Japan has 40,000 varve layers that have been cross-checked with radiometric dating which agrees definitively on its age.[120] Radiocarbon dating has also been cross-checked with tree rings, known dates of volcanic eruptions, plate tectonics, coral, and stalactites, and the results agree with astonishing certainty and accuracy.[121,122] Not only do the independent methods of radiometric dating agree with one another on the antiquity of the earth, they also agree exactly with half a dozen other different natural phenomena to provide us with irrefutable evidence that the earth is beyond doubt vastly older than 6,000 years.

With the damning verdict in, there is only one paltry appeal left on the docket for YECs. They ask: Could radioactive decay rates have been faster in the past? Again, this threadbare argument of highly variable and accelerated phenomena rears its obtuse head. If decay rates were so much faster in the past that radiometric dating gives the impression of a 4.54-billion-year-old earth even though the true age of the earth is 6,000 years, then so much energy would have been given off by this accelerated radioactive decay that it would have literally melted the earth.[123] Even YEC researchers admit that increased radioactive decay of this sort would lead to a 22,000-degree-Celsius temperature (four times hotter than the sun's surface) that would likely cause Earth's entire crust to vaporize.[124,125]

Is it really reasonable to believe that radiometric dating is just plain wrong about the age of the earth? When the dating of tree rings, varves, corals, volcanic eruptions, stalactites, and tectonic plates all agree unanimously and precisely with one another *and* with dates obtained by nine different radiometric dating methods, can we really just dismiss this mountain of evidence? Furthermore, there are many more additional dating methods I have not discussed that show the earth to be at least one million years old, including thermoluminescence, optically stimulated luminescence, electron spin resonance, fission track dating, cosmogenic nuclide dating, magnetostratigraphy, tephrochronology dating and more.[126] Not to mention the eight species of currently living plants with members older than 9,000 years (some much older), the starlight we see from millions of years away, the growth rates of coral and stalactites, the amount of dust on the moon, the layers in ice cores, the varve layers, the seafloor spreading, and record of geomagnetic reversals that all demonstrate far beyond a reasonable doubt that the earth is much older than 6,000 years and is in fact 4.54 billion years old. These pieces of evidence are all multiple independent confirmations that support the reigning paradigm of modern science that it truly is an old earth after all.

The evidences I have presented are not like blocks in a "Jenga" tower; they are more like many strong columns that support a roof. If one, two, or three of the thirty-three pieces of evidence (nine radiometric methods, nine plants, eight natural phenomena, and the seven additional methods briefly mentioned) somehow turned out to be wrong, the roof would not be in danger; there are many other pillars (and much more evidence that would not fit in this book) that would firmly support the roof. In order to knock down the "building," you would need to dispose of almost everything known by nearly every area of modern science. Should we really believe that the fields of chemistry, genetics, paleontology, biology, astronomy, biochemistry, molecular biology, physics, geology, cosmology, astrophysics, geophysics, and anthropology have it all wrong when it comes to the age of the earth? Are 95%–99% scientists wrong about this basic aspect of science? Could the same science that works so well for cellphones, space shuttles, and heart-surgeries be wrong about the age of the earth by over 75,000,000%? I submit to you, that I think we can once and for all close the chapter on this young earth madness.

PART III

THE EVIDENCE FOR EVOLUTION

CHAPTER EIGHT

EVOLUTION

At last we arrive at the critical question undergirding the debate: Is there really anything to the theory of evolution? What evidence is there for or against it? As I did when examining the age of the earth, I will present the evidences I think are most compelling. As far as arguments *against* evolution, I will address those within the arguments *for* evolution.

At the risk of turning this book into a tome, I will assume at least a basic familiarity with the theory of evolution. Evolution at its most basic could be described as the changes in allele (variants of a gene) frequencies over time. Evolution is simply change, and natural selection is the theory which explains a great deal of this change. The theory of evolution by natural selection is based on the fact that species have more offspring than could possibly survive, that these offspring have some inherited variations, and that there is a struggle for existence. Therefore, organisms that possess beneficial variations, which contribute to their fitness, are the "winners" and are able to leave a larger contribution of offspring in the next generation. After many generations of this, a population will have more helpful genetic characteristics and fewer disadvantageous ones. This descent with modification means that over time these gradual changes accumulated from successful inherited variations can produce a new species. Of course this is a grossly oversimplified version of evolution by natural selection. Genetic drift, the founder effect, allopatric and sympatric speciation, phyletic constraint, and stabilizing selection, are just a few examples out of a plethora of other concepts that paint a more accurate picture of evolutionary theory. For the sake of space, however, I will move on to address some common misconceptions.

Many people envision evolution as being like a ladder, as if the theory posits a straight-line progression of one organism turning into another. However, evolution does not proceed in a straight line, as there is a branching pattern of descent that results in a very "bushy" tree of life. For example, some think evolution theorizes that humans evolved from apes or more specifically, from chimpanzees. This is false, however, because although we share a common ancestor with chimps, we did not evolve *from* them. Furthermore, individual organisms do not evolve, but rather entire populations evolve over time to give rise to a new species. Hence, there would not be any instance in which one species gives birth to an entirely different species within one generation, as evolution is a continuous process that may show little change in the small scale of time from one generation to the next. In retrospect, however, over a large timescale, such speciation might be seen.

Lastly, contrary to popular belief, evolution does not hold that life evolves randomly or by chance. Mutation, which gives rise to genetic variation, *is* random; however, natural selection is *nonrandom*, as it selects against organisms that are not as well able to survive and reproduce as others. Therefore, random mutation and natural selection can create complex adaptations over time, but this is due to the nonrandom effects of natural selection.

Regardless, let us dig into the evidence for evolution and examine what best explains the facts that we observe in the world around us. As we journey forward, keep in mind that evolution does *not* imply that there is no creator. We are here only seeking to understand the physical and material outworking of God's unseen hand in the universe. By describing the scientific processes that God has chosen to use, this in no way impugns God or makes creation any less special. Science can answer the "how" questions, but it can never answer the deeper and more challenging "why" questions; that is where God comes in. All truth is God's truth, and as rational creatures made in the image of God, it is incumbent upon us to seek truth no matter what the cost.

CHAPTER NINE

SIMILARITIES

Classification

The fact that all life can be categorized into nested hierarchies based on shared characteristics argues for descent from a common ancestor. Smaller groups of organisms can be classified inside larger groups of organisms like Russian nesting dolls, allowing us to create a tree of life by inferring evolutionary relationships. For example, we can start with a large group of animals like the vertebrates, which has about 66,000 members ranging from fish, frogs, birds, to mammals, and work our way toward a single species. All vertebrates have a backbone—a characteristic that unites them.

Within the vertebrate category, we have the less inclusive group— mammals with only about 5,500 members. These are further defined by not only having a backbone, but also being furry and feeding milk to their young. If we want to move further to a more exclusive group within the mammals, we could consider the ungulates, who have about 450 members such as rhinos and deer, all of them (except whales) bound together by having any number of hooves in addition to the aforementioned traits. Within the ungulates, we have about 220 species of even-toed mammals such as pigs and moose, who only have an even number of hooves in addition to the previous characteristics. We can further pare this group down to the ruminants, which are even-toed ungulates with a special digestive system, and this group contains about 150 species, including cows, goats, and giraffes. Finally, within the ruminants we have a single species such as sheep. The classification of these animals is a reflection of their common ancestry and is easily explained by descent with modification from an ancient ancestor.

Of course this does not prove common ancestry, as one could

arrange any group of items, such as different cars or diversely shaped pots and pans, into a hierarchical classification scheme. However, since animals reproduce with variations in their offspring, and since an animal's environment may favor some variants over others in the game of life, inanimate objects like cars and pots that do not reproduce and are not subject to differential rates of survival may not be an entirely legitimate analogy. While God could easily have created millions of species that might have just happened to be amenable to grouping within nested categories, this reality seems to fit better with common ancestry when taken into account with all of the forthcoming evidence we will explore within this book.

Perhaps the one thing that turns classification from a slightly underwhelming piece of evidence into a strong indication of evolution is the fact that evolutionary trees created by molecular studies match morphological trees (ones created by studying the form and structure of organisms) with a high degree of statistical significance.[1,2] Studies of cytochrome c (a protein),[3] psuedogenes (defunct genes),[4] endogenous retroviruses (viral elements in the genome),[5,6] mutated regions of non-coding regions of DNA,[7] and many other molecular studies continue to vindicate the notion that classification is more than merely arranging items in a way to support a preconceived notion.[8] When the fact that organisms can be grouped by characteristics is coupled with molecular studies, what emerges is the reality that tree-like branching patterns of descent from a single distant ancestor explains both sets of data with better explanatory scope and power than any other theory. This piece of evidence by itself may not be irrefutable, but again, this is but one of many pillars supporting the "roof" of evolution.

Anatomical Homologies

If all life were descended from a common ancestor, we would expect to see deep similarities in groups of closely related animals, but we would also expect to find similarities between distantly related organisms. Such similarities that arise from common ancestry are deemed homologies. There are very deep homologies between all living beings, including anatomical, embryological, and genetic homologies.[9] Such surprising and compelling similarities would be very difficult to explain had each organism been created anew. However, common descent, if true, would make much sense of these homologies.

Charles Darwin remarked in his seminal book *The Origin of Species*:

> What can be more curious than that the hand of a man, formed for grasping, that of a mole for digging, the leg of the horse, the paddle of the porpoise, and the wing of the bat, should all be constructed on the same pattern, and should include the same bones, in the same relative positions?[10]

Indeed, it is very puzzling that in vertebrate animals, limbs for such dissimilar purposes as flying, swimming, digging, leaping, and running would be made up of nearly the same bone and muscle structures (Figure 9.1)[11,12,13] This fact seems to mesh better with evolution from a common ancestor than separately designed creation. Modification of an existing structure would easily explain why lizards, cats, frogs, whales, and humans all have a humerus, ulna, radius, carpals, and metacarpals in the same order in nearly the same place and with similar muscles.[14,15,16] If each of these structures came into being anew, we would not expect to see these striking similarities.

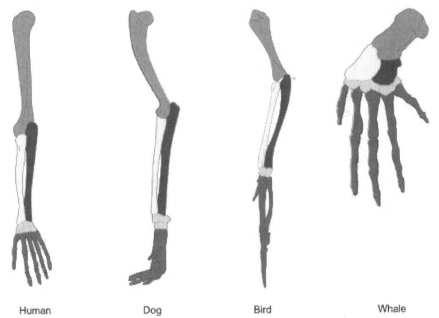

Human   Dog   Bird   Whale

Figure 9.1 Vertebrates display many anatomical homologies such as the same bones and muscles laid out in the same configuration.

Creationists and ID'ers usually tend to downplay this homological evidence. They often refer to different sized cooking pots or model years of cars and claim that these also show similarities but do not prove common descent. However, they are using a false analogy, or what we might call an "apples to oranges" comparison. Cars and cooking pots are not biological beings, do not reproduce, do not have inherited variations, and are not subject to natural selection. The perpetrator of this argument invalidly infers that since cars and living things share one characteristic in common (similarities between "species" or "varieties"), they must share all characteristics in common (e.g., having a designer, being created, not arising naturally).

With the same logic, I could argue that since my computer printer/copier produces copies with slight variations, it is also subject to natural selection as living things are. Of course, this is nonsense. The only other response left to the creationist is that homology is "variation within a kind based on an existing design plan," which to me doesn't sound that far off from evolution. Furthermore, why would the designer use nearly the same parts in the exact same order that would give the impression to millions of scientists over the past 150 years that all life is descended from a common ancestor? Wouldn't God, being all-knowing, know that His "design" would appear more like evolution than special creation and accordingly lead many to the "wrong" conclusion? Why would He desire to lead so many astray?

DNA: The Universal Language

Perhaps the most persuasive and obvious piece of evidence for common descent is the fact that every single living thing on the planet is built on exactly the same genetic code.[17,18,19,20] What I mean by this is that all 8.7 million described species of animals, plants, bacteria, fungi, and everything in between have precisely the same genetic language: DNA consisting of the letters A, T, C, and G (nucleotide bases). These four letters in combinations of three create amino acids, which are then linked together to create proteins. If every single organism is built using this identical four-letter coding system of DNA, doesn't that hint at the fact that all living things are related through the "tree" of life? Not only that, but the "translation table" that determines which combinations of DNA produce which amino acids (which comprise proteins) is nearly universal for every organism; they almost all use this same universal code to create the same twenty amino acids.[21,22,23,24] If the first organism had this DNA code, then it makes sense that all of its descendants would *still* possess this same code, which is exactly what we see today.

Why would God create millions of different life forms consisting of exactly the same four letter biochemical alphabet? Surely He could have created a myriad of organisms with wildly different genetic codes. If God had done this, it would have certainly crushed any chance of belief in common descent during our current genetic age. Wouldn't God, as an omniscient being, know that one day humans would decipher the genetic code of living things and infer that the universal genetic code demands a universal common ancestor?

If God created all species individually, why did He use the same genetic code to make it appear that man, microbes, and moss are all related? If God had created even one species out of 8.7 million with a substantially different genetic code, it would have assuredly thrown the biggest monkey wrench imaginable into the machine of evolutionary theory. Some object that we cannot dictate to God how He should have created life, and that He is free to choose how He creates, even if it doesn't make sense to us (which ironically is the exact same argument that admits the possibility that God *could* have chosen evolution as a means to create), but this brings us back to the earlier question of why God would want to deceive scientists by leaving so many false clues that would trick nearly 99% of them into believing in evolution.

Furthermore, *all* of life on Earth shares DNA that is transcribed into RNA using the help of RNA polymerase. This RNA is then translated into protein by ribosomes, which use very specific molecules for energy (ATP, NADPH). To accomplish this replication, transcription, and translation, all life uses the *same* basic molecular machinery such as small-subunit rRNA, large-subunit rRNA, tRNA, aminoacyl-tRNA synthetases, and multiple ribosomal proteins.[25] All organisms' DNA has the same double helix structure, and new nucleotides are added to the 3' end of the molecule during replication. Consider also that every living being participates in some part of the anearobic glycolysis pathway. More curious a fact is that all living things make proteins from "left-handed" L-amino acids, even though the mirror image "right handed" D-stereoisomers would work just as well.[26]

All life shares a common genetic code (three letters that specify an amino acid), the same twenty amino acids, DNA consisting of A, T, C, and G, RNA consisting of A, U, C, and G, countless similar metabolic pathways, similar methods of DNA replication, similar protein synthesizing systems, and the same phospholipid bilayer cell structure that utilizes ABC transporters.[27,28] All of this to say that all life has astonishingly deep cellular, molecular, and genetic similarities shared by all living organisms—exactly what we would expect were common ancestry true. Things like a universal genetic code and use of only left-handed molecules are effortlessly explained by descent from a single common ancestor. However, if special creation is true, it is difficult to understand why God would choose only to create with "left-handed" amino acids and never right-handed ones that would work exactly the same. Why wouldn't He throw a few "righties" in with the nine million species He created? This would certainly have given scientists pause for consideration, as would just one or two creatures with a significantly different genetic code from the one all current life shares. Such sweeping and unwarranted similarities across all domains of life argue strongly in favor of all life having descended from a first cell.

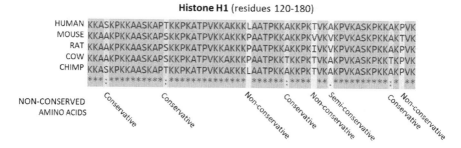

Histone H1 (residues 120-180)

Figure 9.2 A sequence alignment of mammalian histone proteins reveals great genetic similarity between seemingly disparate animals.

Moreover, the nearly identical ordering of certain genes or segments of DNA between ourselves and other species also strongly suggests we share a common ancestor with those species.[29] Such dissimilar species as humans, rats, and cows share the same genes in the same order on certain chromosomes (Figure 9.2).[30] In fact, nearly every gene found on human chromosome 17 is found in the same order on mouse chromosome 11.[31,32] This means that on human chromosome 17, for example, we find the genes ordered as X, Y, and Z and in mice we find the same gene order of X, Y, and Z on their chromosome 11. However, not only do we find *three* genes in the same order between mice and humans, but we find almost *all 1,300* genes on our chromosome 17 in the same order![33] And as world-renowned geneticist Francis Collins (who is a Christian) remarks, "There is no evidence from current understanding of molecular biology that this restriction would need to apply over such substantial chromosomal distances."[34] In other words, there is no other reason why mice should have nearly all of our 1,300 or so genes from chromosome 17 in the same order on their chromosome 11, unless evolution were true.

The chances that the order of our genes would randomly line up with that of mice is so infinitesimally small as to be nearly impossible. Imagine that you and I are playing the card game War, where we both throw down a random card and the highest value card wins the hand. If we both threw down a 2 that would be a slightly uncommon event, and would necessitate us throwing down another card to decide the hand. But then imagine on top of our 2s we both threw down 3s, then 4s and so on, a pretty rare event. Further, imagine that we randomly threw down the *same* card 26 times and then reshuffled the deck, then randomly threw the *same* cards for another fifty games, each consisting of 26 hands. In all, we would have randomly thrown down 1,300 cards and almost every one happened to match. That is roughly similar to the probability of humans and mice "randomly" having the same gene order on their chromosomes. This probability becomes even more unlikely when we consider that we share this "gene ordering" with even *more* animals than just mice.[35,36]

Why would God arrange our genes (or large stretches of DNA) in such a similar way to such seemingly different animals as rats and cows? Why would God order the genes of so many different animals almost exactly the same way if they were each created separately? Either God arbitrarily chose to order our genes in the same way as that of many animals, or these genes lineup because that was the order of the genes of the last common ancestor shared between us and the other species in question. Biologically, there is no reason that such orthologous genes (identical genes in different species) or similar DNA sequences have to be in the same order in different species, so it would appear that if this were "intelligent design," then by ordering genes identically in different animals God intentionally deceived us into believing that evolution occurred. I really can't see any other creationist or ID option; the only plausible explanation for these observations is that many genes and sequences of DNA are ordered in the same way because all species derived from a common ancestor.

Another remarkable illustration of the high degree of genetic similarity between ourselves and other animals can be found in a recent experiment with common yeast. These little unicellular fungi revered for making bread and beer are thought to have had a last common ancestor with humans around one billion years ago.[37] Despite this fact, almost half (43%–47%) of human genes tested were able to function in place of the yeasts' own vital genes, which had either been removed or inactivated.[38] Essentially, researchers replaced a yeast version of a gene for a specific necessary function (e.g., lipid metabolism) with a human version of that gene (called an ortholog). The fact that nearly half of human genes tested are interchangeable with yeast genes shows just how similar all living things are (something to be expected if every species evolved from a common ancestor, but very unexpected in terms of special creation). The yeast experiment facts are certainly better explained by evolution than creationism or Intelligent Design.

DNA Similarity — Just Another Chimp Off the Old Block

You may have been justified in not wanting to eat your brussel sprouts; they are in fact a distant relative of ours. We share about 17% genetic similarity (by method of comparing homologous [similar] genes) with some plants in the mustard family (*Arabidopsis thaliana*).[39] If that percentage seems strangely high and somewhat disconcerting, consider that we share 11% (again by comparing homologous genes) with yeast (*Saccharomyces cerevisiae*),[40] 39% with fruit flies (*Drosophila melanogaster*),[41] 80% with cows (*Bos taurus*),[42] 90% with cats (*Felis catus*),[43] and 96% with chimpanzees (*Pan troglodytes*). The DNA sequence that can be directly compared between the two genomes is almost 99 percent identical. When DNA insertions and deletions are taken into account, humans and chimps still share 96 percent of their sequence.[44,45,46,47,48] We share such a high degree of similarity with all living creatures because, as illustrated above, we all share a lot of biochemical machinery and processes in common. Our metabolic pathways, cell components, genetic storage and replication, and many other biological features are extraordinarily similar. However, we are without a doubt more related to some organisms than others.

Even in Charles Darwin's day, mankind was postulated to have evolved from a common ancestor shared with the great apes. Darwin himself had a fascination with orangutans and surmised that we must share a past with them as well as with the gorillas and chimpanzees. This theory would have to wait over a century to be vindicated by modern genetics. When scientists peered into the genome of the chimpanzee, they discovered that we are by far closest to them genetically than any other organism on the face of the planet. How close? In the most critical sections of our DNA, we share 99.4% genetic similarity with chimpanzees.[49] Think about what this means for a moment: In our most important regions of DNA, the difference between you and a chimp is on average a measly six nucleotide bases (A, T, C, G) out of a thousand!

Let's say you proudly wrote a one-thousand word paper for your college class and triumphantly slapped it onto the professor's desk at grading time. What if I threw a paper right on top of yours that had 994 of the same words and only six different? You would certainly accuse me of cheating! After all, what are the chances that our papers would line up with such uncanny similarity if we both wrote ours independently from scratch? Yet, when it comes to the genetic evidence, many would like to make like the three monkeys and shut their eyes and ears, denying that this incredible degree of genetic similarity means anything at all. But ask yourself this question: Why do we share more DNA with chimps than any other animal if we aren't related in any way? How can this be rationally explained by anything other than common descent?

One key thing to note here is that our genetic similarity lines up very well overall with the hypothetical tree of life that was established *well before* we had all this genetic information. In this case, the genetic information served to confirm and add consistent support to what science had already figured out. Before the genetic age, it had long been determined using phylogenetic reconstruction (a branching diagram showing evolutionary relationships that are inferred by differences or similarities in physical characteristics) that our closest relatives were the great apes followed by other primates (e.g., monkeys). If the percentage of our DNA that is similar to other species shows how recently we shared a common ancestor, then this should be crystal clear when we look at how much our neutral DNA sequences have diverged from other species (this method is based on nucleotide substitutions). And indeed, using this method we find that we differ a mere 1.2% with chimpanzees, 1.6% with gorillas, and with the non-ape baboons we differ by 6.6%.[50,51] Bear in mind that we did not evolve *from* apes or monkeys; instead, we share a common ancestor with them in the distant past and have since gone our own evolutionary ways on our own separate paths. This measure of divergence accounts for the difference between us and other species in the time since we parted ways.

Despite the fact that I have provided seven peer-reviewed and published scientific articles presented by different researchers from different parts of the country publishing in different journals and using more than three distinct genomic methods to establish a 96%–99.4% genetic similarity between humans and chimps, to some this matters not. Some would just counter that we cannot infer anything from the genetic similarity, except perhaps that this is evidence that we were designed by God using a "similar design plan." However, I fail to see how simply being a variation of the "primate plan" is any more special than sharing a common ancestor with other primates. Additionally, this hypothesis of "similar design accounts for DNA similarity" absolutely falls apart when we consider that whales share more DNA in common with artiodactyls (even-toed hoofed mammals like deer) than any other group of animals.[52,53,54,55] This makes sense in light of evolutionary theory, since whales are shown to have evolved from land-dwelling mammals. However, "similar design" would not at all explain why whales, pigs, hippos, and camels share so much of their DNA in common; only evolution would make sense of that.

Most opponents, though, would rather attack the data itself and assert that there is some suppression of evidence going on, or that the numbers are just plain wrong. Some of this stems from a misunderstanding (or possibly a misrepresentation) of how genetic comparisons are carried out. Some researchers test for orthologous genes, some look at single nucleotide polymorphisms, others for similarities in only protein coding regions, and still others the entire genome including introns, exons, and satellite DNA. If you are confused, don't worry—you should be. Genetics is a very complex and difficult area, especially for those without extensive biological training. Creationists and ID advocates will assert that the data is wrong or misleading, but they often cite figures without giving proper context or explaining the method to their audience, who likely wouldn't understand it anyway. They will throw out big numbers with only superficial meaning and mischaracterize studies in order to support their own conclusion. However, the evidence speaks for itself. Every genetic study done to date between humans and chimpanzees has shown that we are more genetically related to them than to any other species on the planet, *no matter what method is used*. Perhaps most telling is that creationists and ID proponents have not published anything on the subject using their own data (of which they have none); this mirage of human–chimp dissimilarity lives only within creationist websites, blogs, books, and magazines.

Monkeying Around With Chromosomes

While the genetic age has confirmed through studies of genetic similarity the long-held conviction that mankind shared a common ancestor with the great apes, it also created a vexing problem that had the potential to shake the foundations of evolutionary theory. The dilemma was that the chimpanzees, gorillas, and orangutans have 24 pairs of chromosomes, but humans have only 23. How could we share a common ancestor with the great apes if we have fewer chromosomes? This seemed like the opportunity of a lifetime to prove evolution false. It was highly unlikely that all the great apes independently evolved an additional chromosome, and just as unlikely that the progenitors of the human species could have completely lost a chromosome along the way, a move that would certainly have resulted in death. This haunting riddle hung heavy like an onerous shroud upon the scientific community for some time. Was this the end of the road for Darwin?

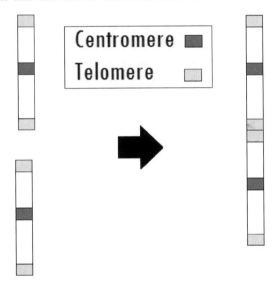

Figure 9.3 Fusion of ancestral chromosomes 2p and 2q into today's human chromosome 2. Chromosomes usually have only one centromere, but in humans there are remnants of a second vestigial centromere as well as telemeric sequences found in the middle of chromosome 2, which normally occur only at the ends of chromosomes.

A definitive answer came in 2005 when the newly sequenced human and chimpanzee genomes were compared. What was found could only be described as stunning and irrefutable proof of our simian heritage. When the chromosomes of the two species had been examined, it was found that chimpanzee chromosomes 2a and 2b corresponded with spectacular similarity to human chromosome 2. In other words, it appeared that the ancestral lineage leading to humans originally contained 24 pairs of chromosomes but then underwent a replication event that left chromosomes 2a and 2b fused head-to-head, creating a uniquely human chromosome: chromosome 2.[56,57,58] This explains why we have one fewer chromosome than chimpanzees.

But could this be a "just-so story" manufactured by biased scientists? The proof of the importance of this study can be found in the unmistakable clues found within the chromosomes themselves. Chromosomes have at their ends "caps" called telomeres, consisting of repetitive sequences of DNA. Chromosomes also normally possess one centromere in their middle, a point where the chromatid pairs are joined. Want to take a guess at what we find nestled away in human chromosome 2? Not only do we find telomeres at the ends of the chromosome like normal, but we also find them in the *middle*. We also find not just one centromere as in all our other chromosomes, but *two* centromeres with one being active and the other inactive. This without a shadow of a doubt proves that the once two separate chromosomes were fused together in the distant past. And if that weren't already powerful and persuasive enough, consider that the banding left by dye-staining chimpanzee chromosomes 2a and 2b matches very closely to that of human chromosome 2.[59,60,61] This again means that we find very similar genes ordered in a very similar way between us and chimps (Figure 9.4).

To say that the implications of these findings are monumental would be a vast understatement. Common descent could be reasonably substantiated on this piece of evidence alone given the magnitude of this discovery. Is there any other reasonable explanation? If God created man and chimpanzee separately, why did he create within them genetic evidence that reads "COMMON DESCENT" in flashing neon lights? If God truly did place within man's genome a forged chromosome fabricated to appear as though it were a fused primate chromosome, what does this say about the character of God? Why would He take such great pains to hoodwink scientists? Could chromosome 2 really be a Holy hoax? The God I worship isn't duplicitous; He is the essence of truth and goodness and to deceive would contradict His character. John 8:44 tells us who the father of lies is, and it's certainly not our Heavenly Father.

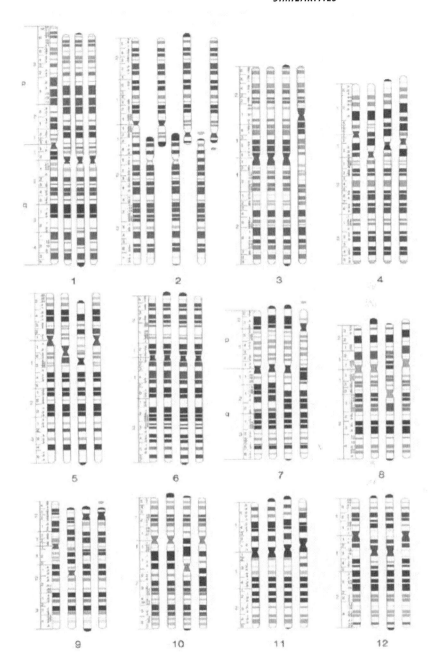

Figure 9.4 Chromosome comparison between humans, chimpanzees, gorillas, and orangutans from left to right respectively. Notice how the dye-staining patterns match up nearly identically for all genes, showing our genes to be mostly in the same place and in the same order. Reprinted with kind permission from: Yunis, Jorge J., and Ora Prakash. "The origin of man: a chromosomal pictorial legacy." Science 215.4539 (1982): 1525–1530.

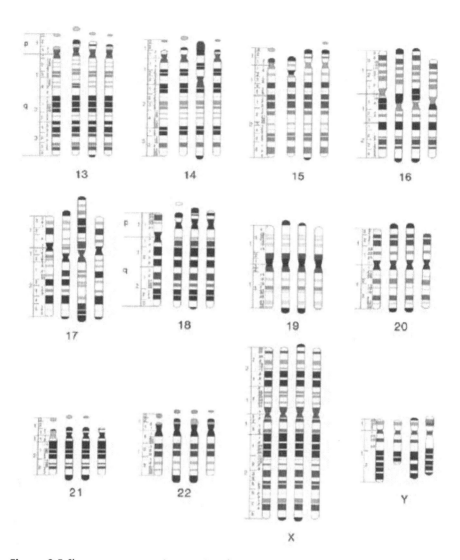

Figure 9.5 Chromosome comparison continued. Reprinted with kind permission from: Yunis, Jorge J., and Ora Prakash. "The origin of man: a chromosomal pictorial legacy." Science 215.4539 (1982): 1525–1530.

Pseudogenes

If I were pressed to provide only one piece of evidence strong enough to make a case for evolution and simultaneously refute creationism/ID, pseudogenes or ERVs would probably be it. These arguments are truly the *coup de grace* for creationism/ID, as when it is properly understood, it is virtually irrefutable and incontestable evidence for macroevolution and common descent. Ironically, this ironclad proof has been hiding in plain sight all along, in every cell you and I possess.

A pseudogene is essentially a broken copy of a functional gene that was at one time working in some distant ancestors, but through mutation it became disabled but was passed on through subsequent generations. About 17,000[62]–18,000[63] human pseudogenes have been identified, which by itself raises the question of why God would place within us so many non-functional, busted genes. Of course there are always exceptions in biology, and in rare cases pseudogenes may have some function.[64] A recent study found that 876 pseudogenes are transcribed from DNA into RNA, but they never actually get to the translation stage where a protein is made, making these largely useless for making protein but sometimes providing important biological roles.[65]

Creationists and ID advocates are now taking this information and running with it, and they are currently trying to overblow the significance of this fact by claiming that since *some* pseudogenes may have a function, then we must conclude that *all* of them will be found to have a function someday, which is simply not true. Or, they try to dismiss the pseudogene evidence entirely since it was once thought that they had no function or transcriptional activity, but this has now been revised by scientists. More importantly, consider that the most optimistic studies place the percentage of functional pseudogenes (meaning only that they are at least transcribed; this doesn't necessarily mean they do anything of importance) at around 12.8%.[66] The bottom line is that the the vast majority of pseudogenes are exactly that: defective genes that were once active, like a genetic fossil from a time longgone by.

As if the fact that we carry over 17,000 decayed and largely non-functional genes doesn't argue strongly enough in favor of evolution rather than intelligent design, there are additional layers of evidence that are even harder to ignore. Take for example the fact that humans carry a corrupt gene for making egg yolk.[67] We carry a vitellogenin pseudogene (VTG) that in chickens is fully-functional and responsible for creating the yellow part of your breakfast eggs. This gene is "scrambled" in humans but still provides important functions in the first several weeks of an embryo's life, although virtually no yolk is produced.[68] This same gene actually produces some usable yolk for nourishment in marsupials,[69] and it produces a considerable amount of yolk for the eggs of monotremes (egg-laying mammals).[70]

Now, if the mammal lineage really evolved from egg-laying reptiles, shouldn't we expect to find shared VTG genes with other egg-layers? Again, this testable scientific hypothesis validates evolutionary theory, as we find the identical VTG gene in chickens.[71] Not only that, but when scientists found the VTG gene in the chickens' genome, they looked at the genetic sequences and genes that flank either side of it and found that the VTG gene in humans is in exactly the same spot in our genome as it is in the chickens' genome![72] Furthermore, this VTG gene has been found in every mammal tested thus far, from dogs and opossums to armadillos and wallabies.[73]

How exactly does intelligent design explain why God would place within humans a mutated egg yolk gene found in precisely the same location and order as in the chickens' genome? Why did God design so many eggless, yolkless animals with egg yolk genes? We can't even chalk this one up to the "fall of man" and decay, since I doubt that in the pre-Fall garden our un-mutated egg yolk genes were doing much of anything for Adam and Eve. Nor can a creation model explain why we have a broken vitamin C synthesizing gene,[74] a busted DNA repair gene (photolyase),[75] inoperative enhanced olfaction (smelling) genes,[76] defunct anti-microbial peptide genes,[77] or any of the other thousands of decayed pseudogenes we all harbor.

But the story gets even more interesting when we compare our pseudogenes to the genomes of other animals. If evolution is correct in that we are most closely related to chimpanzees, we would expect to see some shared pseudogenes that both groups possess by virtue of the pseudogenes being passed down in the two lineages by the last common ancestor. And indeed, we find that among many shared pseudogenes we have in common with chimps is CYP21, a gene that codes for an enzyme that synthesizes glucocorticoids and mineral corticoids.[78] Not only that, but we both share the *same* mutation in the form of an eight-base pair deletion.[79] Literature abounds on shared human–chimp pseudogenes such as cytoplasmic actin, alpha-enolase, connexin, cytochrome b, hgt-2, interferon protein, lanosterol, NADH dehydrogenase, translin and many others.[80,81] What is the more reasonable explanation for why we have the same pseudogenes in the same place as chimpanzees—that both groups independently evolved such mistakes in useless genes placed there by the Creator, or that these same pseudogenes in the same arrangement often with the same mutations are evidence of our common ancestry with the great apes?

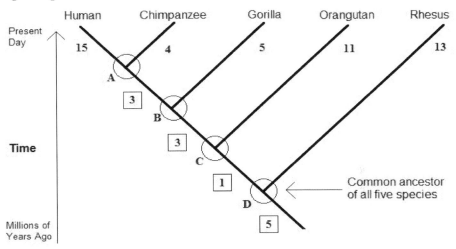

Figure 9.6 The number of olfactory receptor pseudogenes shared by the five species above allows us to ascertain their evolutionary relationships to one another.

We can further test our theory of common ancestry by examining a super-family genes called the "olfactory receptor" (OR) genes. These genes provide mammals with the ability to smell, but many lineages have lost some of their OR genes to mutation, rendering them pseudogenes. While humans still possess the ability to smell, we don't do it as well as some other mammals, having lost functionality in over 60% of our OR genes.[82] Here's where it gets really interesting: OR pseudogenes were compared between humans, chimpanzees, gorillas, orangutans, and rhesus macaques, and, as will soon be demonstrated, the results leave no uncertainties as to the truth of common descent.

Figure 9.6 shows a cladogram representing the evolutionary relationships between these five species. At point A, we have the common ancestor of humans and chimpanzees, likely around seven to eight million years ago. Point B represents the common ancestor shared by humans, chimps, and gorillas even further back in time. Older still, and we have the common ancestor of these three plus orangutans at point C. Finally at point D, we have the common ancestor to all five species.

At this point we can test a prediction of evolution: If humans have any pseudogenes that are not shared by chimps, they should not be shared by the remaining three species. For example, if we found pseudogenes that were shared by gorillas and humans but not by chimps, it would invalidate this proposed evolutionary relationship, because if ancestor "B" had this pseudogene, chimps should have it as well. Does the data on OR pseudogenes support this prediction? You should know the answer at this point . . .

Humans have fifteen OR pseudogenes that are unique to them and are not found in any other species.[83] This is because after the lineage leading to humans split off from the lineage leading to chimps around seven million years ago (point A), fifteen pseudogenes became mutated in the human lineage, so no other species would share these mutant genes since they all diverged at an earlier point. And indeed, no other species does. The same goes for the four unique chimp pseudogenes, five possessed by gorillas, eleven belonging to the orangs, and thirteen associated with the rhesus macaques. Again, if rhesus macaques and humans shared OR pseudogenes that the other three species did not, this would demolish the currently established evolutionary relationship between these five species. But we find all the OR pseudogenes exactly where they should be were evolution and common ancestry true. Not a single one is out of place.

When we look at the bottommost square in Figure 9.6, we see that all five of these species share five OR pseudogenes in common. When we take rhesus macaques out of the picture, we find that the remaining four species share six pseudogenes in common (5+1), as is to be expected from being more related by having evolved from a more recent common ancestor than macaques. Humans, chimps, and gorillas share nine pseudogenes in common (5+1+3), showing the three to be even more related and having an even more recent common ancestor. Lastly, humans and chimpanzees share a full twelve identical pseudogenes (5+1+3+3), verifying that they are in fact our closest relative. Out of all sixty OR pseudogenes in this study, *not one* is found out of place. In fact, every one is exactly where evolution predicts it would be, and this only serves to further strengthen the evidence of common ancestry. And these are just 60 out of about 17,000 pseudogenes in our genome. As mentioned earlier, countless other studies of pseudogenes give similar results.

Endogenous Retroviruses (ERVs)

Endogenous retroviruses (ERVs) are similar to pseudogenes in that most are genetic fossils that have persisted in our genomes for millions of years. However, ERVs differ in that they are remains of a parasitic virus that integrated itself into the germline cell (i.e., egg or sperm) of an organism, not a once functional gene that we lost to mutation. These viruses hijack a sperm or egg cell by breaking into it and then making a DNA copy of their own virus genome, which they surreptitiously insert into the host's genome. The result is that these viruses become part of the host's genome and get passed down to their offspring. This phenomenon then provides us with a golden opportunity to disprove or prove common ancestry, since if the latter were true, we would expect to see a good number of shared ERVs between humans and other species to which we are related.

It should come as no surprise then that all known families of ERVs are shared between chimps and humans.[84] In a recent study, 388 out of 396 ERVs representing every ERV family were found to be shared between chimps and human—an astounding 98%.[85] The numbers become even more impressive when we take all of our ERVs into account, as the initial sequencing of the human genome discovered that we have approximately 203,000 ERVs,[86] and we only have 82 that we do not share with chimps![87] This means we share approximately 202,918 out of 203,000 ERVs with our simian cousins—an astounding 99.96%! Furthermore, all of these shared ERVs were found to be in the same locations on the same chromosomes in humans and chimpanzees.[88] And if that's not enough, when we look at the same ERVs in the same spot in the genome, we find many with identical mutations shared by both species.[89]

If you and I were in separate rooms each with a standard dictionary, and we were asked to randomly and simultaneously flip through the pages and put our finger on a random word 100 times, what are the chances that in the end we'd have come up with 99 of the same random words out of 100 attempts? Almost zero, considering the average dictionary includes around 200,000 words. Now expand this to 203,000 attempts in a genome with three billion base pairs and a 99.96% match rate, and you see how wildly improbable it would be that chimps and humans would share all their ERVs by any other process than derivation from a common ancestor who already had all these ERVs.

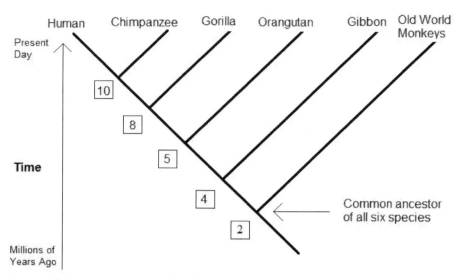

Figure 9.7 Humans share more ERVs with chimpanzees than any other animal.

In an act of sheer overkill and absolute certainty, we can also compare the number of ERVs we share not only with chimps, but also with gorillas, orangutans, gibbons, and old world monkeys to be sure that ERVs prove common ancestry to be true (Figure 9.7). For the group of ERVs called "HERV-K," we find that all six groups share two such ERVs in common. When we exclude old world monkeys, the remaining five groups share four ERVs. When we look at humans, chimps, gorillas, and orangs, we see they share five ERVs. When narrowed down to humans, chimps, and gorillas, we have eight ERVs in common. And finally with our closest relative, the chimpanzees, we share ten ERVs.[90,91] We also have two of our own that no other group shares.

This data only makes sense if we shared a most recent common ancestor with chimps, a second most recent ancestor with the gorillas, a third most recent ancestor with the orangutans, and so on. And again, all the ERVs are where they "should be;" not one is out of place. The ERV data allows us to create a nested hierarchy that shows a clear pattern of common ancestry, much like the pseudogene data. Furthermore, the ERV and pseudogene data are only two pieces of evidence in a sea of other evidences that support this same pattern of common descent.[92,93,94]

Much like with pseudogenes, scientists have learned a great deal more about ERVs in the past several years. The places where the viruses insert themselves into the host's genome were thought to be completely random until recently, but careful study has now revealed that the real picture is a little more complicated than this. Research has found that retroviruses have certain regions within the genome that they prefer to integrate into, but *within* those regions, integration is still mostly random.[95,96] Ever since, creationists and ID advocates have been going absolutely bananas over this revelation and have been excitedly shouting from every rooftop that evolutionists were wrong about ERVs, since they show site specificity. Many ID proponents, therefore, conclude that the ERV evidence for evolution actually proves nothing, since they reason that all of the tens of thousands of ERVs shared between chimps and humans could have integrated separately into the respective lineages since the retroviruses have certain spots they like to splice themselves into, not that they ended up in the same spots as a result of evolution. However, this is certainly not the case, as proponents of this view are either misunderstanding the scientific literature they are quoting, or they are suppressing a great deal of evidence.

First of all, notice that it is the allegedly biased and scheming *mainstream scientists* who made the discovery that some pseudogenes have function, or that ERVs are not randomly integrated, not creationist or ID "scientists" who generally do not perform any original research of their own. Furthermore, notice how, on one hand, creationists and ID advocates say that humans and chimps *are not* genetically very similar (in order to deny the implication of common ancestry), but then on the other hand they argue that, because the two species *are* so genetically similar, that ERVs inserted themselves separately into the *same* genetic places. Anyone see the contradiction? If ERVs could be explained by parallel integration due to genetic similarity, this would underscore the fact that we are nearly genetically identical to chimps and provide good evidence of common descent. But, if creationists want to deny genetic similarities between us and chimps, then they have to deal with the couple hundred thousand shared ERVs that could not have been integrated in a parallel manner due to their view of human–chimp genetic dissimilarity.

The truth of the matter is that retrovirus insertion is *not* truly random per se; there are certainly some parts of the genome they prefer to nestle into.[97,98] However, within those specific parts of the genome is still a great deal of randomness as to where *exactly* the retrovirus will be inserted.[99,100] It's somewhat akin to the retroviruses each preferring to settle down in a certain "city," but the specific neighborhood or street they move to is more or less random. Additionally, some retroviruses show high site specificity (regions where they most often insert), and some show almost no specificity, to the point of near statistical randomness.[101,102]

For our dictionary scenario, this adjustment would mean that it might be more accurate to envision choosing a set number of words from each letter category (e.g., three words from the "A"s, four words from the "B"s, and so on) totaling one hundred words, which would *still* make it almost impossible to match 99 out of 100 randomly. The take-away point here is that the fact that we share nearly all of our 203,000 ERVs with chimps cannot be explained by "parallel integration." While retroviruses do have certain *regions* they prefer, we share many of our ERVs in the *exact same random spot within* those regions. Furthermore, we also share many of the same exact mutations in the same ERVs as chimps.[103]

To explain away this evidence, you would have to believe over 200,000 retroviruses happened to simultaneously invade human and chimpanzee genomes. Not only that, but they all happened to be identical retroviruses that decided to set up shop in identical places in both genomes. What's more, you would further have to believe we somehow developed identical random mutations as chimps did in their ERVs. *Or,* you could believe that the human–chimp common ancestor seven million years ago had all these ERVs, and the reason that chimps and humans have nearly all of them in common is because they both derived from this common ancestor. Be honest now: Which one is really more reasonable? Creationists and ID advocates have no real substantive response to this damning evidence, and as their only retort, they try in vain to obfuscate and muddy the waters by telling half the truth but a whole lie. What this hurting world needs is the Gospel of Jesus Christ, not the deception of well-intentioned creationists.

Psalm 19:1 says, "The heavens declare the glory of God; the skies proclaim the work of His hands" (NIV). I submit to you, the natural world also magnificently declares the glory of God, not through special independent creation, but rather through the laws of natural selection that God designed to bring about a marvelous procession of creatures unimaginable through eons of time. Evolution and common ancestry is not an ugly thing to be ashamed of or fight against; on the contrary, it is the mode of creation that God, in all His wisdom, chose to bring about all life on the planet—much more interesting, creative, amazing, and worthy of worship than rabbit-out-of-a-hat style creation.

CHAPTER TEN

LEFT BEHIND

Vestigial Organs: A Whale of a Tale

Vestigial organs are exciting clues into life's past. Organs of this type are rudiments of ancient structures that have since lost much or all of their original function. To put it another way, they are like evolutionary leftovers; they are no longer needed and so are passed on but may become degenerate due to mutations, or they may maintain some but not *all* of their original functions. Many familiar animals provide tantalizing evidence of their ancestry and very powerfully demonstrate evolution.

Though counterintuitive and seemingly far-fetched, there is very strong DNA evidence that whales evolved from a group of even-toed hoofed land mammals called artiodactyls[1,2,3,4] (more on this in Chapter 11). But if whales were in fact descended from land-dwelling creatures, wouldn't we expect to find other evidences of this? Yes, and indeed we do, as the toothed whales (Odontoceti) and baleen whales (Mysticeti, e.g., Bowhead, Northern Right, Fin, Killer, Sperm) have tiny remnants of a pelvis buried deep beneath their flesh.[5] Dolphins and Manatees also share this evolutionary souvenir.

While the creationists will counter that these bones play a role in reproduction in certain whale species (and they are completely right), they miss the bigger point that these were also once functional pelvises that bore limbs, as I explain further when I discuss the fossil evidence in the next chapter. If you truly doubt that these are in fact remains of a pelvis, look up a photograph showing their location within a whale's body. They are in the exact location you would expect a pair of limbs to be in relation to their front limbs and to the rest of their body. In addition, many whales (e.g., sperm whale) have unmistakable pelvis and even limb structures such as the ilium, ischium, pubis, and femur.[7] These facts mesh very neatly with the evolutionary theory that whales are descendants of four-legged mammals, but they are not plausibly explained by a creation model.

Snakes also bear traces of a pelvis, with boas and pythons having a femur, ilium, and rudimentary hind limb bones buried within their body.[8] All that pokes out is a pair of little spurs which are used as an aid in mating (Figure 10.1). The largest snake family (Colubridae) does not have these spurs and still mates perfectly fine, suggesting that the spurs are not vital to reproduction. And although these pelvis leftovers provide *some* function, they have lost their original function unique to their limbed ancestors (a conclusion reinforced by the initiation of embryonic hind limb buds).[9] And if you look at the spot on a python where these spurs occur, they seem to be conveniently placed in the same area where you would expect legs if snakes were to have them. Again, it is difficult to see why God would purposely confuse scientists by placing what, by all accounts, appears to be pelvis remainders in the spot where hind limbs occur on similar animals, like lizards.

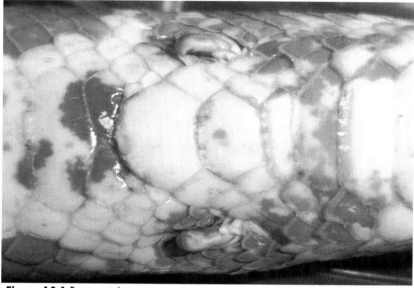

Figure 10.1 Boa constrictor spurs.

Yet, other critters have some anatomical features that have lost all function, not just some. Moles with eyes beneath a layer of skin, blind cave salamanders[10] and cave crayfish with eyeless eye stalks[11] obviously demonstrate evolution. As the fully "eyed" ancestors of these species ventured into darker territories, the function of their eyes became non-essential for their lifestyle and survival, leaving their eye genes subject to mutation over generations. These genes still get passed on, however, and result in the feeble structures these animals now bear. Likewise, an innumerable amount of beetle species have fully formed wings that are *never* utilized.[12] These superb appendages lie beneath an immovable wing cover (elytra), but in a sad irony never once give flight to their owners. How does the creationist/ID model account for fully-formed beetle wings that are never used?

Speaking of wings, have you ever noticed how many birds have wings but can't use them to fly? Ostriches, emus, and penguins are certainly birds, yet they couldn't get off the ground to save their lives. Of course, these appendages still have important purposes. They may serve for propulsion underwater, mating displays, or stabilization when running. A curious case, however, is the flightless kiwi of New Zealand (*Apteryx autralius*). This delightful little bird by all appearances seems to have no wings; it more or less resembles a furry ball with a long beak and large feet. However, if you probe around its side, beneath its feathers you will find a tiny pink nub-like wing smaller than your pinky finger. Just to reiterate, these are small vestigial wings that serve no purpose; they are simply leftover from the flighted progenitor of the kiwi.[13] How can creationism or Intelligent Design account for a bird with wings that have absolutely no function? Doesn't this seem to make more sense in the light of evolution? If the ancestors of all modern birds were flighted, it would make sense that some later branches could develop lifestyles that didn't necessitate flight and thus could co-opt wings for other purposes or lose them entirely.

If you still want more proof of vestigial organs, look no further than a mirror. Humans have many vestigial traits, one of them being goosebumps. Have you ever noticed how you get them when you are cold or frightened? At a time when we had full-body hair, goosebumps once served to make us look larger in order to ward off predators. This fear response would activate our arrector pili muscles to raise our hairs, like the flag raising at Iwo Jima. Likewise, when we were cold, goosebumps would raise our hairs on end to allow them to better insulate us by trapping a layer of air between our skin and the hair. While goosebumps may still serve an important role in maintaining follicular integrity,[14] they have lost much of their original function. The same goes for many or our muscles, including muscles attached to the ear, which cannot move. How would creationism/ID account for extra muscles that don't work?

Yet another example can be found in that of the palmar grasp reflex. This is when an infant clamps its hand around your finger in an adorable death-grip. A study found that 37% of infants can support their own weight with this grip.[15] Babies' feet can also curl inward, unlike adults' feet, which cannot. These prehensile feet and instinctually grasping hands harken back to a time when infants rode on their furry mothers, much like modern apes do today. What purpose could these traits possibly serve today in humans?

Perhaps a bit of wisdom is needed here . . . or maybe not. Studies show that one in three people will have problems with their wisdom teeth, and that up to 20% may experience serious pathology (e.g., infection, inflammation) including in rare cases death.[16] Our ancestors possessed sizable jaws capable of fitting extra molars useful for grinding up plant material. However, human evolution has favored smaller and smaller jaws over time, leaving these third molars out of a job. Human evolution in some groups may be trending toward disposing of these liabilities completely, like the indigenous peoples of Mexico who are almost guaranteed not to have them. On the other hand, some people groups like Tasmanian aboriginees are virtually guaranteed to develop them.[17] How does special creation account for unnecessary extra teeth? Why would God endow us with unneeded molars that in 33% of people become impacted and malformed, causing the potential for sickness and death unless surgically removed?

Vestigial organs certainly are numerous, and the examples that abound provide comprehensive and robust support for the theory of evolution and common descent. Creationism and ID are at a loss when it comes to explaining these phenomena. The evidence provided by vestigial organs is potent, and it cannot easily be ignored.

At a Complete Loss (of Information, That Is)

Perhaps one of the most widely circulated arguments against evolution is the claim that there can only be a loss of genetic information over time as organisms reproduce and change (within "kinds," they might add). Critics allege that there are no mechanisms or processes that can "add" new information to a genome; at best, what we see in the natural world is variation based on existing genetic information, or at worst a "devolution" caused by a loss of information. Animals such as moles with fully-developed eyes beneath a layer of skin, or snakes that have a hidden pelvis left over from when they had legs are often thought to be explained away by this "loss of information" argument. Hence, the proposition that evolution could create anything new or novel would seem to be utterly impossible if only this line of reasoning were valid.

However, this argument betrays a startling unawareness of basic biology. Even if natural selection did just choose from existing variation, this process would still be capable of creating significant change in an organism. If you had a population of organisms that underwent many rounds of natural selection, over time the frequency of beneficial variations would be increased. This would create new combinations that were absent or exceedingly uncommon in the starting population. To give an illustration, imagine that the entire set of genetic information (genome) of an organism is like a huge box of lego bricks. You can take those lego bricks and create an almost endless number of new and unique structures by just rearranging the existing lego bricks in that box. Put another way, the "loss of information" argument is akin to saying that in order to write a new book or poem, you would have to invent more letters in the alphabet, since writers do nothing more than reshuffle letters that are already there. This is ridiculous of course, because with 26 letters, you can rearrange them in any number of infinite ways to create endless new works of literature; the same goes for the four-letter alphabet of the genome. And in any case, beneficial mutations for pesticide resistance in the sheep blowfly (*Lucilia cuprina*) have been verified as actual mutations, *not* as preexisting variation.[18]

When we take the human genome into account, things get even worse for this argument. Consider that when you were conceived, you received a reshuffled version of your parents' genetic material. Each of your parent's gametes (egg, sperm) had a different chromosome combination that could be one of eight million different varieties. Since the egg and sperm can each be assorted in eight million unique ways, this means that when they combine, there is the potential for over 64,000,000,000,000 distinct combinations.[19] This means that you were one out of 64 trillion possible variants that could have been conceived! And this is just due to independent assortment (formation of random pairs of chromosomes in gametes). When you factor in the phenomena of crossing over (where chromosomes swap material), the possible combinations are even higher! All this variation gives evolution plenty of raw material to work with. There is always "new" information, if only for the fact that there is always a combination whose number hasn't yet come up.

But we can add more variation and new information still, in the form of mutations. Put aside notions of X-men and the Incredible Hulk. You currently have about sixty mutations in your genome.[20] Any one of those sixty mutations could create a significant difference in your appearance or behavior, creating yet more material for evolution to work with. There is also new information in the genome created by things called "transposable elements." These bits of DNA essentially pick up and move themselves to another part of the genome where they insidiously reinsert themselves. These transposable elements create structural variation in about 1 out of 21 humans.[21]

What's that? You want more ways organisms can acquire new genetic information? How about horizontal gene transfer? This is where organisms transfer genes outside of reproduction. This is most common in bacteria, where two cells connect and pass genetic information, but this also happens in the plant, fungi, and animal kingdom.[22] Just to be clear, this is a brand new gene being added into another organisms genome. Endosymbiosis also provides new genetic information. This is where one cell begins in a symbiotic (you scratch my back, I'll scratch yours) relationship with another cell but is eventually taken inside that other cell and retained. This accounts for the origin of our mitochondria (the cell's powerhouse) and the chloroplast (photosynthesizing organ) in plants.[23] Also, chromosomes can undergo modifications in the form of deletions, duplications, inversions, translocations, and other ways that can significantly change the genome.[24] Additionally, there can be changes in the number of entire sets of chromosomes, as well as changes in the number of single chromosomes within a set for many organisms, thus providing more variation for evolution to work with.[25]

Deconstructing Devolution

When it comes to organisms only "devolving" in a kind of retrograde evolution, we need only to analyze this claim a little more closely to see that it is fruitless as well. Evolution has no end goal or anything toward which it is striving, at least that science can detect (although by *faith* I believe there is a goal or purpose in the larger sense). Evolution, in its simplest form, is genetic change within populations of organisms in response to their environment. Correspondingly, there is no rule of nature that a type organism must become more complex or more advanced in the course of its evolutionary history. The lay public may place judgements on the biological world as to whether something is evolving in a positive or negative direction, but this distinction does not exist in science. Populations of organisms are simply undergoing change in their allele frequencies; there is no "good" or "bad" or "devolution," as evolution has no inherent directionality.

Additionally, some traits that supposedly show "devolution" may actually be beneficial to the organism. For instance, the mole with eyes beneath its skin may be less prone to infection, as this attribute prevents dirt from entering its eyes. Besides, it lives underground; an eye is presumably of little use in the pitch-black darkness. Likewise, the loss of limbs may be favorable for a snake in that it can surreptitiously sidle up to its prey better than its four-legged forerunners. Similarly, the loss of back limbs in whales would only serve to make them more streamlined and efficient in the water. In short, an organism losing traits its ancestor once possessed does not mean it is "devolving." After all, I don't see anyone lamenting that we devolved since we lost full-body hair coverage and opposable toes!

Are Mutations Always Bad?

Mutations get a bad rap, but things are not so cut-and-dried, and there is much more to the story than most realize. The large majority of mutations in an organism's genome are silent mutations, which don't really affect the owner.[26] This is because the mutations are either in regions that don't code for anything (e.g., "junk" DNA, although this term is somewhat misleading), or the mutation replaces one nucleotide for another one that still ends up creating the same amino acid. Of the small minority of mutations that do matter, most of them are not beneficial, and in fact may be fatal to the organism.[27] However, out of those mutations that do matter, a small proportion of them can be beneficial to an organism.[28,29,30,31,32] This may not sound like a very compelling argument, but consider the fact that mutations that are fatal are not passed on to offspring. In other words, harmful mutations are weeded out because the organisms that have them typically die and don't get to pass on those mutated genes. What we are mostly left with, then, are mutations that either do nothing or provide a potential benefit to a creature. And when beneficial mutations arise in a population, they tend to spread and dominate rather quickly.[33]

Should anyone doubt that beneficial mutations exist, we need not look any further than ourselves. The fact that we have language and the ability to speak is possibly caused by a mutation in our FOXP2 gene.[34] The FOXP2 genes of humans and non-human primates differ by only two amino acids, showing that a small mutation can have a large beneficial impact.[35] If you can drink milk without getting sick, you have a mutation to thank.[36] All infants can process milk, but usually this trait does not carry into adulthood. However, many people groups that historically had a close association with cattle developed a mutation that allowed them to digest milk as adults.[37] Furthermore, nearly all mammals aside from some marsupials and primates have dichromatic vision, which is similar to seeing with red-green colorblindness.[38] However, we have trichromatic vision, which allows us to see a much wider color spectrum than our four-legged friends, likely due to a mutation.[39] Mutations, therefore, are not always bad, and on the contrary are a key driving force of evolution. They provide much variation and raw material for evolution to work with, enabling organisms to evolve in significant ways over time.

Atavisms

Atavisms are perhaps one of the most bizarre and shocking evidences for evolution. An atavism is an ancestral organ or trait that unexpectedly pops up in a modern organism, like a sort of evolutionary throwback. This is only possible because organisms today still harbor plenty of ancient DNA that codes for features that are no longer expressed. Genes such as tails in humans or legs in whales are buried deep within their respective genomes, albeit they are often mutated, repressed, or otherwise inactivated. However, mutations can undo whatever they have previously done, and very rarely a primitive trait from an ancestor millions of years ago expresses itself in a present-day creature in the most freakish of ways.

I am living proof of this concept, as I myself have an atavism. For years I have harbored this shameful secret, but in the name of God and science I must divulge it, if only to help others understand God's magnificent workings through the evolutionary process. I have four— count them—four nipples. Yes, they are truly extra nipples that lie about three inches below my normal ones. However, they are only a quarter inch across, so I'm not quite fit to be a circus sideshow act, although it did make gym class quite interesting. Obvious jokes aside, my supernumerary nipples are reminders of an earlier time in history when mammals had multiple teats.[40] These genes had lain defunct in my genetic lineage for tens of millions of years, only to be reawakened and foisted upon a boy who if he was not already insecure and hairless in a high-school locker room full of mean jocks, surely would become so.

However, there are even stranger cases than mine (thankfully). *Archaeopteryx* was a transitional species between dinosaurs and birds. This ancient bird-like species was unique in that it bore teeth just as its dinosaur ancestors had. So if modern birds really did descend from dinosaurs, shouldn't we expect to see inoperative teeth genes in their genome? Incredibly, that is exactly what we find in every major bird lineage alive today.[41] In fact, not only do the teeth genes still exist in our feathered friends, some mutant bird embryos will actually grow reptilian teeth *instead* of a beak.[42] This is only possible because the dinosaur ancestors of birds passed on this genetic material through the ages. Even when birds stopped expressing teeth, they still carried the gene to do so. All it took for this 70-million-year-old gene to come roaring back to life was a mutation. How exactly does a creation model account for this? Why would God create "bird kind" with ancient teeth genes that are never used? Why does *every single* bird carry within its genome defunct teeth genes when *not one single* modern bird whatsoever has teeth at any point in its life cycle? How could ID or creationism possibly explain this?

Horses provide yet another great example. Modern horses have one toe (what we call a hoof), but their ancestors were dog-sized creatures bearing four toes. The excellent fossil record of horse evolution shows that over time the horse lineage lost these extra toes. So it should come as no surprise that every so often a horse is born with multiple toes.[43,44] As with the other examples, the inactive DNA coding for extra toes lay quiet in the horse genome for millions of years, only to be brought to the surface every now and again by an aberrant mutation.

But things get stranger still. If you remember the movie *Shallow Hal*, you may recall that Jason Alexander's character was revealed at the end of the movie to have on his backside a little tail he could "wag." Truth really is stranger than fiction, however, as this is a very real, albeit extremely rare, phenomenon. There have been multiple documented cases in the medical literature of human beings born with an honest-to-goodness tail attached to their rump.[45,46,47] Some may be described as "psuedo-tails;" however, a small number of these unique humans have true tails with vertebrae and cartilage,[48] endowed with the ability to "wag" them.[49] Furthermore, some of these tails have been passed down in families through generations.[50] This is not at all surprising given that humans have a tail in the early stages of embryonic development.[51] These tails are almost always reabsorbed in a process of programmed cell death, but a mutation is all it takes for the latent tail genes of our ancestors to be switched back on, providing us a sort of biological time machine.

Perhaps stranger still is the disturbing case of whales with atavistic legs. Although, this may not be so surprising given that whale and dolphin embryos have hind limb buds early in their development.[52,53] This fact squares well with the unambiguous and extraordinarily well-preserved fossil record of whales, which shows them to be descendants of land-dwelling four-limbed mammals.[54,55,56]

Examples of whales with legs are not uncommon, with several examples of whales with two hind limbs compiled by Brian Hall.[57] A particularly interesting example was that of a humpback whale captured near Vancouver Island, British Columbia in 1919. This whale had a pair of legs protruding from the back half of its body, each appendage measuring over four feet in length and covered in blubber.[58] These bones consisted of a femur, tibia, tarsus, and metatarsal (Figure 10.2) (the exact same bones we see in land mammals today). Not only that, but they were determined to have likely been attached to the whale's vestigial pelvis.[59]

More recently, in 2006 a dolphin bearing hind-flippers was captured by fishermen off the coast of Japan.[60] This extra set of fins were hand-sized appendages capable of moving as the front flippers.[61] Again, these atavisms are a looking glass into the past. The only reason a whale could sprout a random pair of bony hind legs attached to a pelvis rudiment is if it had these genes in its genome. And the only reason a normally leg-less whale would have "leg" genes is if it had legged ancestors in its past evolutionary history. This evidence is strange yet compelling.

How exactly do creationism and ID account for whales with legs? How does the creation model explain why chickens have the genes to grow reptile teeth (and sometimes do grow them embryonically)? What justification does Intelligent Design give for the designer planting within us tail genes that sometimes give rise to a tail? How can special creation possibly account for a whale with a pair of over four-foot-long blubbery legs dangling from its side, complete with the bones of the femur, tibia, tarsus, and metatarsal attached to a tiny pelvis? Even the most hardened and devoted creationist will stand speechless and at a total loss as to how to explain this. However, when one considers these curious cases in the light of evolution, these findings suddenly seem to harmonize very well.

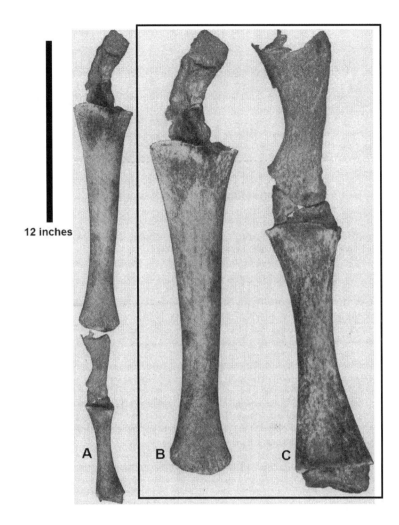

12 inches

Figure 10.2 A. From top to bottom, the bones of the femur, tibia, tarsus, and metatarsal are arranged as they were found on the whale. B. Enlarged photo of the femur and tibia. C. Enlarged photo of the tarsus and metatarsal. Photos B and C are not the same scale as A, as they have been enlarged to show detail.

From: Andrews, Roy Chapman. *A remarkable case of external hind limbs in a humpback whale.* By order of the Trustees of The American Museum of Natural History, 1921

CHAPTER ELEVEN

FOSSILS

Fossil Layers

A striking feature of the fossil record is that when you examine older layers deep down in the earth compared to younger layers close to the surface, you notice something very fascinating. The simplest organisms are found in the bottommost fossil layer, and as you inspect layers closer to the surface, you discover increasingly complex creatures with each successive layer. Furthermore, many of the creatures in the bottom layers are vastly different from those we currently find ourselves surrounded by today.

In the very bottom fossil layer, we find only very simple organisms (e.g., bacteria, algae). Above this layer, we find soft-bodied multi-cellular animals, and above that you'll notice shelled animals have stepped onto the scene. Continue upwards and fishes and land plants have joined in. Up closer to the surface still, we suddenly find the appearance of amphibians and insects. Subsequent higher layers feature reptiles, followed by dinosaurs, followed by birds and flowering plants.[1] The point is, we see a gradual sequence of organisms appearing in the fossil record. And the order in which organisms appear supports the consensus of modern science that life originated billions of years ago and over time evolved into more complex organisms.

For instance, from about 3.5 billion years ago until 600 million years ago in the geologic record, we find only very simple organisms such as bacteria and algae but never find a fossil of a mammal, dinosaur, or insect within that layer.[2,3] Likewise, we never find one single flowering plant in the fossil record until the "dinosaur age" is in full swing.[4,5] We never find fossils of a human and a dinosaur in the same layer, nor do we even find fossils of any modern mammal or modern bird mixed in with the dinosaurs. Similarly, after about 65 million years ago (the date of the Cretaceous-Tertiary extinction), dinosaurs never pop up in any later geologic layers, but mammal fossils afterward show a radiation of diversification.

If all animals were created simultaneously by God, wouldn't we expect to find all types of fossils jumbled together when we dig down into the earth? If evolution did not start with a cell and become more complex, why does the fossil record show simple life in the bottommost layer and increasingly diverse and complex forms progressively higher in the geologic layers? Isn't it curious that we never find a mammal fossil where it shouldn't be, or a dinosaur fossil where it doesn't belong?

And for those who hold on to some hope that the "global flood" explains the vast array of fossils, they are sorely mistaken. Unless the flood was incredibly able to sort all fossils *worldwide* in order from least complex to more complex, taking care to not mix humans with dinosaurs, or modern birds with primitive reptiles, or flowering plants with the first insects, this idea seems fruitless and far-fetched to say the least. Some would advocate that more mobile organisms were able to ascend into higher places to escape the floodwaters and thus would be preserved close to the surface in the geological strata. Therefore, you would expect to find mammals and birds near the top, and fish and marine creatures toward the bottom. However, recall that flowering plants don't arrive in the fossil record until after the appearance of molluscs, arthropods, cnidarians, fish, amphibians, insects, reptiles, and dinosaurs. Are we to believe that these flowering plants were so mobile and swift that they could outrun reptiles and dinosaurs when escaping the flood uphill? The idea that a global flood could produce the very neatly organized and unambiguous fossil record we see today is like imagining a raging typhoon hitting a cluttered junkyard but miraculously leaving in its wake every car in the lot methodically organized by year, make, and model.

Transitional Fossils

A popular creationist website admits, "All the evolutionist has to do is produce one indisputable transitional form between the higher kinds to seriously challenge the creation model."[6] Incredibly, most people who have creationist or ID views truly believe there are no transitional fossils in existence. Every creationist/ID book and website I have read without exception has confidently proclaimed that there is not one single legitimate transitional fossil in existence, and many allege that they are the only proof that would vindicate common descent and evolution.[2] Accordingly, many creationists are genuinely shocked when I tell them there are well over one-hundred transitional fossils, with dozens of very clear examples of transitional fossils therein.[8,9,10,11,12] Most honestly have no idea that there really are transitional fossils, having trusted creationists/ID'ers that there are none. Nothing could be further removed from the truth, however, and I will endeavor to show a few examples that provide the most unambiguous and explicit evidence for macroevolutionary change.

In the proceeding examples, it is important to bear in mind that evolution and common descent are not supported solely by the fossil record. A sufficient case could be made on the DNA, homology, biogeography, or other evidences alone. The existence of transitional fossils is merely the icing on the cake that makes the theory of macroevolutionary change even more airtight. Another item to keep in mind is that the fossil record is certainly not complete by any means, and that it is unreasonable to expect to find a transitional fossil for a specific group or for most groups even. The creation of a fossil is an exceedingly rare event, and we are fortunate to have any at all. The ones that we have found, however, are powerful pieces of evidence that leave no doubts as to their implications.

Storming the Beaches — Water to Land

Deep in the Devonian, from about 380-360 million years ago, a monumental event took place that would change the course of life on this planet. Lobe-finned fishes began to transition to four-legged creatures capable of leaving the water, laying the groundwork for all tetrapods (four-legged animals) yet to come.[14,15] While the seas were full of predators and competitors in the Devonian, the shallower swampy areas presumably contained better opportunities for space, food, and breeding for the lobe-finned fishes. This would have provided a great benefit to variants subtly more suited to inhabiting the shallows, and thus

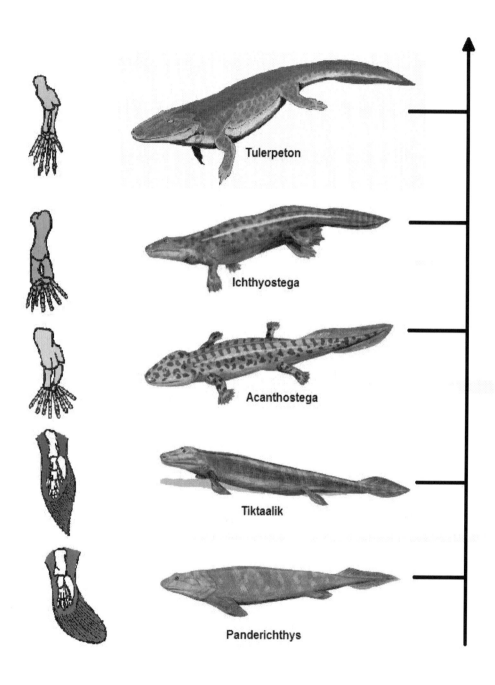

Figure 11.1 The lineage that gave rise to modern tetrapods is comprised of several fossil animal species that establish a morphological bridge between fishes and tetrapods.

natural selection in this group trended toward favoring fins that were increasingly limb-like and capable of supporting weight, toward respiratory systems that depended less on water, and toward resistance to desiccation (drying out). Eventually, some of these early tetrapods would have spent increasing amounts of time on land exploiting predator-free ecological niches rife with food, to the point that over time they became mainly land-dwellers (if this seems implausible, look up frogfish, walking catfish, mudskippers, and climbing perch). Thus, the origin of tetrapods has its root in the lobe-finned fishes of the Devonian.

The evidence of this monumental event is made manifest by the fossil witnesses to this occasion (Figure 11.1). The early lobe-finned fishes such as *Panderichthys* had a fish-like body and a rounded head with spiracles (breathing holes) that indicate it was already breathing air.[16] This fish had paddle-like pelvic and pectoral fins, but by this period had already lost dorsal (top) and anal (bottom near tail) fins.[17] By the time *Tiktaalik* emerges, the eyes have moved more toward the top of a flattened skull, as in most modern amphibians. This stage also sees the development of a neck that allows for movement, and a jointed pectoral fin.[18] When we get to *Acanthostega* in the late Devonian, we now see limbs bearing eight digits, an indication of the first "footed" animal.[19] However, this critter still had internal gills and a lateral sensory system, indicating it was still predominantly aquatic.[20] *Ichthyostega* later changes things up and spends more time on land[21] and also moves to having seven digits on each limb.[22] Enabling this move is a robust skeletal system comprised of reinforced vertebrae, limbs, and ribs.[23]

Now, this is not a comparison of different sized pots or models of car; this is a progression of fossils over time that show very clear intermediates between fishes and tetrapods. Each step in the evolution of these animals shows a mix of primitive traits and new traits, inextricably linking these animals to one another in a macroevolutionary sequence. This is not an act of rummaging around the fossil drawer and sorting specimens in a way that supports a preconception; this is a series of fossils that are all *themselves* transitional species, and taken together with the geological age in which they were found create a coherent and persuasive narrative chronicling how tetrapods came about. One would be very hard-pressed to come up with a creation model that could account for *Panderichthys* being created by God 380 million years ago, *Tiktaalik* being made 5 million years later, and *Acanthostega* and *Ichthyostega* another 10 million or so after that, each species being individually "designed" to look like one proceeded the other in an evolutionary fashion over time.

Why would God specially create such extinct animals for any other purpose than confusing us? I sincerely believe God is the ultimate truth, and that there is no deceit in Him. To conclude that God would create so many evolutionary "clues" that were false would seem to me to contradict the supremely good God of the Bible.

Horses: A Nightmare for Creationism

The fossil record of horse evolution is by far the most complete of any animal, with almost all the intermediate species linking the primitive *Hyractotherium* to modern *Equus* known through an excellent series of fossils.[24,25,26,27,28,29,30] The fact that we can trace horses' past throughout the last 55 million years using fossil proof at nearly every step is simply incredible, and it provides explosive evidence for macroevolution. During this time, many significant changes took place, as a dog-sized four-toed animal became a 1,000 pound, one-toed creature with many anatomical differences.

It is important to understand that the evolution of the horse family much like most other groups is more like a bush than a tree,[31] (Figure 11.2). There was not a linear progression toward the modern horse but rather many different side branches in which some evolved in different directions.[32] Some of these offshoots kept certain structures and lifestyles that others did not, and at times multiple lineages of different horse existed concurrently, especially in the mid to late Miocene (15–5 million years ago).[33] Horses were not the "goal" of all of this; they are simply the only ones to have survived to the present day. I say this so as not to oversimplify the evidence and mislead readers, as many textbooks have traditionally done a disservice to this subject.[34] As I have done throughout this book, I do my best to present all of the evidence as objectively as I can, no matter how sophisticated and complicated the material is. Additionally, I believe the slightly more complex but accurate picture of horse evolution adds to the veracity and utility of this transitional fossil series more so than does the grossly oversimplified version.

We start off deep in the Eocene about 55 million years ago. Here we had *Hyracotherium* (Eohippus), a minuscule leaf-eating creature standing only 25–50 centimeters at the shoulder, replete with four toes

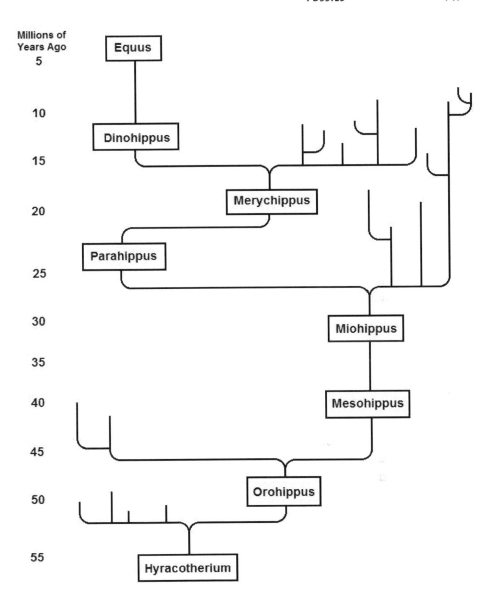

Figure 11.2 The evolution from the small four-toed *Hyracotherium* to the modern-day horse is spanned by a number of fossil intermediates. Morphological characteristics link all these species together and show gradual change over time.

on its front legs and three on its back, all with little proto-hooves attached.[35,36] About 50 million years, there was *Orohippus*, who possessed a similar sized but slimmer body with a slightly longer head and limbs.

Around 10–15 million years later, *Mesohippus* hit the scene, standing 60 centimeters tall but sporting one fewer toe on its front limbs.[37] At 32 million years ago, *Miohippus* had become heavier than its predecessor, with a longer face as well. In the early Miocene around 24 million years ago, *Parahippus* had started to browse less foliage and incorporate more grasses into its diet.[38] In addition to being larger than *Miohippus*, this species differs in that it had smaller side-toes that became less useful.[39,40] *Merychippus* had become a full-blown grazer by 20 million years ago,[41] and aside from its three toes, looked very much like a modern horse with a tall stance of 90 centimeters.[42] It also had a larger brain than its predecessors, a trend that started with *Mesohippus*. Lastly, we have *Dinohippus* who turned up roughly 13 million years ago, with some individuals having lost the two extra toes and others still hanging on to a vestige of them.[43] This last species looked nearly indistinguishable from our modern horse.

When it comes to tracing the lineage that led to our modern horses, some overall trends are apparent. Size increases gradually from 25–50 centimeters in the Eohippus to 150 centimeters in the modern horse. The number of toes decreases steadily from four on the front and three on the back, to three on both sets of limbs, to species where there is variability between three toes and one, to finally one toe on each limb. The main toe (third digit) becomes consistently longer and thicker throughout this series, and the length of the limbs increases overall. The crown heights of the molars also become longer through time, as early horses are browsers but later horses are grazers. It is all but inescapable to conclude that these fossils are indisputably transitional forms. The layers in which these specimens are found and the dating of said layers preclude the possibility that all these species existed simultaneously. This is truly a *sequence* of evolutionary change over long periods of time, with a multiplicity of fossils at every single stage to provide ample evidence to that effect. Dozens, and in many cases, over a hundred complete skeletons of each species exist,[44] and I have personally viewed several of them.

Again, it seems the only other possible interpretation besides evolution is the unattractive and *ad-hoc* explanation that God created Eohippus, only to later kill off that species in order for it to be replaced with *Orohippus*, and so on until we arrive at the modern horse. This would of course, again, mean that God was creating species individually over time that would appear to be evolved from one another, when in fact they were specially created. Others may be tempted to chalk the series up to "variation within a kind," but can you really call a four-toed creature the size of a small dog evolving into a half-ton animal with one toe over the span of 55 million years "variation within a kind?" It seems that one could easily play a semantics game and call anything "variation within a kind" to avoid admitting the reality of macroevolution. However, this is not microevolution by anyone's definition; this is a rock-solid example of macroevolution at its clearest.

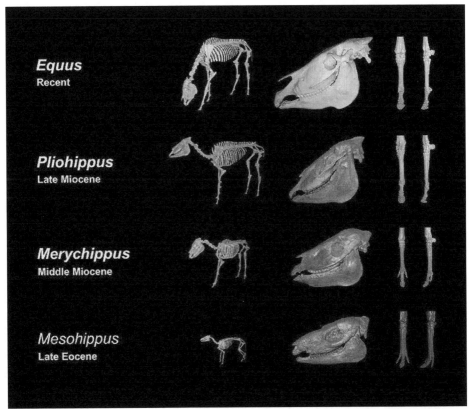

Figure 11.3 Skeletal reconstructions demonstrate an increase in size as well as a loss of digits over time. Cranial and dental changes reveal a gradual shift from browsing to grazing.

Whale Transitional Fossils

When I was a creationist, I laughed at the thought that whales derived from land mammals. That amusement quickly turned to dismay, however, when I not only found that there was an excellent fossil record to support this conclusion, but I observed some of the transitional fossils in person. There is nothing quite like seeing the unmistakable skeleton of a whale with small, yet recognizable hind limb bones (Figure 11.4). The macroevolutionary fossil sequence of whales from their origins as land-dwelling four-limbed mammals to their present condition is unambiguous and exceptionally well-preserved.[45,46,47] These forms show a gradation of terrestrial four-limbed creatures becoming aquatic two-limbed animals over time. The intermediate steps along the way are well represented with distinct transitional fossils, which provide tremendous support for macroevolution.

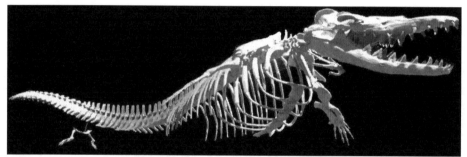

Figure 11.4 *Dorudon* skeleton. Note the tiny pelvis and hind limbs.

About 52 million years ago, we have the first true whale in the form of the ostensibly un-whale-like *Pakicetus*. Though this wolf-sized animal may not look like a cetacean (whale), the ear region of its skull is a dead giveaway that it certainly is, as the bony wall surrounding the ear in whales is unmistakable and unlike that of any other mammal.[48] Don't miss this point: The skulls of whales have certain features that are not shared by *any other* animal group, confirming that *Pakicetus* was a primitive whale, not any other kind of animal. Not only was the skull of *Pakicetus* the beginning of specialization for hearing underwater, but it was intermediate between land mammals and modern whales in that capacity, further establishing this fossil as a transitional form.[49]

A few million years later, the crocodile-like *Ambulocetus* has become an amphibious whale, in contrast to its more terrestrial predecessor.[50] This creature possessed the unmistakable skull of a cetacean yet still had toes terminating in hooves as did *Pakicetus*, a testament to their artiodactyl (even-toed hoofed mammal) origins.[51] Chemical analysis also supports the idea that this early whale spent much time in and near water, as its fossils have been found in what is likely ancient estuary environments,

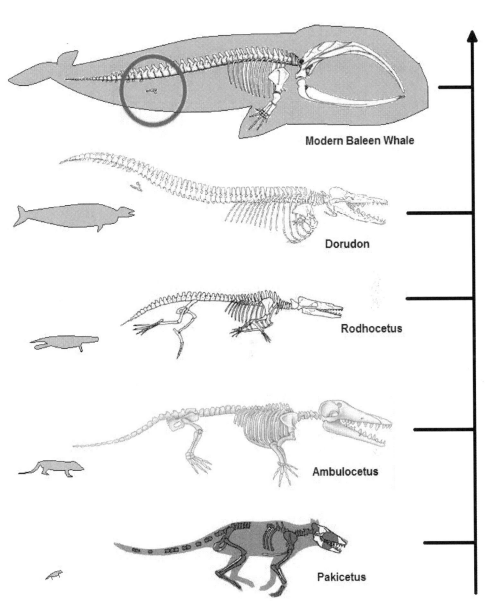

Figure 11.5 Transitional fossil series leading to modern whales. Shown to the left in shading are the relative sizes of each animal. Note the vestigial pelvis in the modern baleen whale.

with the ratios of oxygen isotopes in its bones suggesting it spent its time in both fresh and salt water.[52,53] Fast forward to 47 million years ago, and *Rhodocetus* has become predominately aquatic, evidenced by smaller hindlimbs, a shorter pelvis,[54] and an overall limb structure that strongly suggests limited ability for movement on land.[55] The skull also becomes more elongated and whale-like, especially in that the nostrils are placed further back along the snout, closer to where modern whale's blow-holes are placed.[56] By 40 million years ago, *Dorudon* has largely dispensed with the hind limbs, as this 16-foot-long creature retains only a rudimentary pair.[57] This whale was fully aquatic, further shown by the fact that its blow-hole was nearly midway between the tip of its snout and the top of its head, having migrated even closer to the position of a modern whale's.[58]

We see a very clear progression of intermediate forms over geological time when we examine the fossil record of whales. For the sake of brevity, I chose only a few examples, but other transitional whale species such as *Indohyus, Kutchicetus, Artiocetus, Remingtonocetus, Maiacetus, Aetiocetus, Takracetus, Dalanistes, Basilosaurus, Georgiacetus,* and literally dozens of other species are clearly transitional whale forms that cannot be denied.

In addition to the evidence of the sequential appearance of fossils midway between artiodactyls and modern whales, the artiodactyls share with ancient whales a distinctive double-pulley astragalus (ankle bone) that is like an anatomical fingerprint inextricably linking these two groups.[59] This is very important evidence for whale origins, as the only two groups of animals that have this characteristic ankle bone are the artiodactyls and ancient whales; *no other animal groups* possess them.[60] Now, this unique astragalus was predicted to be found in ancient whale fossils by the DNA evidence linking whales and artiodactyls.[61,62] In the early 2000s, this is exactly what was found, providing a brilliant example of how evolution is a testable theory that makes predictions and passes them with ease.[63] Lastly, the fact that additional recent DNA studies have shown whales to be more related to artiodactyls than any other group of animal provides even further proof of their common ancestry.[64,65,66]

As with our other series of transitional fossils, neither creationism nor ID can provide an empirically based explanation for any of this evidence. Creationism and ID can only resort to religious, faith-based arguments that are by definition not scientific, or that deny the evidence altogether. And in doing so, they denigrate the handiwork of the Creator and deprive Him of the glory He deserves for bringing about these marvelous forms through His chosen method of evolution.

It's a Bird ... It's a Dinosaur ... It's *Archaeopteryx*!

Archaeopteryx is perhaps one of the most controversial fossils ever discovered. With the first of eleven specimens found just two years after the publication of Charles Darwin's *On the Origin of Species* in 1859, this fossil seemed to be a fulfilled prophecy of what Darwin predicted paleontologists should find were evolution to be true. *Archaeopteryx* was the first major transitional fossil that truly left dissidents of Darwin unnerved and unsettled. The reason for this is that this creature appeared to have been a fully feathered dinosaur. Additionally, this animal shared a mosaic of bird and dinosaur traits, which seemingly defied attempts to definitively place it in either category. The result is that this fossil was and still is the poster child for evolution.

Some discerning readers may object that this species is not the direct ancestor of modern birds, and that it was more likely a member of the primitive bird-like dinosaur group that gave rise to modern birds. The jury is still out on this matter; however, there is very good evidence that has surfaced in the last five years that validates *Archaeopteryx* as being, in fact, a primitive bird.[67,68] Whether *Archaeopteryx* was just a close "cousin" to modern birds in that it was part of the basal group of feathered dinosaurs that would eventually give rise to modern birds, or it was in fact a primitive bird, it is a transitional species between dinosaurs and birds nonetheless, and this in-house dispute does not minimize or invalidate its importance as a powerful transitional fossil.

The criterion for a transitional fossil is that it must be an intermediate showing a mix of both ancestral traits of one group and derived traits of another, which *Archaeopteryx* fits to a "T." The theropod dinosaurs (the group of bipedal dinosaurs that included T. Rex) share a great number of characteristics with *Archaeopteryx* in that they both had a toothed jaw, long bony tail, nasal openings very far forward, spine that attached to the rear of the skull, unfused pelvic bones, flat cartilaginous sternum, gastralia (belly ribs), semilunate carpal (wrist bone), killing "toe," and clawed fingers.[69,70] The similarities *Archaeopteryx* shares with modern birds is that it had a reversed first toe on its feet, furcula (wishbone), reduced fingers, and feathers that are, in ornithologist Frank B. Gill's words, "indistinguishable from modern feathers."[71]

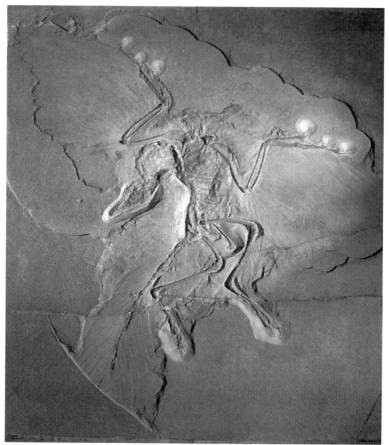

Figure 11.6 *Archaeopteryx* fossil showing clawed fingers, long bony tail, and feathers.

Also, theropods are thought to have laid and incubated eggs in protected nests, much like modern birds. Theropods and extant birds also share lightweight bones, similar feet, respiratory systems, and shoulder sockets that allow them to tuck their arms (or wings) close to their body.[72,73] As far as the similarities between modern birds and reptiles (the group from which dinosaurs evolved), they both lay eggs, have scales (ever look at a bird's feet?), and have similar soft anatomy.[74] Perhaps the most telling evidence is that scales and feathers are both made of the protein keratin, and both of the genes that produce scales and feathers have been found to be very similar.[75]

Creationists and ID proponents seem to have schizophrenia when it comes to what *Archaeopteryx* really is. Neither group believes it is a transitional fossil, but some creationists and ID'ers insist it is merely a bird, while others insist it is nothing more than a dinosaur. The Center for Scientific Creation tries to beguile readers and soothe terrified minds by stating that "leading paleontologists are coming to the conclusion that *Archaeopteryx* is a dinosaur."[76] Meanwhile, the Institute for Creation Research claims, "*Archaeopteryx* was a true bird."[77] Clearly, the lack of agreement within the creationism/ID community only serves to illustrate how powerfully this fossil demonstrates itself as a true macroevolutionary transition.

Those who contend that this animal was only a bird often point out that *some* modern birds (exceedingly few) have clawed wing digits (e.g., ostrich, hoatzin). While this is true, *all* modern birds have a pygostyle, which is a fused triangular-shaped group of tail vertebrae; this is in sharp contrast to the long bony tail found in *Archaeoptyerx*.[78] Furthermore, modern birds do *not* have a toothed jaw, whereas our fossil in question most certainly did.[79] I could go down the list, but suffice to say this creature had many features that *no* modern bird possesses. On the other side of the coin, *Archeapoteryx* had asymmetrical feathers identical to those of modern birds.[80] Asymmetrical feathers create an airfoil shape that allows for the creation of lift and therefore flight. In contrast, symmetrical feathers do not allow for flight. Though this animal likely only used its wings for gliding or as an aid in climbing trees (answering the question what half a wing is good for), its asymmetrical feathers provide proof that this was not merely some structure unrelated to those of modern birds. The feathers of *Archaeopteryx* are undoubtedly a carbon copy of those of modern birds.

Lastly, for those who maintain that *Archaeopteryx* is merely a bird, why does it show over one-hundred anatomical differences from modern birds?[81,82] How can we believe this is a bird when its only major similarity to a bird is feathers? Why is this "bird" that God created individually so vastly different in so many ways from any other bird He created? For those who contend that it is a dinosaur, are you admitting that dinosaurs evolved feathers? Wouldn't a dinosaur sprouting feathers demolish any hope of special creation for all animals? If you can chalk up a feathered dinosaur to "variation within kinds," then what else is not possible? If dinosaurs get feathers, why can't fish become land-dwellers and protohominids become human?

As a last resort, some will insist that since we haven't found the intermediate between dinosaurs and *Archaeopteryx*, or between *Archaeopteryx* and more advanced birds, that this is not a genuine transitional fossil. This tactic is nothing more than the cleverly placed rhetorical device of "moving the goalposts." It seems that if a fossil linking an extinct and extant group is found, then cries demanding intermediates between *those* specimens are heard, and so on *ad infinitum*. Additionally, there are even more bird to dinosaur transitional fossils out there such as *Anchiornis*, *Confuciusornis*, *Ichthyornis*, and *Eoalulavis*, along with others. However, there is a reason the *Archeaopteryx* fossil in particular has not faded in its infamy in the last century and a half. This fossil has defended its place in the spotlight by confirming the darkest fears of evolutionary critics.

Human Transitional Fossils — So Easy a Caveman Can See It's True

As contentious of an issue as evolution is, perhaps within that argument, no area is more controversial than that of human evolution. Just as Copernicus and Galileo upset our sense of "specialness" by revealing that our planet isn't the center of the universe, many see the revelation that humans and apes share a common ancestor as a full-on assault on Christianity and our identity as special beings capable of relationship with our Creator. Some therefore reject the possibility of primate ancestry out of hand, based merely on a gut reaction and perceived incompatibility with Scripture, not dissimilar to the situation centuries ago with Copernicus and Galileo. But believing that all truth is God's truth, and that He is the ultimate truth, we are obligated to seek the truth and should have no fear of it. Setting aside any emotional or theological issues, what does the evidence say in regard to human evolution?

Modern evolutionary theory posits that the lineage leading to chimps and the lineage leading to humans split off at least seven to eight million years ago.[83] During this period of several million years, many different species of human-like ancestors came and went out of existence (Figure 11.9). Rather then being a straight line progression toward modern humans, our history was "bushy," with many species branching off and becoming dead ends. Furthermore, multiple species of ancient human coexisted at various times in the past. However, despite many creationist claims that there are almost no ancient human fossils, over 6,000 individual specimens have been found to date.[84,85] While many of these specimens are not complete skeletons and are fragmentary, a small number are nearly complete, and many of those that are incomplete have the parts that tell us the important story—the skull and pelvis.

The reason the skull and pelvis of the hominid fossils are so important is that they can tell us whether or not the individual in question was bipedal (walked upright). Walking upright requires a different skeleton from that needed to walk on all fours, and the difference is not difficult to spot. One of the most obvious differences between a quadruped (walking on all fours) and a biped is that quadrupeds have a very tall and narrow pelvis, while bipeds have a very short and wide pelvis (Figure 11.7).[86]

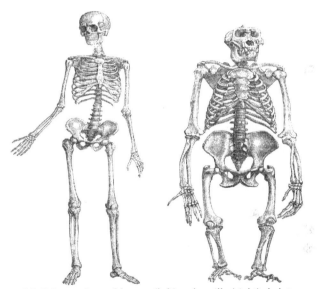

Figure 11.7 Comparison of human (left) and gorilla (right) skeletons. Note the many differences in bipedal and quadrapedal anatomy.

The skull is equally as important in determining whether a specimen walked upright or not, based on the foramen magnum (the hole where the spinal cord enters the skull).[87] A quadraped such as your dog will have the foramen magnum at the back of its skull, which makes sense, as this would be the most natural place for the spinal cord to enter the skull in an animal that walks around on all fours. Bipeds, however, have the foramen magnum directly underneath their skull, as necessitated by an upright posture (Figure 11.8).[88] Apes have a foramen magnum that is a little more forward than that of a quadraped but not directly underneath as in bipeds. This is due to the fact that apes are more erect than other primates and are able to briefly walk upright briefly. These facts allow us to objectively and accurately assess hominid fossils to ascertain whether they are just apes, just human, or truly a transitional species.

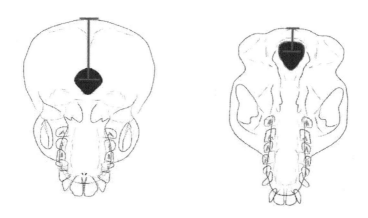

Figure 11.8 Comparison of human (left) and chimpanzee (right) skulls. Note the position of the foramen magnum.

We begin our journey at six to seven million years ago,[89] around one million years or so after the human–chimp lineage split.[90] Here we find two species, *Sahelanthropus tchadensis* and *Orrorin tugenensis*. The *Sahelanthropus* fossil consists of a skull, which shows that it had a cranial volume (brain size) very similar to that of a chimpanzee (about 360cc).[91] The skull shows a mix of primitive and modern hominin characteristics [92,93] and also has a very prominent brow ridge suggestive of that of a male gorilla.[94] However, the foramen magnum in this specimen is positioned and oriented in such a way that it is apparent this species walked upright.[95] Furthermore, the foramen magnum of *Sahelanthropus* is positioned about midway between a chimp's and a human's, exactly where we would expect to find it if this were an early bipedal transitional form.[96] The *Orrorin* specimen, on the other hand, is missing its skull but instead contains a partial femur that suggests bipedalism,[97] and in both species the canine teeth, although still large and prominent, are smaller than those of modern male apes.[98] These fossils show a mix of ancestral traits (small brain size and large canines) and derived traits (bipedal locomotion, foramen magnum position), making them good candidates for human transitional fossils.

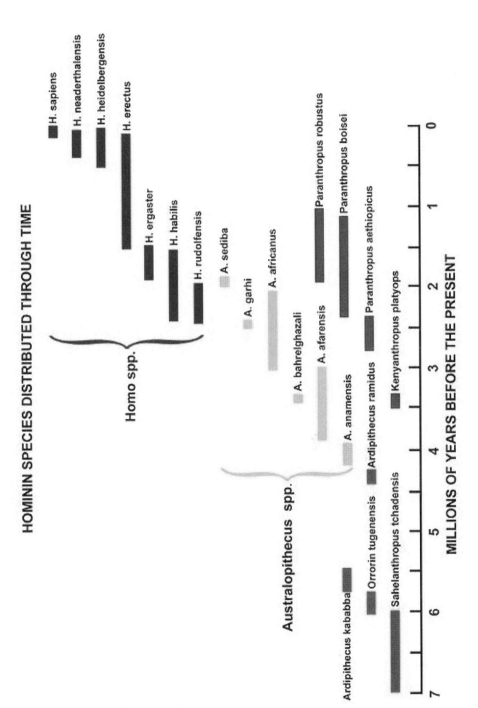

Figure 11.9 Hominin distribution through time.

The story continues with a species that has multiple fossil specimens, of which one is surprisingly complete—that of *Ardipithecus ramidus*.[99] This species lived approximately 4.4 million years ago and possessed a skull that was very chimp-like in brain volume and appearance (300–350cc), but it had a foramen magnum near where a modern human's is, indicating that it walked upright.[100] This assertion is also bolstered by the fact that the pelvis of this specimen was shorter, much like ours.[101] Interestingly, although this ape-like creature walked upright, it still had an opposable grasping first toe on its foot (hallux) that further suggests this is truly an intermediate species between ape-like predecessors and modern humans.[102] Furthermore, the species also had reduced canines, a trend initiated with our previous two species.[103]

Three million years ago, *Australopithecus afarensis* arrives on the scene, with a very short and bowl-shaped pelvis that, along with the low placement of the foramen magnum, dispels any doubt that this was a bipedal species.[104,105] This fact is also attested to by well-preserved *Australopithecus* footprints, fossilized in volcanic ash dating to around 3.6 million years ago,[106] showing this creature walked upright with an arched foot similar to that of humans but with ape-like long curled toes.[107] Additionally, this species still had a brain volume similar to that of a chimp or gorilla (375–550cc)[108] and possessed ape-like long forearms and digits.[109] However, the skull was not completely ape-like, as the lunate sulcus (the front boundary of the brain's visual area) was placed farther back than it is in apes, and more toward where it lies in humans.[110] We also see more humanlike teeth, in part due to a further reduction in canine tooth size, which along with all the other traits again points to this species being a transitional fossil.[111]

We don't get a member of our own genus until about two million years ago with *Homo habilis*. This bipedal species marks the beginning of stone tool use, perhaps made possible by this species' larger brain (average 650cc).[112] *Homo habilis* began to move toward looking somewhat more like us, as it had a less protruding face than previous species[113] and even more humanlike teeth than *Australopithecus*.[114] Between 1.8 million and 100,000 years ago, we have the first hominid species to move out of Africa and subsequently colonize Asia and Europe: *Homo erectus*.[115] The skull of this bipedal species had an increased brain volume of 750–1,250cc, with more recent specimens having larger brain sizes and older specimens smaller sizes.[116] In addition to being human-like in that the pelvis and foramen magnum show *Homo erectus* to be bipedal,[117] this species also bears a projecting nose unlike its antecedents.[118] The canines were also reduced in *Homo erectus* nearly to the point that they are in modern humans.[119] However, the skull was still long with a small forehead, noticeable brow ridge and robust jaw, making this species still not completely human-like.[120]

It isn't until about 160,000 years ago that *Homo sapiens* are recognizable as one of our own.[121] By this time, our cranial capacity has averaged out to 1,350cc,[122] our brow ridge is either absent or quite small, and our jaws are delicate and small with very inconspicuous canine teeth. And although controlled fire appears around 400,000 years ago, it is not until about 30,000 years ago that we have painting, jewelry, and carving, and not until 10,000 years ago that we have agriculture. Lastly, the dates of early human fossils and artifacts are confirmed by over a dozen different dating methods.[123] Bear in mind too, that these species are just a sampling of the many intermediate fossils between modern humans and ape-like ancestors; there are others that I have omitted for the sake of brevity.

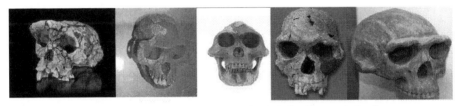

Figure 11.10 Hominin skull series. From left to right: *Sahelanthropus, Ardipithecus, Australopithecus afarensis, Homo habilis,* and *Homo erectus.*

The takeaway point is that most of the 6,000 individual specimens of ancient hominids show a mixture of ape-like and modern human characteristics. The fact that creationists and ID'ers cannot agree on which ones are "just apes" or "just humans"[124] serves to underscore the fact that these actually *are* intermediate forms. And remember, we *know* definitively whether or not these species walked upright based on the skull and pelvis of a specimen; these are not guesses or wishful thinking on the part of scientists. Many species such as *Ardipithecus* were ape-like in almost every way except they walked upright. Can creationists really call that "just an ape?" How exactly does a bipedal ape fit into a creation model? Similarly, can we really call *Homo habilis* "just a human," when its skull volume was half the size of ours with a flattened nose, pronounced brow ridge, and slightly protruding face suggestive of an ape? But remember, it also used stone tools and walked upright, so it is not really "just an ape" either.

The hominid fossil evidence shows trends that are consistent with evolution from an ape-like common ancestor seven million years ago, and with 6,000 specimens, it cannot be ignored or explained away. We see that cranial volumes over time tend to increase, canine sizes tend to decrease, skeletons become less adapted for life in trees, pelvises change from a quadrapedal to a bipedal form, and over time we see foramen magnums that move from a more chimp-like position to that of modern humans. Although the hominid tree of life is bushy with exact relationships unresolved, what is undeniably clear is that there is certainly a sequence of forms showing indisputable intermediates between ape-like ancestors and today's modern humans. The fossil evidence alone would be enough to prove common ancestry in humans, as would the ERV, pseudogene, or genetic similarity evidence. Taken together with the evidence from anatomical homology and phylogenetics, all these independent evidences provide corroboration and conclusive evidence far beyond a reasonable doubt for the theory that man descended from a common ancestor shared with chimpanzees.

Although in my initial research and investigation years ago I found this proposition to be highly unpalatable and repugnant, I eventually had to concede that the evidence for the conclusion was inescapable and unavoidable. Though formerly I dearly wanted human evolution to be false, I refused to seek comfort in illusory and hollow creationist explanations, and I forced myself to come to grips with the truth that was so plainly made clear. I had to be honest with the evidence, honest with myself, and most of all honest with God. While at the time I didn't see how human evolution could possibly fit into His plan, I trusted in His wisdom and sovereignty and eventually found peace that surpasses all understanding, and a renewed sense of awe and wonder worthy of worship for the One who made it all possible.

Living Fossils

When I was a creationist, I was particularly fascinated by "living fossils." If I had a mascot in those days, it would have been the coelacanth that lived 230–80 million years ago (*Laugia groenlandica* and *Macropoma mantelli* respectively,) who seemingly vanished from the fossil record, only to reappear in 1938 off the coast of Africa. Other "living fossil" organisms such as horseshoe crabs (Limulidae family) and ginko trees (*Ginko biloba*) seemed to further fuel my doubt in evolution; I just couldn't see how these creatures could remain nearly unchanged for millions of years were evolution true. It wasn't until I did a little more research into these mysterious creatures and gained a better understanding of biology that I realized this key piece of "evidence" against evolution falls flat in a rather disappointing way.

For starters, many of today's so-called "living fossil" species are very different in some key ways. The modern coelacanth (*Latimeria chalumnae* and *menadoensis*), for example, has some key anatomical differences from its distant relatives.[125,126] Additionally, superficial similarity between a fossil and a modern organism may seem profound until one considers what cannot be seen. Behavioral traits, soft tissue, physiology, and genetic makeup cannot be compared between fossils and their modern-day descendants, and these can make all the difference when comparing two species.

Also consider that the fossil record is imperfect. Most people are surprised when I admit this, but I have never been taught anything to the contrary in all my schooling and have never read any scientific material that states otherwise. Science is very open and honest about the scarcity of fossils in existence. Ironically, creationist and ID materials are the only places where I have read about scientists supposedly making grand claims regarding the fossil record. This inadequacy of the fossil record also means that the last fossil we have of a species may not accurately represent the time that it went extinct. Remember, absence of evidence does not mean evidence of absence. Therefore, coelacanth species did exist between 1938 and 80 million years before present, but the sparse fossil record either failed to capture a specimen, or we are yet to discover such a fossil.

Lastly, this "living fossil" objection stems from a general misunderstanding of how evolution works. Many think of evolution as something compulsory, that organisms must necessarily be evolving in some significant way at all times. Along with this notion is often the misnomer that an organism must be evolving "toward" something or must be changing into something more complex. But remember, populations of organisms are merely responding to their environment. There is no rule or law of nature that they must change toward something or even change at all. Sometimes a creature's best bet is to stay the same; this is what is called stabilizing selection. Basically it means that if you live in a fairly stable and constant environment (like our coelacanth, who lives deep in the Indian Ocean) with few predators, you may best be benefited by not changing much. In this case, a lot of variation from the already successful plan may be selected against, which means you don't get to reproduce and pass on those genes. It's not completely dissimilar to the mantra, "if it ain't broke, don't fix it." While "living fossils" may be extremely interesting, they don't advance the creationist/ID cause, as they pose no challenge to evolutionary understanding.

An Explosion of Cambrian Proportions

If I had a nickel for every time I've heard or read of apologists, creationists/ID'ers, and Christian radio talk show hosts abusing the facts surrounding the Cambrian explosion, I certainly wouldn't still owe $56,000 on my student loans! The Cambrian explosion is arguably the sacred cow of creationism and Intelligent Design and is perhaps the biggest piece of "evidence" they believe they have. However, this period of evolutionary history is either very, very poorly understood by anti-evolutionists or underhandedly misrepresented. For the uninitiated, the Cambrian explosion was a period that began around 543 million years ago, which marked the sudden appearance of most animal phyla.[127] Many major animal "body plans" appeared during this time, and many have likewise existed until the present. ID advocates often credit this explosion as having created nearly every type of organism we see today and largely deny the existence of animal life prior to the explosion. But is this really the case? What does the evidence show?

The fossil record provides the answer. Complex multicellular life was present at least 2.1 billion years ago,[128,129] approximately 1.5 billion years *before* the Cambrian. Furthermore, directly preceding the Cambrian explosion, there already existed a particularly diverse and complex multicellular assemblage of organisms termed the "Ediacaran fauna," which preceded the explosion by at least 40 million years.[130,131,132] However, these soft-bodied creatures of the Eidiacaran were much less likely to preserve as fossils than their hard-shelled Cambrian counterparts, resulting in far fewer fossils and thus a preservation bias. And though these strange precursors to the Cambrian are subject to much discussion pertaining to where exactly they fit on the family tree, most scientists agree that there were at least two phyla of animals present (Cnidaria and Porifera, which include such animals as jellyfish and sponges respectively), with some scientists arguing that there were up to six phyla Pre-Cambrian.[133,134,135,136,137,138,139]

Furthermore, some of these animals had radial and bilateral symmetry, with a few attaining a length of six feet![140,141] And remember, bacteria were already hanging around for almost three billion years by this point, and multicellular life had already existed for 1.5 billion years *prior* to the Cambrian explosion. The takeaway here is that animal life did not emerge all at once in the Cambrian, there was a rich history of life *before* the explosion, which is often ignored in the creationist account.

Figure 11.11 Fossil of *Spriggina flounensi* from the Ediacaran fauna which preceded the Cambrian.

Not only were phyla of animals present *before* the Cambrian, many phyla appeared long *after* the "explosion." The phyla Acoelomorpha, Rotifera, Platyhelminthes, Loricifera, Acanthocephala, Gastrotricha, Gnathostomulida, Phoronida, Xenacoelomorpha, and Bryozoa[142] are such animal groups that made their first appearance millions of years *afterward*.[143] Interestingly though, no land plants whatsoever have been found anywhere close to the time of the Cambrian. All twelve phyla (divisions) of land plants that have ever existed occurred long *after* the Cambrian explosion.[144] The first land plants occurred a full 100 million years *afterward*,[145] and in the case of the flowering plants, they appeared an astounding 400 million years *after* the Cambrian explosion.[146,147] Additionally, *none* of the phyla of fungi (four to seven phyla, depending on classification scheme) left any verifiable fossils earlier than the Devonian approximately 100 million years after the start of the Cambrian.[148] Furthermore, mammals, birds, insects, dinosaurs, reptiles, spiders, and amphibians, along with many other animal groups were not present at all during the Cambrian but instead appeared *much later* in the fossil record.[149]

To sum it up, out of 35 animal phyla, at least two but possibly six were around *before* the Cambrian, with ten appearing *after* the Cambrian.

All twelve phyla of land plants showed up *after* the Cambrian, as did all seven phyla of fungi. Therefore, out of the 54 animal, plant, and fungi phyla, more than half (31–35) did *not* make their first appearance in the "Cambrian explosion." So what exactly is the Cambrian explosion supposed to prove for creationism/ID? Though certainly many Cambrian groups *have* gone extinct, to claim that we see "more" phyla in the past with a subsequent "winnowing" down to the present is misleading, and moreover, just plain false.

And although ID advocates still try to paint a picture of a dead lifeless earth instantaneously exploding with oodles of critters in a matter of minutes, nothing could be further from the truth. The majority of the scientific evidence shows that the Cambrian explosion lasted 20 million[150,151,152,153] to 25 million years,[154,155,156] with some conservative estimates placing the duration at 10 million.[157] On the popular level, even smaller estimates of 5 million are often tossed about; however, scientific literature supporting this is scant, and some liberal estimates come in at 45 million years.[158,159] For creatures that reproduce either annually or every few years, even five million years would certainly be long enough for evolution to have taken place, as the fossil record clearly shows.

Figure 11.12 *Dickinsonia costata* from the Ediacaran.

The important thing to remember is that all these Cambrian animals evolved over a span of *millions* of years; they didn't show up overnight in a giant eruption at exactly 12:00 midnight 543 million years ago. These organisms evolved in a stepwise evolutionary fashion over a period of 20–25 million years. In fact, we even find transitional fossils such as lobopods and velvet worms (intermediate links between crustaceans and other forms) *within* the Cambrian "explosion,"[160,161] further demonstrating that this was a period of evolutionary radiation, not creation out of nothing. If the creationist/ID contention is that God "intervened" to create the Cambrian phyla, why did He spend 20 million years doing so? And why did He create the other half of the phyla previously mentioned either before or after the Cambrian?

Show Me the Fossils

Although I have shown transitional fossil sequences for five major animal lineages, explained how the fossil strata demonstrate evolutionary change, and explained the facts surrounding living fossils and the Cambrian explosion, to some this matters not. Some critics of evolution claim that it is incumbent upon scientists to produce transitional fossils for *every* described species (of course, even if scientists *did*, critics would demand intermediates between *those*, and so on *ad infinitum*). Likewise, some would argue that all the fossil record reveals is "fully-formed" species with no intermediates. This misguided refrain of "show me the fossils" is often based on the assumption that if evolution is true, there should be billions of fossils in existence, with many of them consisting of transitional forms. However, this line of thinking demonstrates a severe lack of knowledge regarding both fossilization and evolution.

As touched on earlier, fossilization is an extremely rare event. Though over 99% of all species that have ever lived are now extinct,[162] we have exceedingly few of them as fossils. Creationists and ID proponents often imagine fossilization as a frequent, commonplace occurrence, however, exactly the opposite is true. Paleontologist Donald Prothero notes that only 5% of currently living species of plants and animals have been found as fossils.[163] He goes on to state that even when considering only the nine well-skeletonized phyla (the type that are most likely to leave a fossil), 85–97% of such species have *never left a single fossil*.[164] Another study has postulated that only 10 or 15 fossil species are found in certain tropical river bank habitats that would have held around 10,000 species, which means that in these environments, only 0.1–0.15% of species ever become fossilized.[165] Perhaps most telling is that in the environments most likely to create fossils, such as ocean limestone reefs, fossilization is no greater than 1–2% of species.[166]

Also contributing to the rarity of fossils is that when most animals perish, they are readily scavenged or soon decay. Even if an organism could avoid these fates, it would then also have to be in the appropriate environment, such as marine waters, rivers, lakes, bogs, or other types of suitable settings, typically for at least 10,000 years. Furthermore, many fossils are also destroyed by geological processes such as erosion and weathering. Additionally, many areas where fossils are located may be difficult to reach. For example, fossils located very deep underground may simply never be discovered. Other areas with rich fossil deposits may be difficult to access, such as Antarctica, where many fossils have been recently unearthed. Also, political enmity between countries can prevent paleontologists from accessing potential fossil sites in certain regions. And, countless unexamined fossils already lay in storage at many museums and universities awaiting study; sadly, the number of persons with the skills and knowledge to classify these fossils is limited.

Compounding these problems is that new species often arise in small geographic areas, since isolated populations generally experience more rapid evolutionary change. And, evolution does not proceed at some gradual, steady rate throughout history (more on this shortly). Species tend to be characterized by long periods of stasis (very little change) punctuated by relatively short periods of rapid evolution (short in geological time, meaning on the order of 50,000–100,000 years).[167] Because of all these factors, we should consider it a great blessing that we have even a couple hundred transitional fossils.

In addition to the human, whale, horse, tetrapod, and bird transitional fossils, we find many others as well. Transitional fossils between land mammals and manatees,[168] lizards and snakes,[169] and fossils of limbed snakes[170] are all real and can be verified by anyone with an internet connection. There is also a complete fossil record of planktonic forams (single-celled, shelled, ocean protists) that actually documents a speciation event and the evolution of a new feature.[171] A continuous two-million-year fossil record of diatoms (single-celled, glass-like ocean organisms) also records a speciation event[172] (one species splitting into two). A brief search by those so inclined will reveal many more transitional fossils that cannot be covered here. And although science readily admits that the fossil record is regrettably lacking, there are *more* than enough transitional fossils to clearly and unequivocally demonstrate evolution. Indeed, evolution could be substantiated even without the fossil record, based solely on the other evidences covered in this book;

fossils only serve to add another layer of proof upon the heaping pile that already exists.

For those who still imagine that fossilization is such a common occurrence that we should find more transitional forms, consider the passenger pigeon. Not much more than a hundred years ago, passenger pigeons numbered around three billion birds (yes, billion with a "b"). However, they were hunted to extinction, with the last one dying in captivity in 1914. Now, how many have been unearthed since that time? If fossilization were as common as creationists would have us believe, why isn't anyone digging up any of the billions of easier to find, unfossilized passenger pigeons? Yet, creationists and ID'ers demand fossils of much rarer creatures. If fossilization were such an ordinary event, then wouldn't we expect to see fossils from all the animals leaving Noah's Ark in the Near East, dispersing around the globe? But we find nothing of the sort.

Lastly, to those who contend that the fossil record shows "fully-formed species" appearing and then disappearing, this again shows surprising ignorance of evolutionary biology and the fossilization process. In Figure 11.13, we have the scenario of a hypothetical organism evolving throughout time. The circles surrounding certain stages represent the rare occurrence of fossilization (of course, the rate of fossilization in this scenario is much higher than the actual rate). However, the figure clearly shows why having only a very small percentage of species present in the fossil record gives the impression of fully-formed species with no antecedent or subsequent forms. If you look at Figure 11.13a, you can see how these four seemingly different creatures give the appearance of fully formed, unrelated, and distinct species. However, if we look at the hypothetical 100% complete fossil record of Figure 11.13b, we can easily see that these forms *are* related through a series of intermediates. Hence, were the fossil record even halfway complete, we would likely see the patterns of descent in the fossil record even more clearly than we already do. With only one to two percent of species appearing in the fossil record, it is no wonder why to some it appears that organisms show up fully formed in the fossil record, seemingly out of nowhere. Even so, this is not the case, as we have just seen there are very many transitional series with intermediate forms linking every step of the transition. To say there are no transitional fossils is to be willfully ignorant of the fossil record.

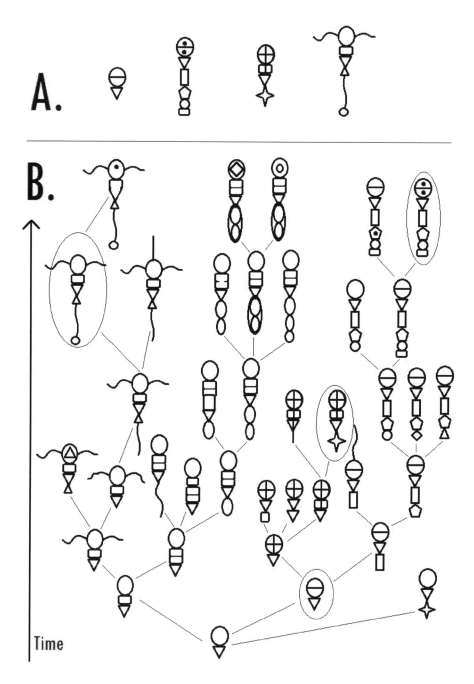

Figure 11.13 In "B," we see the complete fossil record if all species had been preserved. The circled species represent those that actually get preserved as fossils. In "A," we see that the small percentage of fossils we find gives the false impression of organisms appearing "fully-formed" with no predecessors or successors.

CHAPTER TWELVE

DOUBTS MISPLACED

Biogeography

Biologist Jerry Coyne once wrote, "The biogeographic evidence for evolution is now so powerful that I have never seen a creationist book, article or lecture that has tried to refute it. Creationists simply pretend that the evidence doesn't exist."[1] Indeed, biogeography, which studies how plants and animals are distributed across the globe, is truly the *bête noire* (black beast) to creationists and ID proponents. As we will see, creationist views cannot give any explanations to facts that are easily made clear in light of evolutionary theory.

The recognition of the significance of biogeography goes all the way back to the well-traveled naturalist Charles Darwin. Darwin was deeply impressed by the distribution of plants and animals on oceanic islands around the world. He noticed that islands far from a mainland were conspicuously absent of frogs, salamanders, and native mammals, despite suitable habitat therein.[2] However, these islands contained plants, insects, and birds, some of which were unlike any other species found elsewhere in the world. Darwin stumbled upon something that would be a keystone in his argument for evolution by natural selection.

Prevailing views of dispersal from a single center (i.e., the hypothesized landing site of Noah's ark on Mount Ararat in modern-day

Turkey), or creation from multiple centers face a very serious challenge when scrutinized under the light of biogeography. Why would it be that God created polar bears in the Arctic but not in the identical habitat of Antarctica? Conversely, why should penguins be found only in Antarctica but not the Arctic? Furthermore, cacti (family Cactaceae) are only native to the Americas, even though there are deserts elsewhere with nearly identical environments but that do not have cacti.[3] Moreover, when cacti are introduced to these foreign deserts, they absolutely thrive there, showing that improper habitat is not the reason why God did not choose to put them there.[4] Why are the nearly 100 species of lemur found *only* on the island of Madagascar and no where else in the world?[5] And perhaps equally as interesting—why are Australia's only native terrestrial mammals either marsupials or those that lay eggs?[6]

The answer to these questions is that there is generally a single point of origin from which a species arises, and its geographic distribution is limited by its ability to travel to new suitable environments. Accordingly, the reason we don't see freshwater fish on oceanic islands is because they can't tolerate the saltwater swim to make it to this perfectly suitable island habitat.[7] Similarly, we don't typically see frogs and salamanders on oceanic islands because the salt water journey would be fatal to their sensitive skin.[8] The same goes for terrestrial mammals, who cannot swim over great exspanses of ocean. Consider the lush tropical island of Hawaii that, for its entire existence of tens of millions of years, never had one single native frog or terrestrial reptile but now has several introduced varieties that have flourished so well in this new environment that some have become pests![9] Why did God not create frogs on Hawaii originally, even though the island is a suitable habitat for them? Why did God not put terrestrial reptiles, mammals, frogs, freshwater fish, or salamanders on oceanic islands despite the fact that these islands are perfect habitats for them?

More curious perhaps is the fact that Australia's only native mammals are the egg-laying echidna and platypus, marsupials, seals, sea lions, and bats.[10] According to evolutionary theory, egg-laying mammals (monotremes or prototheria) are the most ancient branch, since among other traits they lay eggs like their reptile ancestors.[11] Marsupials (metatheria) are considered more derived since their young are essentially surrounded by an eggshell while in utero, similar to the shell of a snake or egg-laying mammal.[12] Marsupials, however, are born live and subsequently migrate to the mother's pouch where they are nourished. Mammals that have a placenta (organ that nourishes the fetus through an umbilical cord) are called eutherians and evolved later than monotremes and marsupials.[13]

All these pieces fit well into our puzzle when we consider that 160 million years ago, the continents were much closer together, with South America, Antarctica, and Australia being part of a supercontinent called Gondwana.[14] Fossil evidence suggests that early prototheria and metatheria originated in North America and moved southward into South America before traversing the Antarctic on their way to Australia.[15] As the continents subsequently drifted apart and oceans opened up between them, the marsupials and monotremes were marooned on Australia, while they were largely replaced by placental mammals elsewhere. Cut off from the rest of the world, the marsupial lineage adaptively radiated (rapidly evolved) to fill almost every possible ecological niche on the Australian continent.[16] These similar ecological niches and selective pressures between Australia and elsewhere led to convergent evolution, whereby unrelated organisms evolve similar traits. In Australia we have marsupial sugar gliders that look like eutherian flying squirrels from North America, marsupial tasmanian wolves (recently extinct) that looked like eutherian wolves, marsupial moles that look just like eutherian moles, marsupial mice that look like eutherian mice, and the list goes on and on.[17]

All of this may sound like a "just-so" story, but it provides a testable challenge for evolution. If marsupials truly did travel from the Americas across Antarctica before being isolated in Australia, we should certainly find marsupial fossils in Antarctica to prove this assertion. But do we? In an amazing confirmation of evolutionary theory, marsupial fossils *have* been found just off the Antarctic Peninsula on Seymour Island exactly as predicted, and of the precise age expected.[18,19]

Furthermore, although reptiles generally do not inhabit oceanic islands, there have historically been some risk-takers who were apparently unaware of this rule. Likely by rafting on vegetation a few million years ago or more, iguanas and tortoises made their way to the Galapagos Islands (this is not just wishful thinking—several such tortoise and iguana dispersals have actually been documented).[20,21] While these species bear a close relation to their mainland cousins, they differ in some significant ways. The marine iguanas forage in the ocean, unlike their mainland counterparts, and they also possess a salt-excreting gland and modified skeletal anatomy for swimming.[22] Likewise, the Galapagos tortoises, while most closely related to the Chaco tortoise of South America, differs in that the former can reach a size of six feet while the latter is usually less than a foot long,[23] among other traits. Darwin noticed these details and was also fascinated by the strong fossil resemblance between fossils of *Glyptodon* in South America and today's armadillo living in the same location, with the former appearing to be a Volkswagen Beetle-sized version of the latter.[24] The point here is that species on oceanic islands are most closely related to species on the nearest mainland, yet they are also distinct from them in some respects. Similarly, the location where we find a fossil of an ancient creature is often the same location we find a present-day creature that strongly resembles it.

All of these facts are understandable given the theory of evolution; however, they cannot be apprehended by creationism or ID. If one believes that all modern creatures derived from Noah's Ark, then one must explain why *all* of the monotremes and *all* of Australia's two hundred plus species of marsupials decided to migrate across Asia then "swim" thousands of miles of open ocean to Australia (except the directionally challenged opossum group), but the placental mammals refused to set foot on the island. Likewise, it cannot explain how *flightless* kiwis traveled 10,000 miles from Mount Ararat to New Zealand. Nor can it account for why *all* one hundred lemur species would have swum to one specific island off the coast of Africa and *nowhere* else in the world. Why did polar bears decide to go only north from Noah's Ark, but penguins only went south, despite the fact that the two habitats are identical? How did cacti make it thousands of miles to the Americas from Noah's Ark, but they failed to become established right in Noah's backyard?

Even if one imagines *multiple* centers of creation, this does nothing to help the case for creationism. Multiple centers of creation would seem to imply that God arbitrarily created many island species that are found *only* on those islands and nowhere else in the world. Additionally, it would not make sense of the fact that ecologically identical habitats across the planet have an unequal distribution of species, such as cacti being only in the deserts of the Americas, or polar bears being only in the Arctic, or freshwater ponds on oceanic islands being devoid of freshwater fish. Ask yourself this question: Do fishless freshwater ponds on islands fit better with a creation model or with evolution? Does creation better explain why islands have endemic species found nowhere else in the world, or does evolution? Why has God not created any terrestrial mammals, freshwater fish, newts, frogs, or salamanders on ancient oceanic islands? Can creation explain why a distinct island species has its closest relative on the nearest mainland?

How does creation account for the discovery of current species in the same place as the fossils of their clearly related but very different ancestors? The facts of biogeography fit exactly with what we would expect to find were evolution to be true; however, the facts are simply unexplainable in terms of a creation model.

Micro vs. Macro

One thing that creationists, ID proponents, and evolution adherents can all agree on is the reality of microevolution. The term describes the change of gene frequencies within a population and can be thought of as evolution on a small scale. I have never once read of, heard, or spoken to any person or group that opposes microevolution, not even by the staunchest of Young Earth Creationists. This is not surprising given that this small-scale process does not involve any dramatic changes and is even sometimes touted by creationists as a mechanism created by God to allow organisms to adapt to changing environments, or to create more species within a "kind" after the flood. This latter hypothesis, however, is plagued by unresolvable problems. For example, creationists and ID'ers will sometimes assert that Noah took an ancestral member of "cat kind" onto the Ark, which afterward diversified through microevolution into the different members of "cat kind" that we see today.

Macroevolution, however, is evolution on a large scale and is roundly condemned by the majority of creationists and ID proponents. This term denotes change at or above the species level and involves one species giving rise to other new species over time. While macroevolution occurs over a very large time scale, many examples of microevolution may actually be observed within one's lifetime, providing undeniable proof that is impossible to refute.[25] Perhaps the example closest to home is that of antibiotic resistance. The Second World War ushered in the age of antibiotics with the wonder drug penicillin, but bacteria have quickly evolved to become resistant to not only this but many other antibiotics.[26] Natural selection has selected against bacteria that succumb to antibiotics, leaving the few mutants able to survive to spread their genes through the population and shift the whole toward resistance. This is also happening with over 440 pest species of arthropod,[27] where heavy application of insecticides over time have seen crop pests and other nuisances such as bedbugs evolving resistance to some heavy-duty chemical agents.[28]

And for those who contend that these are merely examples of "selection from existing variation," recall that the sheep blowfly has evolved resistance to pesticides from a beneficial mutation and *not* from preexisting variation, disproving the hypothesis that these insects were "created" with resistance genes already in their genome.[29] And in any case, why would God create insects with insecticide resistance genes that result in human sickness and loss of food crops? Or alternatively, how could the effects of the "fall of Man" have the creative power to craft new resistance genes in insects? This "fall of Mankind is responsible for resistance genes" hypothesis also invalidates other creationism/ID arguments that claim no new genetic "information" can be created apart from supernatural intervention.

Darwin's finches are perhaps the best known example of microevolution, where a single species of finch from the Central or South American mainland colonized the Galapagos islands and subsequently split off into over a dozen different species, each adapting to a specific diet and developing unique physical characteristics such as beaks suited to their respective ecological niche.[30] Peppered moths are another classic example of microevolution. Two hundred years ago, before the Industrial Revolution, nearly all peppered moths were light-colored, as to blend in with light-colored tree bark and lichens. The gene for the black variant of the peppered moth occurred with a frequency of only 0.01%, making this morph very rare.[31] However, new coal-fired factories began belching soot, and the trees and much of the environment became covered with it and darkened. Subsequently, light-colored moths stuck out like sore thumbs against a dark background and became much more vulnerable to predation. In contrast, the dark-colored moths prospered, as they were now camouflaged against the blackened trees. By the turn of the 19th century, black peppered moths made up about 98% of the peppered moths captured, as the population had evolved from being almost completely white to predominately black.[32]

But perhaps the clearest and most powerful observed evidence for microevolution can be found in the example of the Italian wall lizard.[33] In 1971, researchers transplanted five pairs of these lizards onto a tiny island in the Adriatic Sea. Shortly after seeding the island with these reptiles, however, the Croatian War of Independence broke out, barring scientists from the island for over thirty years. When they returned, they were absolutely astonished at what they found. The ten lizards had mushroomed to a population of five thousand, and more surprisingly, they had evolved an entirely new digestive structure, replete with larger heads capable of delivering a mightier bite.[35] These lizards, while originally insect eaters, had adapted to eating plentiful plant material and evolved a new structure called the "cecal valve," which is essentially a muscle between the large and small intestine that allows food to be slowed down and fermented in chambers, allowing the lizards to extract nutrients from digested plants.[36] This cecal valve was something brand-new for this lizard, not some "preexisting variation" that came to dominate the population. In only thirty generations, these lizards underwent a major evolutionary change, demonstrating observed, verified, and undeniable microevolution in action.

While all Christians are probably still on board at this point, many would object if we go one step further to microevolution being used as evidence for macroevolution. While presumably all Christians are okay with the former, many steadfastly deny that microevolution could ever add up to macroevolution. Lizards that change their guts are still lizards, as are moths that turn from white to black, or finches that develop different beaks, and this presents little challenge to the creationist/ID worldview. However, this comfortable distinction dissolves when we discover that macroevolution is little more than microevolution on a larger time scale![37]

Small changes over the span of thousands or millions of years can easily equal large changes. The same mechanism that produces new digestive systems in the Italian wall lizard *will* create macroevolutionary changes in any species given the right selective pressures and sufficient time. There is nothing whatsoever that can possibly stop microevolution from becoming macroevolution given a long enough period of time; no mechanism or process exists in nature to prevent the possibility of large-scale change.[38] Modern evolutionary theory is wholly sufficient to explain macroevolutionary change—no "missing mechanism" is needed to rebuff the theory, contrary to creationist/ID claims.

Denying that microevolution adds up to macroevolution is like saying that millimeters could never add up to kilometers. Of course they could! Given enough millimeters, they will eventually add up to kilometers. Put another way, this denial is akin to saying that walking will get you from your house to the corner store, but walking could never get you from New York to Portland. Microevolution and macroevolution are quantitatively different, but qualitatively they are the same.[39] The only tactic left to avoid the inevitable conclusion is to never define microevolution, so as to be able to move the goalposts and call anything "microevolution within a kind." Thus, some will try to explain away the dog-sized, four-toed Eohippus becoming the one-toed, thousand-pound modern horse over fifty million years as "microevolution."

Punctuated Equilibrium

Punctuated Equilibrium (PE) is perhaps more misunderstood than any other concept in science. This poor football of a theory has been relentlessly kicked around without any regard to what it actually says and has been hijacked so often that even Somali pirates are impressed. PE is undoubtedly the dead horse that continues to be flogged with reckless abandon by creationists and ID advocates. It is the theory that species are characterized by periods of stasis, punctuated by periods of rapid evolution.[40] In other words, the theory states that for most of a species' long history, it changes little but then undergoes periods where it experiences rapid evolution and significant change. Creationists and ID'ers have taken this to mean that the scientific evidence points more toward special independent creation rather than evolution over millions of years, and they have quote mined the papers advocating this theory in such a way that without the proper context, the quotes *appear* to fly in the face of modern evolutionary theory. Evolution critics further claim that PE is an admission of the lack of evidence for the theory of evolution and is in fact a tacit confession from a scientific turncoat. However, there are many problems with these highly dubious interpretations of PE.

For starters, creationists are trying to use "rapid" in a different way than the author who discovered PE intended. This "rapid" period of change is still on the order of 50,000–100,000 years according to PE, not something that happened overnight.[41] The theory does *not* contend that one species becomes another species in one generation, as if the parent of one species gives birth to a new and different species. Furthermore, PE is not an exclusive theory that competes with or doubts evolution by natural selection; rather, it is an expansive theory that sheds more light on precisely how the evolutionary process works at the "nuts and bolts" level. This theory is a very nuanced, in-house argument for scientists about the minutia of evolution over time. No one is disagreeing that evolution by natural selection occurs, but PE just tries to make the point that evolution is not something compulsory that happens at an even and predictable rate. Evolution proceeds in a variable fashion, with different paces at which changes occur over time.

To give a helpful example, think about your drive home from work. You have places where you are going different speeds—places where you are stopped, and places you slow down and speed up. In this analogy, the speed you are driving represents the pace of evolutionary change. From your starting point to your finish, you may have periods where you are driving seventy on the freeway (rapid evolution), periods when you are driving thirty in a residential area (slow evolutionary change), or times when you are at a stop sign or stop light (stabilizing selection and no change). If anything, PE may be faulted for being preoccupied with the stops and freeways, but it is a theory that just wants to make the valid point that the whole ride is not a constant fifty-five miles an hour from start to finish.

PE in no way undermines, doubts, or supplants evolution; it merely seeks to further define how evolution works. The scientists who developed this theory never once wavered in their belief in evolution, and they repeatedly bemoaned how creationists have distorted this theory and twisted it to say something it never said.[42] Furthermore, this theory does *not* say that transitional forms do not exist, as the co-founder of the theory has made explicitly clear that there are indeed many transitional fossils in existence.[43] PE in no way advocates instantaneous evolutionary change, but instead emphasizes incremental evolutionary change within a short geological time frame (e.g., 50–100k years). PE has thus been best described as a "minor gloss" and an "interesting but minor wrinkle on the surface of neo-Darwinian theory" that "lies firmly within the neo-Darwinian synthesis."[44]

Though creationists and ID advocates are eager to spin PE as an "admission of gaps" or as a theory trying to cover up a "lack of evidence," PE is nothing of the sort. Try as one might, PE cannot be shoehorned to fit a creation or ID model; it is simply another piece of the puzzle put into place, providing a more complete and comprehensive picture of how God has used evolution to bring about the enchanting life forms we see around us today.

Irreducible Complexity

I must confess, I became slightly nostalgic when I dusted off my copy of biochemist Michael Behe's book *Darwin's Black Box*. The argument contained within once invigorated my ID worldview and gave a sense of mainstream scientific legitimacy to my convictions, which I thought were unassailable. That argument to which I am referring is that of "irreducible complexity" (IC), which contends that some biological systems are composed of many interacting parts that are all necessary for their basic function, and that removal of even one of these parts would render the system inoperable. Behe's contention is that such irreducibly complex systems could not have arisen through naturalistic processes such as natural selection and thus are best explained by an intelligent designer.

In 1802, theologian William Paley wrote hypothetically about "crossing a heath" and pitching his foot against a stone. He concluded that if one asked how the stone got there, it would be reasonable to assume it had always lain there. However, Paley argued that if one found a watch, it would be absurd to say that it had always just been there, for something so designed as a watch must have surely had a maker. This analogy, known as "Paley's Watch," has been subsequently redressed in the slick and snazzy clothing of modern biochemistry and relabeled "irreducible complexity." After nearly two hundred years, this resuscitated argument has become part of the creationist and ID movement canon, though it may not fare much better than the original under the careful scrutiny of science, philosophy, and theology.

While Paley's watch as applied to biology was convincing for its time, the analogy suffers irreparable damage from the fact that it compares reproducing biological organisms with non-reproducing inorganic objects, a very important distinction that renders this analogy disanalogous. Furthermore, while watches and biological entities may share one attribute in common (complexity), that does not necessarily mean they share all attributes in common (having a designer). While IC is not quite as guilty of the same preceding fallacies, like Paley's watch it is culpable for the lesser charge of "argument from incredulity," which essentially says, "I just *can't imagine* how 'X' could be true; therefore 'X' must not be true." And in this case, IC would add that intelligent design must account for the phenomena that seem improbable naturalistically.

While IC is perhaps on shaky ground philosophically, in the interest of fairness, we will push forward and evaluate this argument scientifically as well. IC contends that some biological systems are irreducibly complex, much like a watch or a car engine. All the parts of your engine are critical to its functioning, and you can't change or remove any parts without turning your engine into a giant paperweight. If you remove your car's crankshaft for instance, you won't be going anywhere, since all parts of the engine are crucial to its basic operation. IC argues that the molecular motor that turns the flagellum (a hair-like structure that allows a cell to move) is made up of dozens of different components and is likewise an irreducibly complex structure. IC also posits that the immune system, blood clotting cascade, cellular protein transport system, and AMP biosynthesis are similarly irreducibly complex systems.[45]

Furthermore, IC contends that these systems must have had an "all or nothing" evolution. That is, all the parts of the system must have evolved at the same time or else the product would not function, as if it had even one fewer part, it would be rendered useless. And so the argument goes, there could not be intermediate evolutionary stages of irreducibly complex systems since precursor systems would have no function, and therefore natural selection could not act to further enhance and develop these systems into something useful. Therefore, IC argues that irreducibly complex systems could not have evolved by means of slight, stepwise modifications by way of natural selection; the whole thing must have come about in "one fell swoop," which IC proponents claim is impossible naturalistically. The conclusion of IC is that since these irreducibly complex systems cannot be evolved naturally, an intelligent designer must be needed.

But *could* the aforementioned systems have evolved without obvious intelligent intervention? Even Michael Behe concedes that, "Even if a system is irreducibly complex (and thus could not have been produced directly), however, one can not definitively rule out the possibility of an indirect, circuitous route."[46] Furthermore, during the much-publicized 2005 Kitzmiller versus Dover Area School District trial that ruled against the teaching of ID in public schools, Michael Behe made a very candid admission that grants us another clue. The memorandum opinion states:

> Professor Behe conceded that there are no peer-reviewed papers supporting his claims that complex molecular systems, like the bacterial flagellum, the blood-clotting cascade, and the immune system, were intelligently designed. In that regard, there are no peer-reviewed articles supporting Professor Behe's argument that certain complex molecular structures are "irreducibly complex." In addition to failing to produce papers in peer-reviewed journals, ID also features no scientific research or testing.[47]

Nevertheless, let us take up the challenge set forth by IC and investigate whether or not there are any plausible explanations for how such irreducibly complex systems could have evolved through natural selection. Let's start with Behe's contentions regarding the immune system. Behe claims that such a system is irreducibly complex; however, as the memorandum for the aforementioned court case reveals:

> [I]n Darwin's Black Box, Professor Behe wrote that not only were there no natural explanations for the immune system at the time, but that natural explanations were impossible regarding its origin. However, Dr. [Kenneth] Miller presented peer-reviewed studies refuting Professor Behe's claim that the immune system was irreducibly complex. Between 1996 and 2002, various studies confirmed each element of the evolutionary hypothesis explaining the origin of the immune system. In fact, on cross-examination, Professor Behe was questioned concerning his 1996 claim that science would never find an evolutionary explanation for the immune system. He was presented with fifty-eight peer-reviewed publications, nine books, and several immunology textbook chapters about the evolution of the immune system; however, he simply insisted that this was still not sufficient evidence of evolution, and that it was not "good enough."[48]

We could end the chapter right there, but there's more evidence against IC to be found. In regards to the supposedly irreducibly complex clotting cascade, the same court found that,

> [W]ith regard to the blood-clotting cascade, Dr. Miller demonstrated that the alleged irreducible complexity of the blood-clotting cascade has been disproven by peer-reviewed studies dating back to 1969, which show that dolphins' and whales' blood clots despite missing a part of the cascade, a study that was confirmed by molecular testing in 1998. Additionally and more recently, scientists published studies showing that in puffer fish, blood clots despite the cascade missing not only one, but three parts. Accordingly, scientists in peer-reviewed publications have refuted Professor Behe's predication about the alleged irreducible complexity of the blood-clotting cascade.[49]

But that's not all. Jawless fish also have a clotting cascade system that functions with fewer components than ours.[50] Similarly, annelids (worms), echinoderms (e.g., starfish), molluscs, insects, and others have even more primitive mechanisms that prevent them from bleeding out when they are injured, achieving a similar end to that of the clotting cascade.[51] Were IC true in regards to the clotting cascade, we should not be able to find a simpler but still functional clotting system, yet we do find this with whales, dolphins, puffer fish, and many other animals,[52] making the possibility of this mechanism evolving through natural selection very plausible.

But what about that classic icon of design—the human eye? Although many find it hard to believe that such a complicated and complex organ as the human eye could arise by natural means, the big mistake here is in thinking that only very complicated eyes such as our own are useful. There exist in nature a wide variety of eyes, perhaps the simplest being patches of pigment cells used by microscopic organisms such as algae and other single-celled photosynthetic organisms, and they are useful only for distinguishing between light and darkness. Other critters such as the mollusc *Pleurotomaria* have a simple eyecup, a step up in the world of eyes but still incapable of forming an image. The *Nautilus* has a pinhole camera-type eye that lacks a lens yet is capable of forming a low-resolution image. Lastly, the marine snail *Murex* has yet an even more advanced eye since it contains a primitive lens that allows for the focusing of light and protection of the eye.

The fact that there abound so many gradations of eyes from utterly simple eyespots to sophisticated vertebrate and cephalopod eyes dismantles any hope of the human eye being irreducibly complex. Simple pigment clusters allow algae to swim toward light needed for photosynthesis and thus provide a serious advantage to these organisms. From here it is "off to the races," as natural selection can modify, hone, and otherwise produce increasingly complex eyes in response to selective pressures, as evidenced by the many diverse forms of eyes in the animal kingdom. Far from being impossible, the evolution of the human eye is very explicable and plausible in terms of evolution and is evidenced by a variety of eye types.

For those still not convinced of the futility of IC, let us examine the flagellum, a little whip-like appendage protruding from certain cells. Michael Behe contends that these structures and their accompanying molecular motors are irreducibly complex and could not have evolved from simpler precursors, which he holds would not be functional. And although Behe states that the flagellum consists of over two hundred different proteins all crucial to its basic function,[53] biologist Kenneth Miller has pointed out in his book *Finding Darwin's God*, that many flagella have fewer than two hundred proteins and vary wildly in their arrangement and number of parts.[54] Therefore, flagella are very diverse and flexible in terms of their evolution. They are not irreducibly complex, as many "versions" exist, with some being more sophisticated than others. Finally, many scientists have proposed persuasive scenarios for the evolution of the flagellum and have successfully rebuffed claims of it being irreducibly complex.[55,56,57]

Rather than spend twenty more pages rebutting every IC claim, let me just cut to the chase. Not only is IC bad science, it is dangerous and irresponsible when we try to incorporate it into our theology. IC is little more than an elaborate "God of the gaps" argument, whereby something that is currently unexplained is pressed into service as a proof for God. And what is the result when science ends up explaining something that previously could only be explained by invoking God? That specific argument *for* God becomes an argument *against* God, and God is seen more and more as "something that used to explain how things work" but isn't needed anymore. We should argue for God based on what we *do* know, not argue for God based on ignorance and what we don't know. Those who advance such reckless and imprudent arguments as IC do so to the great detriment of practicing and potential believers.

For Christians who had hoped that IC could demolish Darwin and provide solid evidence of design, the prognosis is grim. IC has been defeated not only in a court of law but by countless scientists, journal articles, and books. Ironically, creationists and ID proponents may have had their faith misplaced in Behe all along, as Kenneth Miller recalls,

> In a 1995 debate, I presented him [Behe] with molecular evidence indicating that humans and the great apes shared a recent, common ancestor, wondering how he would refute the obvious. Without skipping a beat, he pronounced the evidence to be convincing, and stated categorically that he had absolutely no problem with the common ancestry of humans and the great apes. Creationists around the room – who had viewed him as their new champion – were dismayed.[58]

It bears repeating that our faith should not be placed in any human construct, be it creationism, evolution, or ID. Faith placed in anything but God will ultimately leave us sorely disappointed.

Specified Complexity

Specified complexity (SC) is arguably the number one "go to" argument for Intelligent Design proponents. Along with irreducible complexity, this concept forms the backbone of the modern ID movement. Specified complexity is the brainchild of ID advocate William Dembski, who claims that specified complexity is an "explanatory filter," which can distinguish design from the products of chance or regularity (i.e., laws of nature) by detecting complex specified information. Dembski provides the example of a single letter of the alphabet which he defines as specified but not complex. Conversely, he defines a sentence of random letters as complex but not specified. Lastly, he states that a Shakespearean sonnet is both specified *and* complex.[59]

Therefore, Dembski reasons that if something is both complex *and* specified, then it must be the product of an intelligent cause and not natural processes. Moreover, SC can be thought of as a measure of improbability. Spilling the contents of a supersized bag of Scrabble letters has an infinitesimally small chance of randomly spelling out a Shakespeare sonnet; therefore, Dembski reasons that this complex and specified information is necessarily attributable to intelligent design, as the probability of this event occurring through chance or regularity is virtually nonexistent. Consequently, Dembski contends that DNA and other biological systems exhibit this same type of SC and therefore must be attributed to an intelligent designer. Anyone else experiencing a sense of *déjà vu?*

This argument is similar to irreducible complexity in that it makes the claim that biological organisms are so complex that it is inconceivable that they could have arisen by natural processes, and therefore they could not have. Accordingly, SC could be interpreted as another "argument from incredulity," as the conclusion of the SC argument is based primarily on a lack of understanding of how certain improbable events could have come about. SC could also be seen as a circular argument, since Dembski has defined SC in such a way that it *cannot* occur naturally. Other scientists also take issue with Dembski's hypothesis, brusquely stating that, "Dembski's work is riddled with inconsistencies, equivocation, flawed use of mathematics, poor scholarship, and misrepresentation of other's results."[60] Additionally, the mathematical basis for specified complexity is regarded as unsound by many mathematicians.[61] But regardless of what the critics say, we will examine SC on its own merits and see if it holds water.

SC makes many assertions regarding the improbability of certain genetic patterns or biological systems arising through naturalistic processes. However, how can one truly place an accurate statistical probability on a genetic code developing via natural processes? Or a certain biological structure coming about through natural selection? Harvard professor of biology and mathematics Martin Nowak concurs, remarking, "We cannot calculate the probability that an eye came about. We don't have the information to make the calculation."[62] There are numerous probabilities and countless variables that factor into something such as the eye evolving, and finding objective and precise values with which to calculate its probability of evolving would certainly prove impossible, rendering any supposed calculation of such a biological system meaningless.

Some calculations may admittedly be more feasible and realistic than others. For instance, the chance of a specific sequence of one hundred nucleotides forming randomly is about one out of 10^{60}. Astronomer Fred Hoyle raises the bar for improbability even higher when he claims that the probability of cellular life evolving is about one out of $10^{40,000}$ (that is ten with 40,000 zeros after it); keep in mind, the entire universe only has 10^{82} atoms in it!

However, for one, improbability is not the same as impossibility. If you take a deck of 52 cards, and shuffle then deal them one at a time, the probability that you would deal the specific sequence of cards you just laid down is approximately one out of 10^{67} (the number of stars in the universe is 10^{23}), an extremely improbable event. But of course *after* the fact, the probability of obtaining that specific sequence is 100%, since we know it just occurred. The statistics are impressive because we are validating what we see, like shooting the broad side of a barn with an arrow and then painting a target around the spot that was hit.

Put another way, consider the probability that your parents would meet each other, compounded with the probability that they would have intercourse on the exact day and time you were conceived, multiplied by the probability that out of millions of sperm and many eggs, the two specific ones that would create you would be joined, and now extend this improbability to include your grandparents and so on. It's astonishingly improbable that you exist, yet you are here reading this book.

Another factor that renders such improbable biological calculations utterly impotent is the fact that these calculations consider the probability of such events occurring sequentially and not simultaneously. It's like entering one of those supermarket kiosk contests. If I apply to one contest and my chance at winning is one out of a million, my odds are exactly that. Even if I apply to one every week, it is still more likely than not that I would never win in my lifetime. However, if I applied to one million of these contests at the same time, there is an over 62% chance of me winning at least one contest. The same goes for things like the first peptide or first enzyme. If you simultaneously have trillions of groups of prebiotic chemicals subject to the nonrandom laws of chemistry over a billion year's time, you are much more likely to draw the "lucky number" than if you proceeded with only one group of prebiotic chemicals at a time.

Perhaps most important to the discussion of biological improbabilities is the fact that complex biological structures do not come about in one step, and that precursors are often simpler than ones currently observed. As we previously discussed, something such as the flagellar motor or clotting cascade did not evolve in one fell swoop, but by a process of accumulating and preserving small changes. Dawkins created an insightful experiment that lends credence to this observation. He designed a program that started out with a sentence consisting of twenty-eight characters of gibberish that then copied itself (reproduced) with a random chance of error (mutation). Whichever "progeny" of the original phrase was most like the target phrase, "METHINKS IT IS A WEASEL," would then be chosen to proceed. In this simulation, it took only forty-three generations to get from twenty-eight characters of gibberish to the target phrase, which is incredible given that the number of possible combinations for twenty-eight characters is 10^{40}. Although this experiment does suffer from the fact that real-life evolution does not have a discernible goal toward which it is working (science cannot detect "goals" or purpose), it is still successful in demonstrating that changes can be quickly and easily reached by accumulating a series of simpler changes. Lastly, and on a similar note, biological improbability calculations are often rendered useless by the mere fact that evolution is not completely random, as natural selection acts in a *nonrandom* fashion. This makes calculations based on an assumption of "random chance" invalid.

Despite Dembski's pronouncement that evolution cannot create specified complexity, examples abound that invalidate this claim.

Researchers who use evolutionary algorithms (EAs) in artificial life studies have found that novelty and increasing complexity are produced in their simulations.[63] Evolutionary algorithms are also used to design electronics, boat hull designs, and many other systems that are deemed to be too complicated of a problem for an intelligent designer such as a person.[64,65] These EAs take two parent designs and produce multiple offspring that have a mix of characteristics from the parent designs. The EAs then select the best offspring and re-breed them and so on until the best designs are produced. One could argue that the computers and programs on which these simulations are run are "intelligently designed;" however, once the simulation is begun, it closely mimics real biological evolution, as the "designer" is hands-off at this point and lets the mutation and selection run at liberty. In any case, the EAs contradict the claim that specified and complex systems require an intelligent designer.

Further doubt is cast upon SC when we examine observable evidence of novel genes being evolved. Recall that beneficial mutations (not preexisting variation) for pesticide resistance in the sheep blowfly have evolved recently,[66] even though it would seem that a DNA sequence coding for pesticide resistance would be "complex and specified," and according to Dembski could only be created supernaturally. Additionally, one experiment removed the genes that allowed for sugar digestion in bacteria, then allowed the deficient bacteria to grow in a sugar-rich medium. The result was that the impaired bacteria quickly evolved new enzymes allowing them to once again digest sugar[67] —again a case of specified and complex information arising though naturalistic processes.

And who could forget our Italian wall lizard that evolved a completely new digestive structure in thirty years?![68,69] If evolution creating an entirely brand new and never before seen digestive structure isn't complex and specified information, I don't know what is. Lastly, bacteria with novel genes evolved for eating nylon were discovered in 1975[70] (these genes did not exist prior to nylon's invention in 1935), another instance of SC brought about by natural selection, something Dembski denies is possible. And as already discussed in the section "At a Complete Loss: of Information, That Is," we can see that there are many biological mechanisms that add information. Information *is* added to genomes; this is not hypothetical or subject to interpretation—this is *actually observed* in the real world.

Dembski's SC filter flounders as an explanatory filter for detecting design. Nylon-eating bacteria, pesticide-resistant flies, vegetarian lizards, and sugar-loving bacteria all demonstrate that specified complexity *can* and *has* arisen from naturalistic processes such as evolution, and that information can be added to the genome in non-supernatural ways. This alone completely disqualifies SC from being a "design detector." Even Dembski himself admits, "[I]f things end up in the net that are not designed, the criterion will be useless."[71] Add to this the EAs that also show that not only can evolution produce novel specified complexity, but it can even outdo intelligent human designers. Lastly, Dembski's "gee-whiz" probabilities are meaningless, as the true probabilities for the first cell, organs, DNA, and biological systems are incalculable in principle and are rendered sterile by overlooking simultaneous processes, nonrandom natural selection, and *post hoc* validation.

Overall, SC is but another argument from ignorance, where the lack of evidence for something (e.g., abiogenesis) is used as proof of God. Dembski writes, "Worse by far is to impose as an *a priori* requirement that all gaps in our knowledge must ultimately be filled by non-intelligent causes."[72] However, Dembski's own SC theory imposes an *a priori* requirement that all gaps in our knowledge must ultimately be filled by supernatural causes! While I do believe (as hopefully most Christians do) that there *is* a designer, and that there *is* objective purpose in the universe and throughout the biological kingdom, there is no mathematical formula or filter that can detect God. Theories such as SC only serve to further alienate us from the people we are trying to reach and provide us with false hope that is sorely misplaced.

Second Law of Thermodynamics

Although this argument is so unsound and flawed that it is seldom used by any apologists anymore, it still makes its rounds on the popular level and thus merits our attention. The claim in question is that the second law of thermodynamics makes evolution physically impossible. What this law states is that for a closed system, entropy (disorder) must necessarily increase. This also means that overall, the universe is moving toward disorder. This is why when a glass breaks, it never gathers itself up and reforms, or why when you drop ink into a glass of water, it permeates the whole liquid and cannot easily be reversed. Thus, the creationist/ID argument goes that evolution violates the second law, as an increase in order (i.e., biological complexity) goes against the trend toward disorder and as such is impossible under the laws of physics. But is this correct?

Seeing as the majority of theologians and apologists are not trained in science, it is perhaps understandable that the very few who use this argument are wrong about this basic scientific concept. The key distinction is that the second law pertains to *closed* systems, not open ones. For example, if you have a chemical reaction taking place inside a sealed flask, then that *is* a closed system where the disorder as a whole will decrease. However, living things are not closed systems; they are *open* systems. The reason for this is that the sun radiates energy into our biosphere, a good deal of which is taken up by plants and other autotrophs who are able to utilize free energy and nutrients like all living things. And even though disorder in the universe as a whole is increasing, there can still be increasing order in some places as long as overall the whole is decreasing in order. Such is the case with living beings; they can increase in order by using energy they borrow from other places.

Proof that the second law of thermodynamics does not prohibit evolution is as close as your bathtub. Ever notice what happens when you let the water drain out? It forms a whirlpool, which is an increase in order. The same goes for crystals, snow flakes, stalactites, and tornadoes, all of which are increases in order and complexity from their former states that would be impossible were the creationist understanding of the second law really the case. Were their revisioning of the second law true, God would have to step in to circumvent the second law in order to create life (in the past as well as presently), and He would also have to do the same for every single snowflake, since both are increases in order and complexity. The bottom line is that the second law applies to *closed* systems like you might find in a laboratory experiment, *not* to open systems such as our earth. To try to apply the second law of thermodynamics to evolution is to fundamentally misunderstand both concepts.

Abiogenesis: The First Cell

I could not possibly think of ending this book without at least briefly dealing with perhaps the most vexing question about life itself: Where did it come from in the first place? The theory of abiogenesis seeks to answer that question and posits that the first cell arose from nonliving material. However, it must be stated at the outset that biological evolution and the origin of the first cell are entirely separate disciplines. The theory of evolution deals with what happened from the first living cell up to today and everything inbetween; abiogenesis deals with what happened from nonliving matter up to that first cell. Evolution does not depend on a viable theory of abiogenesis and is in no way "disproven" by the paucity of evidence surrounding the first cell's origin. Frankly, the question of how life arose is not even necessarily relevant to evolution; life exists, and that is all that is required for the theory of evolution to be plausible. Creationists, ID'ers, and scientists all believe that the earth was once lifeless and at one point it came to have life; science, however, seeks to illuminate exactly how this process took place on an empirical level.

I'll spare you the suspense and tell you that the origin of life is shrouded in mystery. However, science is getting ever closer to answering this "mother-of-all-questions," and great advances toward solving the mystery have been made in the past sixty years. That being said, what we do know is that the oldest undisputed fossils we have show that the first organism likely appeared around 3.5 billion years ago.[73,74,75] The Miller-Urey experiment is infamous for attempting to replicate this incredible first cell event by combining elements thought to comprise the early Earth's atmosphere, along with water and electricity cycled through an apparatus. What scientists discovered when they ran this experiment was that much of the original inorganic material spontaneously developed into organic compounds; most important among these compounds present were amino acids, the building blocks of life.[76]

Amazingly, a 2011 reanalysis of the original sealed vials from the experiment found 18 additional amino acids along with the original five found in 1952,[77] making this experiment even more relevant than previously thought. Though some critics unjustifiably contend that the Miller-Urey experiments are "discredited" since science has now learned more about the early Earth's atmosphere and suspect it was slightly different from the conditions in the experiment, this is not the case. More recent Miller-Urey-type experiments have used a wide range of conditions to simulate early Earth and all have created organic molecules necessary for life out of inorganic material.[78,79,80]

While none of these experiments created life, they do show that under early Earth conditions, most of the ingredients necessary for simple life could have arisen fairly easily. Furthermore, there are additional sources of organic compounds from which life could have originated. Meteorites often contain organic matter, such as the 1969

Murchison meteorite that contained nitrogenous bases, fatty acids, hydrocarbon chains and over one hundred different amino acids.[81]

From simple organic chemicals, there would likely have been the formation of polymers (large molecules with repetitive units), and then eventually replicating polymers. These first replicating molecules have been persuasively argued for by the RNA world hypothesis. This RNA world took place in the early Earth and preceded the arrival of DNA and proteins. These early RNA molecules were catalytic (they could speed up reactions) and self-replicating, and were precursors to the first cell. This plausible scenario has good evidence behind it and is generally accepted in the scientific community.[82,83]

More support for the RNA world has been provided by the Spiegelman Monster. This "monster" is an RNA chain 218 nucleotides long and capable of reproducing. It was created by placing virus RNA into a solution containing RNA replicase, free nucleotides, and salts whereafter the monster commenced replication.[84] The Spiegelman Monster is a "proof of concept" so to speak and shows the plausibility of an RNA world of self-replicating molecules.

Perhaps more interesting, however, are laboratory-made protocells or protobionts. These would have been the next step between self-replicating molecules and the first cell. Many protocells are simply phospholipids submerged in water, a process which results in the spontaneous formation of miscelles and vesicles. Essentially, these drops of fatty acids in water create a spherical compartment, which has a selectively permeable membrane capable of performing some of the same tasks as living cells. Some of these protocells can capture enzymes, polysaccharides, and nucleic acids and are able to perform simple polymerization reactions. Moreover, some protocells can diffuse in smaller molecules and even grow and divide like living cells.[85] From here, the first true living cell would not be a far leap and likely would have been much simpler than any living bacteria or other organism today.

One commonly held misconception about abiogenesis is that it was something like a primordial soup of inorganic chemicals that suddenly got zapped by lightning and instantaneously created something like a bacterium. It is important to stress, however, that the theory of abiogenesis posits that there were probably many intermediate stages between inorganic matter and the first cell, which could have been much simpler than today's most basic living cell. This is very different from the caricature of bacteria or other organisms suddenly popping into existence from a pile of inert chemicals—which abiogenesis certainly does *not* postulate.

Furthermore, some are suspicious of abiogenesis due to the profusion of many "gee-whiz" probabilities thrown about by opponents of the theory. Stephen C. Meyers states in Lee Strobel's book *Case for a Creator* that:

> Run the odds of these things [the first protein molecules] falling into place on their own and you find that the probabilities of forming a rather short functional protein at random would be one chance in a hundred thousand trillion trillion trillion trillion trillion trillion trillion trillion trillion trillion. That's a ten with 125 zeroes after it![86]

However impressive that sounds, recall from the chapter, "Specified Complexity," that these probabilities rest on the premise of sequential events and not simultaneous ones and fail to take into account the fact that biological systems evolve incrementally by accumulating and preserving small changes (selection also happens at the chemical level). Furthermore, the true probability of such an abiogenesis event cannot ever really be known with any degree of certainty, making most of these probabilities meaningless. Lastly, these probabilities are plagued by the problem of arbitrary but specific outcomes, like the 52-card sequence example previously given.

The take-home message here is that although science hasn't nailed down life's origin, it has many reasonable theories and is making strides in understanding abiogenesis. Many evolution skeptics, no doubt, will scoff at the inability of modern science to clearly elucidate the beginnings of life, but remember, delving into the unknown and trying to answer difficult questions is at the heart of the scientific enterprise. Though some might see abiogenesis as speculation, as long as this speculation is subject to testing, it is still a valid part of the scientific process. Right on cue, it is usually at this point that creationists and ID'ers will be inclined to offer an alternative supernatural explanation in the absence of a solid scientific one.

Admittedly, the very first cell may very well have popped into existence out of nothing at the command of God, or God may well have caused nonliving materials to form into organic molecules and then caused those organic molecules to assemble into the first living cell. However, science could never prove nor disprove these beliefs. Science may in time tell us how the first cell arose, but the question of possible directed purpose behind the first cell is out of bounds for science. Similarly, just because science may explain the physical process behind something does not mean God could not have been involved. However, just as science cannot prove or disprove faith, our faith is not science. The lack of a complete scientific theory for abiogenesis is not proof for God anymore than an airtight theory of abiogenesis would be proof against God. We are still embracing all our rational and spiritual faculties when we accept the scientific account or life's origin while believing that God had a plan and a purpose for life and was intimately involved in the process. What we must *not* do as Christians at this point is make an argument from ignorance.

Just because science cannot fill in all the blanks surrounding life's origin, we cannot simply insert God and claim victory. Though many creationists and ID'ers see the incompleteness of the theory of abiogenesis as their last defensible stronghold, it would be supremely foolish and irresponsible to use our current state of ignorance surrounding the origin of life as "evidence" of God's involvement in the process. "Science cannot explain the origin of life; therefore, God must have done it" is a very dangerous God of the gaps argument to make and will in time prove disastrous to our Christian witness. Remember, science has a very good track record of figuring out things that are very hard to explain, and if history is any guide, science will figure out the origin of life as well. It is precisely at this point that the argument *for* God (based on the lack of a scientific explanation of life's origin) becomes an argument *against* God by the same logic, and unbelievers will see God as being "out of a job," and He will be pushed further and further into obscurity and irrelevance in the minds of many. This is why we must take great care *not* to advance such dangerous arguments and flawed logic. We must argue for God from what we do know and not from what we do not know. When people's eternal destiny is at stake, we cannot be so reckless.

Evolution Summary

Though one could spend a lifetime sifting through the mountains of evidence regarding evolution, I have done my best to objectively present the arguments and evidences that I personally find most convincing, as well as those which provoked deep thought and earnest examination when I was a creationist. Much like the case for an old earth, each piece of evidence by itself is an independent confirmation of the theory of evolution, and when you have multiple independent confirmations of a theory, the case is much stronger, more persuasive, and more conclusive. The evidence for evolution is not like a house of cards, where the refutation of one piece of evidence is like the removal of one card, an act which can topple the entire structure. Rather, the evidence for evolution is like a strong house constructed with steel girders, then reinforced with stone pillars, iron rebar, concrete colonnades, and oak beams. Any one of these supports would suffice in holding the house together, but when all of these supports are combined, they serve to make the structure even stronger yet. You would have to tear down almost all the different supports to topple the house of evolution, and given the amount of evidence for evolution, this seems extremely unlikely.

The great force of these multiple independent confirmations of evolution becomes readily apparent when we consider even one example —the evidence concerning whales. For one, embryology has shown that whale embryos develop hind limb buds early in development, only to have them gradually reabsorbed. Since whales do not have hind limbs, this suggests evolution from a four-limbed ancestor. Next, consider that the front limbs of a whale are patterned on the same muscle and bone structure and placement as many other mammals, which is an extremely odd coincidence were all mammals *not* related by common ancestry. Additionally, whales share the same astragalus (anklebone) with and only with artiodactyls (even-toed hoofed mammals), and when paired with the fact that whales share more of their DNA with artiodactyls than any other animal, this is further evidence that whales evolved from artiodactyls. If all of this weren't enough, remember that the fossil record of whales is astonishingly complete, showing an overall gradual transition from four-limbed land mammals to whales over time. Furthermore, evidence of this can be found in the vestigial pelvis that whales still possess, with bones that correspond to those of other mammals' pelvises. To top all that off, every once in awhile a whale will develop an atavism whereby it will sport a real flesh and bone pair of back legs, reminding us of their evolutionary heritage. And this is just with one animal! Any of these evidences by themselves are enough to validate evolution, but taken together, these evidences provide confirmation that is essentially undeniable.

CHAPTER THIRTEEN

COMFORT IN THE END

Monsters Under the Bed

If you are a stalwart creationist/Intelligent Design advocate, I know how you are probably feeling at this point, because I've been there. I remember the pit-of-my-stomach feeling I would get anytime someone would mention evolution. I remember being apprehensive and anxious when arguments against my creationist beliefs were challenged, and when I was being confronted with the intimidating and distasteful evidence for evolution. Your heart flutters, your palms perspire, and somewhere deep in your brain a little synapse fires, alerting you to the unpleasant possibility that you may be wrong about this whole evolution deal. You brush it aside, assuaging your fears with your "proofs" espoused by pastors, pundits, and apologists galore. You pour over your books, CDs, and websites, but still deep inside of you, possibly even subconsciously, the doubt lingers and festers like an open wound. You are afraid to take an honest look at the evidence itself (not to be confused with what Christians present to you as "the other side"), because you are afraid of what you might find. You are afraid of fundamentally changing the way you see the God you love and for whom you live. The seed has undoubtedly been planted and will assuredly sprout and mature. How you shape and care for this new being is entirely up to you.

Will the Jenga tower collapse? Will the brick wall tumble? Will the almighty fall off His throne or be eaten by a terrifying creature from under a rock? I proclaim a confident and resounding "NAY!" Once you accept evolution as part of God's divine plan—however confounding to your senses—and you rest in His omnipotence and sovereignty, you will promptly realize that the monsters under the bed existed only in the mind. You were but Don Quixote, tilting at windmills, believing you were a knight jousting a dreadful enemy; in reality, you were fighting an invented adversary. You now see that the emperor has no clothes! What was once reviled is now revered, and as a reward to seeking truth, you have as C.S. Lewis said you may have, "comfort in the end."

Did you ever stop to consider that the doubt you feel may be the Holy Spirit provoking you to ask the scary questions and explore the difficult mystery? Just like physical pain motivates us to change what we are doing, spiritual pain can motivate us to seek understanding by humbling ourselves before God, and to use the curious mind He gave us to explore the truth. God always meets you where you are, but He never leaves you the same. Do we not grow immensely when we are pushed out of our comfort zones? He did not intend for us to live insular and comfortable intellectual lives but instead challenges us to get out of the boat and walk on the water. Do we trust Him?

I made the leap of faith and followed where I felt the Holy Spirit was leading me. Though initially it didn't make much sense to me, I obeyed God and prayed for guidance. When I came out the other side of my evolution–creation crisis, I found I had unnecessarily feared an imagined enemy for far too long. I garnered newfound appreciation for the majesty of God, and the box in which He had previously been contained within my mind was blown to pieces. My understanding of Him has been fabulously enriched, and I have confidence and conviction that no truth needs to be feared. In truth we find Him.

Maybe you need to pray about this area of your life. I can be an extraordinarily obstinate man, and it was only through much prayer, long conversations with my wife late into the night, digging into the Word and seeking the wisdom of wise and learned Christian men and women that I came to be in the place I am in now. God has lit a fire in my heart and placed upon me a burden to bring healing and truth to this divisive and corrosive dispute. The enemy delights when we snare ourselves in such counterproductive and dangerous arguments as creationism and ID. He laughs when we damage our witness to the non-Christian community by advancing bogus theories. The enemy would love nothing more than to distract and divide the body of believers.

It is time to end this Christian Civil War! Let's take back *real* science in the name of our Lord. Let us love our God with all our mind by fully embracing the incredible mental faculties with which we have been blessed. Indulge your God-given curiosity and discover the nuts and bolts of the universe; don't be ashamed of how He has created us and the rest of creation. Today's Christianity is known for what it is against. What if it was known for what it was *for?*

CONCLUSION

During the Allied invasion of World War II, hundreds of life-like rubber dummy paratroopers were dropped into the French countryside. These distractions drew German fire away from the Allies and wasted a great deal of the Germans' ammunition and other military resources. While the Germans were busy firing at dummies, Allied troops were busy sneaking behind enemy lines. The real battle was taking place elsewhere, while the unwitting Germans were squandering their firepower and energy on mere rubber dummies.[1] I submit to you, as Christians we are attacking the "rubber dummy" of evolution, while the real enemy slips past us unnoticed and unchallenged. How will we answer God on judgment day when He asks us why we pointlessly besieged so many distractions, meanwhile the real battle was taking place elsewhere?

Science is *not* the real enemy. While some antagonistic scientists themselves may make bold assertions about God and faith, they are merely giving their own metaphysical philosophies, a discipline in which science by definition cannot participate. And while some of these may claim that only science alone can give us knowledge about the universe, they step on their own tongues in doing so, as this is a philosophical statement and not a scientific one.

Don't fall for the false dichotomy preached by both atheists and Christian fundamentalists that illegitimately proclaims that you must choose between either atheism and science *or* God and creationism/ID. What these odd bedfellows fail to understand is that if an event can be explained in scientific terms, this does *not* in any way exclude God. Just because God does not bring something about by way of a direct action (i.e., supernatural or miraculous intervention) by *no means* justifies the assumption that God was not involved at all.

While presumably creationism and ID are well-intentioned attempts to "defend" the God of Scripture, they are bad science and even worse theology. The biggest threat of these ideologies is that they endanger the Christian faith by pointing to the improbable or unexplained as evidence of God. As philosophies built wholly on negative evidence (i.e., how do you explain "X"?), every scientific discovery then further serves to make God an "endangered species" by the same token.

In the same vein, creationism and ID only serve to alienate the lost, whom we desperately long to reach, as many see denial of the plain truth of evolution as a brain amputation prerequisite to Christianity, something they are unwilling to undergo. These ideologies also set practicing believers up for future failure, as in time many faithful will look beyond the sound and fury of creationism and discover the forgery that has deceived them. At this point, they may be disillusioned and discard God along with creationism. Lastly, creationism/ID disenfranchises the 22–46% of Christians who understand the validity of evolution, leading to possible estrangement (to which I can personally attest) and division among the body of believers.

Creationism and Intelligent Design are the Marianas Trench of Christian thought, whose practitioners are merely polishing brass on a sinking ship. I hesitate to be so blunt, but I dearly want to avoid a repeat of the Galileo blunder that for centuries has served as a continual source of embarrassment for the church. The crime of course was not just that the church was humiliated, but that this arrogance and obtuseness has left baggage for those witnessing for the faith, and suspicion for those considering the faith. This time, we would do well to be on the right side of history.

The words of St. Augustine, written 1,600 years ago, cry out to us more relevant than ever, pleading with us to exercise extreme caution and humility:

> [I]t is a disgraceful and dangerous thing for an infidel [non-Christian] to hear a Christian, presumably giving the meaning of Holy Scripture [referring here to Genesis], talking non-sense on these topics; and we should take all means to prevent such an embarrassing situation, in which people show up vast ignorance in a Christian and laugh it to scorn. The shame is not so much that an ignorant individual is derided, but that people outside the household of the faith think our sacred writers held such opinions, and, to the great loss of those for whose salvation we toil, the writers of our Scripture are criticized and rejected as unlearned men. If they find a Christian

mistaken in a field which they themselves know well and hear him maintaining his foolish opinions about our books, how are they going to believe those books in matters concerning the resurrection of the dead, the hope of eternal life, and the kingdom of heaven, when they think their pages are full of falsehoods on facts which they themselves have learnt from experience and the light of reason?[2]

Anti-evolution rhetoric does not enhance our faith; on the contrary, I truly believe it weakens our faith.

When we realize that biblical inerrancy does not mean that everything in the Bible is *literally* true (e.g., Jesus being the "true vine" does not mean He *is* a vine, or that there really are creatures with six wings and many eyes all over their front and back [Revelation 4:6–8]), but that everything the Bible *teaches* is true, we can examine the question of our origins with newfound honesty and confidence. We must remember that God inspired human authors, and their writings are imbued with the fingerprint of their culture and place in time. Just as God humiliated Himself in taking on human form, He allows His Word to be colored by human perspective and frame of reference in order to reach us. Genesis is an extraordinary book about a God who brings everything into being out of nothing, and about the one true God who desires that we should know Him. To treat the Bible as a science textbook would be a categorical mistake and a dishonor to the author's intent.

Though we may not think that God would have created through evolution (or we may not like it if He had), this does not mean He didn't. It would be very presumptuous to unequivocally assert that God would not have brought about life in this way, as we are not in the position of telling God how to do things. As Romans 9:20 (NIV) says, "But who are you, a human being, to talk back to God? Shall what is formed say to the one who formed it, 'Why did you make me like this?'" Isaiah 45:9 (NLT) also tell us, "Does a clay pot argue with its maker? Does the clay dispute with the one who shapes it, saying, 'Stop, you're doing it wrong!' Does the pot exclaim, 'How clumsy can you be?'"

Though Christians may be uncomfortable with such concepts as macroevolution and perhaps ape-like ancestors in particular, we must remind ourselves that God tells us in Isaiah 55:9 (NIV), "As the heavens are higher than the earth, so are My ways higher than your ways and My thoughts than your thoughts." Who is wiser? Do we know how to create better than God does? Who are we to speak for God and tell others He would not or could not have used evolution as a tool for His purposes? Who are we to talk back to God and complain about how we were made?

And for those in positions of teaching (I include myself here) remember that teachers will be judged more strictly (James 3:1), and that if we cause a little one to stumble, it would be better if we had a millstone hung around our neck and were drowned in the sea (Matt. 18:6). I say this to warn those imperfectly-equipped freelancers who espouse anti-evolutionary views to take a hefty spoonful of caution and humility. "Let anyone who thinks he stands take heed lest he fall" (1 Cor. 10:12).

The truth is that when science and faith are both properly understood in terms of their limitations, intent, scope, and purpose, there truly is no conflict. Though ID'ers talk of God's majesty revealed by his direct "programming" of the genetic code or "assembly" of molecular motors, the truth is even grander than that. God programmed the entire universe in a way that would produce and sustain living creatures by laws He had created before the foundation of the universe was in place, and He was intimately involved in the process, not by magic or intervention, but by His guidance and purpose. Evolution does not rob God of the glory or credit any more than the musical instruments rob Beethoven of the credit for his *Fifth Symphony*.

We are told in Romans 12:2 to be transformed by the "renewing" of our minds, not the "removing" of our minds. Our beliefs, no matter how sincerely held, will never change the facts. The facts, however, should change our beliefs. Rather than continuing to shadowbox this imagined enemy, we should shift our focus back onto Christ, the One without whom nothing else matters. For, "if Christ has not been raised, your faith is futile; you are still in your sins" (1 Cor. 15:17).

Let us praise God for His sovereignty and marvelous handiwork, and let us fully appreciate His creation by acknowledging and respecting His methods, and the ways He chose to create. When we accept evolution as His elected process, we find creation more beautiful in that we see how exceedingly elaborate and brilliant the mind of the Creator truly is. He has created mysteries for us to solve in order for us to know Him better and enjoy His creation, and in these truths He is reflected and glorified. Therefore, let us not condemn evolution. We cannot be so reckless when souls hang in the balance.

NOTES

CHAPTER ONE: INTRODUCTION

1. Lewis, Clive Staples. *Mere Christianity*. Zondervan, 2001.
2. Murray, Abdu; personal communication.
3. Bell, Rob. *Velvet Elvis: Repainting the Christian Faith*. Harper Collins, 2006.

CHAPTER TWO: THE NATURE OF SCRIPTURE

1. Walton, John H. *The Lost World of Genesis One: Ancient Cosmology and the Origins Debate*. InterVarsity Press, 2010.
2. http://www.vanderbilt.edu/AnS/physics/astrocourses/ast203/Copernicus.htm
3. D'Souza, Dinesh. *What's So Great About Christianity?* Tyndale, 2007.
4. https://www.lhup.edu/~dsimanek/ussher.htm
5. https://diogenesii.wordpress.com/2007/06/22/what-is-the-smallest-seed-in-the-world/
6. Ibid.
7. Norman, Steve; personal communication.
8. Augustine, Saint. *The literal meaning of Genesis*. No. 41. Newman Press, 1982.
9. http://www.relevantmagazine.com/god/have-we-made-bible-idol-0
10. Lamott, Anne. *Traveling mercies: Some thoughts on faith*. Anchor, 2000.
11. Miller, Kenneth R. *Finding Darwin's God: A Scientist's Search for Common Ground Between God and Evolution*. Cliff Street Books, 1999.
12. Bonhoeffer, Dietrich. *Letters Papers from Prison*. Simon and Schuster, 2011.

CHAPTER THREE: WHAT SCIENCE CAN AND CAN'T SAY AND DOES AND DOESN'T SAY

1. https://answersingenesis.org/what-is-science/two-kinds-of-science/
2. Phillip E. Johnson, "The Church of Darwin," Wall Street Journal, August 16, 1999.
3. Strobel, Lee. *The case for a Creator: A journalist investigates scientific evidence that points toward God*. Zondervan, 2004, 19.
4. Ibid., 22.
5. Ibid., 24.
6. Ibid., 28.
7. Hodge, Charles. *Systematic Theology*. Wm. B. Eerdmans Publishing Co, 1975, vol. 2, 15.
8. Geisler, Norman L., and Ronald M. Brooks. *When Skeptics Ask: A Handbook on Christian Evidences*. Baker Books, 1990, 211.
9. Geisler, Norman L., and Frank Turek. *I Don't Have Enough Faith to Be an Atheist (Foreword by David Limbaugh)*. Crossway, 2004, 117.
10. Wilson, E.O. *On Human Nature*. Harvard University Press, 1978.
11. On Debating Religion, The Nullifidian, Dec 94.
12. "Evolution, Climate Change and Other Issues". PewResearch. 2009-07-09. Retrieved 2013-03-06.
13. Newport, Frank (2028-05-11)."In U.S., 42% Believe Creationist View of Human Origins". Gallup. Retrieved 2015-07-29. http://www.gallup.com/poll/170822/believe-creationist-view-human-origins.aspx
14. http://www.pewinternet.org/2015/10/22/strong-role-of-religion-in-views-about-evolution-and-perceptions-of-scientific-consensus/ The 46% statistic includes those who believe that human evolution was guided by a supreme being (27%) and those who believe that human evolution was guided by natural processes (15%). However, I would argue that "guided by natural processes" does not exclude God in any way and is perhaps implied, especially since the persons polled attended religious services weekly or more.
15. http://www.encyclopediaofarkansas.net/encyclopedia/entry-detail.aspx?entryID=2243

16. http://ncse.com/media/voices/religion

17. "The Clergy Letter Project" *The Clergy Letter Project*. Indianapolis, IN: Ovation Agency, Inc. Retrieved July 4, 2012.

18. "The Clergy Letter - from American Christian Clergy – An Open Letter Concerning Religion and Science".The Clergy Letter Project. Indianapolis, IN: Ovation Agency, Inc. Retrieved December 12, 2013.

19. Strobel, Lee. *The case for a Creator: A journalist investigates scientific evidence that points toward God*. Zondervan, 2004, 31.

20. http://www.discovery.org/scripts/viewDB/filesDB-download.php?command=download&id=660

21. Chang, Kenneth (21 February 2006). "Few Biologists But Many Evangelicals Sign Anti-Evolution Petition". *The New York Times*. Archived from the original on 25 December 2007. Retrieved 4 January2008.

22. Decker, Mark Lowry; Moore, Randy. *More than Darwin: an encyclopedia of the people and places of the evolution-creationism controversy*. Westport, Conn: Greenwood Press, 2008.

23. Strobel, Lee. *The case for a Creator: A journalist investigates scientific evidence that points toward God*. Zondervan, 2004, 66.

24. Kreeft, Peter; Tacelli, Ronald K. *Handbook of Christian Apologetics*. InterVarsity Press, 1994, 107.

25. *Answers to Evolution*. Rose Publishing, 2004.

26. http://www.pewinternet.org/2015/10/22/strong-role-of-religion-in-views-about-evolution-and-perceptions-of-scientific-consensus/

27. http://www.people-press.org/2009/07/09/section-5-evolution-climate-change-and-other-issues/

28. http://www.pewinternet.org/2015/07/23/an-elaboration-of-aaas-scientists-views/

29. http://www.religioustolerance.org/ev_publia.htm

30. http://www.pewforum.org/2009/11/05/scientists-and-belief/

31. Ibid.

32. *Science and Creationism: View from the National Academy of Sciences*. National Academy Press, 1999.

33. Burkett, Andrew. *The Ministry of Chance: British Romanticism, Darwinian Evolutionary Theory & the Aleatory*. ProQuest, 2008.; also available at:
http://creationism.org.pl/groups/ptkrmember/szkola/2005/nobel_letter.pdf

34. Amicus Curiae brief in *Edwards v. Aguillard*, 85-1513 (United States Supreme Court 1986-08-18).

35. http://www.bbc.co.uk/science/space/universe/questions_and_ideas/steady_state_theory

36. http://www.npr.org/templates/story/story.php?storyId=4655517

37. Young, Davis A. *The Biblical Flood: A Case Study of the Church's Response to Extrabiblical Evidence*. Eerdmans Pub Co, 1995.

38. http://www.youngearth.org/index.php/archives/rmcf-articles/item/21-transcript-of-ken-ham-vs-bill-nye-debate

39. https://answersingenesis.org/about/faith/

40. Walton, John H. *The Lost World of Genesis One: Ancient Cosmology and the Origins Debate*. InterVarsity Press, 2010.

41. D'Souza, Dinesh. *What's So Great About Christianity?* Tyndale, 2007.

42. dictionary.com

43. http://www.nas.edu/evolution/TheoryOrFact.html

44. https://answersingenesis.org/blogs/ken-ham/2014/06/11/should-we-unite-around-mans-fallible-word-or-gods-infallible-word/

45. Plantinga, A. 1991. An evolutionary argument against naturalism. *Logos* 12: 27-49.

CHAPTER FOUR: THE BEGETTER OF ALL EVILS?

1. http://creationtoday.org/tyrannosaurus-rex-was-a-cannibal/
2. http://www.dallasobserver.com/news/footprints-of-fantasy-6403234; "Footprints of Fantasy," by Kaylois Henry, Dallas Observer, December 12, 1996.
3. Strobel, Lee. *The case for a Creator: A journalist investigates scientific evidence that points toward God.* Zondervan, 2004.
4. http://www.lwbc.co.uk/Genesis/results%20of%20believing%20evolution.htm
5. Ham, Ken. *The Lie: Evolution.* Master Books, 2012.
6. http://creation.com/evolution-makes-atheists-out-of-people
7. Strobel, Lee. *The case for a Creator: A journalist investigates scientific evidence that points toward God.* Zondervan, 2004.
8. Geisler, Norman L., and Ronald M. Brooks. *When Skeptics Ask: A Handbook on Christian Evidences.* Baker Books, 1990, 211.
9. Dawkins, Richard. *The Blind Watchmaker: Why the Evidence of Evolution Reveals a Universe without Design.* W. W. Norton & Company, 1996.
10. Larry A. Witham. *Where Darwin Meets the Bible: Creationists and Evolutionists in America.* Oxford: Oxford University Press, 2002, 23.
11. Dawkins, Richard. *Reason Rally*, National Mall, Washington, DC, March 24, 2012.
12. Closing statements of presentation at *Beyond Belief : Science, Religion, Reason and Survival*, November 5, 2006.
13. Lewontin, Richard. "*Billions and Billions of Demons*" in: The New York Review of Books, 9 January 1997, 31.
14. http://www.gallup.com/poll/155003/Hold-Creationist-View-Human-Origins.aspx
15. D'Souza, Dinesh. *What's So Great About Christianity?* Tyndale, 2007.
16. Polkinghorne, John. *One World: The Interaction of Science and Theology.* Templeton Press, 2007.

CHAPTER FIVE: YOUNG EARTH BY THE NUMBERS

1. Numbers, Ronald. *The Creationists: From Scientific Creationism to Intelligent Design.* Harvard University Press., 2006.
2. http://creation.com/where-are-all-the-people
3. http://www.interacademies.net/10878/13901.aspx
4. http://ncse.com/rncse/30/3/americans-scientific-knowledge-beliefs-human-evolution-year-
5. Ibid.

CHAPTER SIX: SENIOR ORGANISMS

1. http://www.rmtrr.org/oldlist.htm
2. Brutovská, Eva, et al. "Ageing of trees: application of general ageing theories." *Ageing research reviews* 12.4 (2013): 855-866.
3. Sussman, Rachel. *The oldest living things in the world.* University of Chicago Press, 2014.
4. "Great Basin Drama" (1991); http://www.sfgate.com/news/article/Staying-Alive-High-in-California-s-White-2995266.php
5. Stokes, Marvin A., and Terah L. Smiley. *An Introduction to Tree-Ring Dating.* University of Arizona Press, 1996.
6. Swetnam, Thomas W., Marna Ares Thompson, and Elaine Kennedy Sutherland. "Using dendrochronology to measure radial growth of defoliated trees." (1985).
7. http://www.esi.utexas.edu/component/content/article/36-tree-project/124-an-introduction-to-dendrochronology
8. http://www.ltrr.arizona.edu/lorim/basic.html
9. https://journals.uair.arizona.edu/index.php/radiocarbon/article/view/16947/pdf
10. Brutovská, Eva, et al. "Ageing of trees: application of general ageing theories." *Ageing research reviews* 12.4 (2013): 855-866.

11. Augustine, Saint. *The literal meaning of Genesis*. No. 41. Newman Press, 1982.
12. http://msue.anr.msu.edu/news/trees_and_flooding_faqs
13. Veres, Aniko, et al. "CONSERVATION GENETICS-GENETIC ANALYSIS AND CLONING OF THE OLDEST MAGYAR BLACK LOCUST (Robinia pseudoacacia) TREE PLANTED IN 1710 (Babolna) FOR PHYTOREMEDIATION PURPOSES."
14. Öberg, Lisa, and Leif Kullman. "Ancient subalpine clonal spruces (Picea abies): sources of postglacial vegetation history in the Swedish Scandes."*Arctic* (2011): 183-196.
15. World's oldest living tree discovered in Sweden". Umeå University. Retrieved 6 May 2008 http://info.adm.umu.se/NYHETER/PressmeddelandeEng.aspx?id=3061
16. "Native Conifers of Tasmania". Paks and Wildlife Service, Tasmania http://www.parks.tas.gov.au/index.aspx?base=3240
17. Booth, Carol. "Enduring Australians: Millenarians and centenarians." *Wildlife Australia* 50.3 (2013): 4.
18. Krussmann, G. *Manual of Cultivated Broad-leaved Trees and Shrubs*. Vol II:E-Pro. Timber Press.Portland, OR, 1977, 445
19. Moldenke, H. N. 1950. The oldest flowering plant. *Horticulture* 18:456–457.
20. Wherry, E. T. 1972. Box huckleberry as the oldest living protoplasm. *Castanea* 37:94–95.
21. Willaman, J. J. 1965. The oldest living plants. *Morris Arboretum Bulletin* 16:65–66.
22. http://arnoldia.arboretum.harvard.edu/pdf/issues/248.pdf
23. http://141.243.32.146/resources/nature/recoveryplanDraftEucalyptusRecurva.pdf
24. Frank C. Vasek. 1980. Creosote Bush: Long-Lived Clones in the Mojave Desert. *American Journal of Botany* 67(2):246-255.
25. Feldman, Annette. "California Desert Protection Act, The." *Environs: Envtl. L. & Pol'y J.* 16 (1992): 60.
26. May MR, Provance MC, Sanders AC, Ellstrand NC, Ross-Ibarra J (2009) A Pleistocene Clone of Palmer's Oak Persisting in Southern California. *PLoS ONE* 4(12): e8346. doi:10.1371/journal.pone.0008346
27. Ibid.
28. http://eprints.utas.edu.au/7645/1/Lynch1998.pdf
29. Arnaud-Haond S, Duarte CM, Diaz-Almela E, Marbà N, Sintes T, Serrão EA (2012) Implications of Extreme Life Span in Clonal Organisms: Millenary Clones in Meadows of the Threatened Seagrass *Posidonia oceanica*. PLoS ONE 7(2): e30454. doi:10.1371/journal.pone.0030454
30. Ibid.

CHAPTER SEVEN: ANCIENT NATURAL PHENOMENA

1.   Christopher Gregory Weber. (1980) The Fatal Flaws of Flood Geology *Creation Evolution Journal* 1(1):24–37 .
2.   Wonderly, Daniel E. *God's time-records in ancient sediments: evidences of long time spans in Earth's history*. Crystal Pr, 1977.
3.   Ibid.
4.   Guzmán, Héctor M., and Jorge Cortes. "Growth rates of eight species of scleractinian corals in the eastern Pacific (Costa Rica)." *Bulletin of Marine Science* 44.3 (1989): 1186-1194.
5.   http://oceanexplorer.noaa.gov/explorations/12lophelia/background/growth/growth.html
6.   Hubbard, Dennis K., and David Scaturo. "Growth rates of seven species of scleractinean corals from Cane Bay and Salt River, St. Croix, USVI."*Bulletin of Marine Science* 36.2 (1985): 325-338.
7.   Wonderly, Daniel E. *God's time-records in ancient sediments: evidences of long time spans in Earth's history*. Crystal Pr, 1977.
8.   Ibid.
9.   Christopher Gregory Weber. (1980) The Fatal Flaws of Flood Geology *Creation*

Evolution Journal 1(1):24–37.

10. Ibid.

11. Ibid.

12. Wonderly, Daniel E. *God's time-records in ancient sediments: evidences of long time spans in Earth's history.* Crystal Pr, 1977.

13. Christopher Gregory Weber. (1980) The Fatal Flaws of Flood Geology *Creation Evolution Journal* 1(1):24–37.

14. Wonderly, Daniel E. *God's time-records in ancient sediments: evidences of long time spans in Earth's history.* Crystal Pr, 1977.

15. Ibid.

16. Dahl-Jansen
http://www.gfy.ku.dk/~www-glac/papers/pdfs/151.pdf

17. Seely, Paul H. 2003. The GISP2 ice core: Ultimate proof that Noah's flood was not global. *Perspectives on Science and Christian Faith* 55(4): 252-260.
http://www.asa3.org/ASA/PSCF/2003/PSCF12-03Seely.pdf

18. Ruddiman, William F. *Earth's Climate: past and future.* Macmillan, 2001.

19. Lambert, Fabrice, et al. "Dust-climate couplings over the past 800,000 years from the EPICA Dome C ice core." *Nature* 452.7187 (2008): 616-619.

20. Jouzel, Jean, et al. "Orbital and millennial Antarctic climate variability over the past 800,000 years." *science* 317.5839 (2007): 793-796.

21. Lüthi, Dieter, et al. "High-resolution carbon dioxide concentration record 650,000–800,000 years before present." *Nature* 453.7193 (2008): 379-382.

22. Petit, Jean-Robert, et al. "Climate and atmospheric history of the past 420,000 years from the Vostok ice core, Antarctica." *Nature* 399.6735 (1999): 429-436.

23. Ritz, Catherine, Vincent Rommelaere, and Christophe Dumas. "Modeling the evolution of Antarctic ice sheet over the last 420,000 years: Implications for altitude changes in the Vostok region." *Journal of Geophysical Research: Atmospheres (1984–2012)* 106.D23 (2001): 31943-31964.

24. Seely, Paul H. 2003. The GISP2 ice core: Ultimate proof that Noah's flood was not global. *Perspectives on Science and Christian Faith* 55(4): 252-260.

25. Cole-Dai, Jihong, et al. "A 4100-year record of explosive volcanism from an East Antarctica ice core." *Journal of Geophysical Research: Atmospheres (1984–2012)* 105.D19 (2000): 24431-24441.

26. Palais, Julie M., Mark S. Germani, and Gregory A. Zielinski. "Inter-hemispheric transport of volcanic ash from a 1259 AD volcanic eruption to the Greenland and Antarctic Ice Sheets." *Geophysical Research Letters* 19.8 (1992): 801-804.

27. Petit, Jean-Robert, et al. "Climate and atmospheric history of the past 420,000 years from the Vostok ice core, Antarctica." *Nature* 399.6735 (1999): 429-436.

28. Morris, Henry. *Scientific Creationism, California.* Creation- Life Publishers, 1974.

29. Brown, Walter Tarleton. *In the beginning.* Center for Scientific Creation, 1989.

30. Snelling, Andrew A., and David E. Rush. "Moon dust and the age of the solar system." *Creation Ex Nihilo Technical Journal* 7.1 (1993): 2-42.

31. Ibid.

32. Awbrey, Frank T. "Space dust, the moon's surface, and the age of the cosmos." *Creation/Evolution, XIII* (1983): 21-29.

33. Ibid.

34. Dalrymple, G. Brent. "How Old is the Earth." *A Reply to" Scientific* (1984).

35. d'Almeida, Guillaume A.; Peter Koepke & Eric P. Shettle. *Atmospheric Aerosols - Global Climatology and Radiative Characteristic.* Deepak publishing, 1991.

36. Ceplecha, Zdenek "Luminous efficiency based on photographic observations of the Lost-City fireball and implications for the influx of interplanetary bodies onto Earth" *Astronomy and Astrophysics* 311(1): 329-332 (July 1996).

37. Ceplecha, Zdenek "Influx of interplanetary bodies onto Earth" *Astronomy and*

Astrophysics 263: 361-366 (1992).

38. Wasson & Kyte, 1987 *Geophysical Research Letters*, 14:779, 1987.

39. Dohnanyi, J. S. "Interplanetary objects in review: Statistics of their masses and dynamics." *Icarus* 17.1 (1972): 1-48.

40. The amount of moon dust varies from 1/8 inch to 3 inches in depth but averages around two inches in depth. See: Snelling, Andrew A., and David E. Rush. "Moon dust and the age of the solar system." *Creation Ex Nihilo Technical Journal* 7.1 (1993): 2-42.

41. Awbrey, Frank T. "Space dust, the moon's surface, and the age of the cosmos." *Creation/Evolution, XIII* (1983): 21-29.

42. https://answersingenesis.org/kids/astronomy/moon-dust-argument-no-longer-useful/

43. Snelling, Andrew A., and David E. Rush. "Moon dust and the age of the solar system." *Creation Ex Nihilo Technical Journal* 7.1 (1993): 2-42.

44. http://www.universetoday.com/110858/how-far-can-you-see-in-the-universe/

45. Willott, Chris J., et al. "Four quasars above redshift 6 discovered by the Canada-France High-z Quasar Survey." *The Astronomical Journal* 134.6 (2007): 2435.

46. Moreland, James Porter, and John Mark Reynolds. *Three views on creation and evolution.* Zondervan, 1999.

47. Ibid.

48. Willott, Chris J., et al. "Four quasars above redshift 6 discovered by the Canada-France High-z Quasar Survey." *The Astronomical Journal* 134.6 (2007): 2435.

49. Nehme, Carole, et al. "Geomorphology research in Jeita cave, Lebanon: speleogenesis study for a scientific valorization of a touristic cave." Poster Session, International Congress on scientific research in Show Caves, Karst Research Institute ZRC Sazu, Slovenia. 2012.

50. Moore, George William, and Gerardus Nicholas Sullivan. *Speleology: the study of caves.* Zephyrus Press, 1978.

51. Short, Martin B., James C. Baygents, and Raymond E. Goldstein. "Stalactite growth as a free-boundary problem." *Physics of Fluids (1994-present)* 17.8 (2005): 083101.

52. Harmon, R. S., et al. "Uranium-series dating of speleothems." *National Speleological Society Bulletin* 37 (1975): 21-33.

53. Ford, Derek C. and Carol A. Hill, 1999. Dating of speleothems in Kartchner Caverns, Arizona. *Journal of Cave and Karst Studies* 61(2): 84-88.

54. Moore, George William, and Gerardus Nicholas Sullivan. *Speleology: the study of caves.* Zephyrus Press, 1978.

55. Ibid.

56. Bradley, Wilmot Hyde. The varves and climate of the Green River epoch. *U.S. Geol. Survey Prof. Paper* 158:87-110. 1929.

57. Van Till, Howard J. *Portraits of creation: Biblical and scientific perspectives on the world's formation.* Wm. B. Eerdmans Publishing, 1990.

58. Anderson, Roger Yates, et al. *Meromictic lakes and varved lake sediments in North America.* No. 1607. USGPO,, 1985.

59. Schadewald, Robert. "Six 'Flood' arguments Creationists can't answer. Creation." *Evolution* 9 (1982): 12-17.

60. Bradley, Wilmot Hyde. The varves and climate of the Green River epoch. *U.S. Geol. Survey Prof. Paper* 158:87-110. 1929.

61. Smith, M. Elliot, Brad Singer, and Alan Carroll. "40Ar/39Ar geochronology of the Eocene Green River Formation, Wyoming." *Geological Society of America Bulletin* 115.5 (2003): 549-565.

62. Smith, M. Elliot, Alan R. Carroll, and Brad S. Singer. "Synoptic reconstruction of a major ancient lake system: Eocene Green River Formation, western United States." *Geological Society of America Bulletin* 120.1-2 (2008): 54-84.

63. Bradley, Wilmot Hyde. The varves and climate of the Green River epoch. *U.S. Geol. Survey Prof. Paper* 158:87-110. 1929.

64. Ibid.
65. Ager, Derek, and Derek Victor Ager. *The new catastrophism: the importance of the rare event in geological history.* Cambridge University Press, 1995.
66. Schadewald, Robert. "Six 'Flood' arguments Creationists can't answer. *Creation/Evolution* 9 (1982): 12-17.
67. Bates, R.L. and Jackson, J.A. (Eds.), *Dictionary of Geological Terms*, 3rd ed., Anchor Press/Doubleday, Garden City, NY, 1984.
68. Ibid.
69. Smith, G. R., and R. L. Elder. "Environmental interpretation of burial and preservation of Clarkia fishes." *Late Cenozoic History of the Pacific Northwest: San Francisco, American Association for the Advancement of Science* (1985): 85-93.
70. Batten, David J., Jane Gray, and Rex Harland. "Palaeoenvironmental significance of a monospecific assemblage of dinoflagellate cysts from the Miocene Clarkia Beds, Idaho, USA." *Palaeogeography, palaeoclimatology, palaeoecology* 153.1 (1999): 161-177.
71. Drever, J.I., 1997, The Geochemistry of Natural Waters, 3rd ed., Prentice Hall, Upper Saddle River, NJ 07458.
72. Fischer, Alfred G., and Lillian T. Roberts. "Cyclicity in the Green River Formation (lacustrine Eocene) of Wyoming." *Journal of Sedimentary Research* 61.7 (1991).
73. McGREW, PAUL O., and Alan Feduccia. "A preliminary report on a nesting colony of Eocene birds." (1973): 163-164.
74. Leggitt, V. Leroy, H. Buchheim, and ROBERTO E. Biaggi. "The stratigraphic setting of three Presbyornis nesting sites: Eocene Fossil Lake, Lincoln County, Wyoming." *National Park Service Paleontological Research* 3 (1998): 61-68.
75. Fischer, Alfred G., and Lillian T. Roberts. "Cyclicity in the Green River Formation (lacustrine Eocene) of Wyoming." *Journal of Sedimentary Research* 61.7 (1991).
76. http://www.indiana.edu/~ensiweb/lessons/varve.ev.pdf
77. Smith, M. Elliot, Brad Singer, and Alan Carroll. "40Ar/39Ar geochronology of the Eocene Green River Formation, Wyoming." *Geological Society of America Bulletin* 115.5 (2003): 549-565.
78. Machlus, Malka, et al. "Eocene calibration of geomagnetic polarity time scale reevaluated: Evidence from the Green River Formation of Wyoming." Geology32.2 (2004): 137-140.
79. Smith, M. Elliot, et al. "High-resolution calibration of Eocene strata: 40Ar/39Ar geochronology of biotite in the Green River Formation." *Geology*34.5 (2006): 393-396.
80. Kitagawa, Hiroyuki, and Johannes van der Plicht. "A 40,000-year varve chronology from Lake Suigetsu, Japan; extension of the (super 14) C calibration curve." Radiocarbon 40.1 (1998): 505-515.
81. Williams, D. F., et al. "Lake Baikal record of continental climate response to orbital insolation during the past 5 million years." Science 278.5340 (1997): 1114-1117.
82. Anderson, Roger Y., et al. "Permian Castile varved evaporite sequence, west Texas and New Mexico." Geological Society of America Bulletin 83.1 (1972): 59-86.
83. Pennington, R. Toby, and Christopher W. Dick. "The role of immigrants in the assembly of the South American rainforest tree flora."*Philosophical Transactions of the Royal Society of London B: Biological Sciences*359.1450 (2004): 1611-1622.
84. Yih, David. "Land bridge travelers of the Tertiary: the Eastern Asian-Eastern North American floristic disjunction." *Arnoldia* 69.3 (2012): 14-23.
85. http://pubs.usgs.gov/gip/dynamic/understanding.html
86. Lambert, David. *The field guide to geology.* Infobase Publishing, 2006.
87. https://www.unavco.org/software/geodetic-utilities/plate-motion-calculator/plate-motion-calculator.html
88. http://education.nationalgeographic.com/encyclopedia/continental-drift/
89. Sinnhuber, Miriam, et al. "A model study of the impact of magnetic field structure on atmospheric composition during solar proton events." Geophysical research letters

30.15 (2003).

90.   http://www.geomag.bgs.ac.uk/education/reversals.html

91.   http://www.nasa.gov/topics/earth/features/2012-poleReversal.html

92.   Ibid.

93.   Vine, Frederick J.; Drummond H. Matthews (1963). "Magnetic Anomalies over Oceanic Ridges". Nature 199 (4897): 947–949.

94.   http://oceanexplorer.noaa.gov/edu/learning/2_midocean_ridges/activities/seafloor_spreading.html

95.   Tomascik, Tomas. *The Ecology of the Indonesian Seas*. Periplus Editions, 2013.

96.   http://paleobiology.si.edu/geotime/main/foundation_dating4.html

97.   Gee, Jeffrey S., et al. "Geomagnetic intensity variations over the past 780 kyr obtained from near-seafloor magnetic anomalies." *Nature* 408.6814 (2000): 827-832.

98.   Zagatto, V. A. B., et al. "Natural radioactivity in bananas." *The Natural Radiation Environment: 8th International Symposium (NRE VIII)*. Vol. 1034. No. 1. AIP Publishing, 2008.

99.   http://w.astro.berkeley.edu/~dperley/areopagus/isotopetable.html

100.   Dalrymple, G.B., Izett, G.A., Snee, L.W., and Obradovich, J.D., 1993, 40Ar/ 39Ar age spectra and total fusion ages of tektites from Cretaceous- 32 Argon Thermochronology of Mineral Deposits Tertiary boundary sedimentary rocks in the Beloc Formation, Haiti: *U.S. Geological Survey Bulletin* 2065, 20.

101.   Hall, Brian; Halgrimmson, Benedikt. *Strickberger's Evolution*. Jones and Bartlett Publishers, 2007.

102.   Smith, M. Elliot, Brad Singer, and Alan Carroll. "40Ar/39Ar geochronology of the Eocene Green River Formation, Wyoming." *Geological Society of America Bulletin* 115.5 (2003): 549-565.

103.   Swisher, Carl C., and D. R. Prothero. "Single-crystal 40Ar/39Ar dating of the Eocene-Oligocene transition in North America." *Science* 249.4970 (1990): 760-762.

104.   Mark, Darren F., et al. "A high-precision 40 Ar/39 Ar age for the Young Toba Tuff and dating of ultra-distal tephra: Forcing of Quaternary climate and implications for hominin occupation of India." *Quaternary Geochronology* 21 (2014): 90-103.

105.   Bonnet, Nicolas J., et al. "First 40 Ar/39 Ar dating of intense late Palaeogene lateritic weathering in Peninsular India." *Earth and Planetary Science Letters*386 (2014): 126-137.

106.   Wiens, Roger C. "Radiometric Dating." *A Christian Perspective. The American Scientific Association*. (2002).

107.   Carlson, Richard W. "Absolute Age Determinations: Radiometric."*Encyclopedia of Solid Earth Geophysics*. Springer Netherlands, 2011. 1-8.

108.   Bowen, R. "Radioactive Dating Methods." *Handbook of Nuclear Chemistry*. Springer US, 2011. 761-816.

109.   Simon A. Wilde, et al.: *Evidence from detrital zircons for the existence of continental crust and oceans on the Earth 4.4 Gyr ago,* Nature Geoscience, 2001.

110.   Brent Dalrymple, *The age of the Earth*. Stanford University Press, 1991.

111.   Dalrymple, G. Brent. *Ancient Earth, ancient skies: the age of Earth and its cosmic surroundings*. Stanford University Press, 2004.

112.   Bowring, Samuel A.; Williams, Ian S. (1999). "Priscoan (4.00-4.03 Ga) orthogneisses from northwestern Canada". *Contributions to Mineralogy and Petrology* 134: 3.

113.   Norman, Marc D., et al. "Chronology, geochemistry, and petrology of a ferroan noritic anorthosite clast from Descartes breccia 67215: clues to the age, origin, structure, and impact history of the lunar crust." *Meteoritics & Planetary Science* 38.4 (2003): 645-661.

114.   Dalrymple, G. Brent. *The age of the Earth*. Stanford University Press, 1994.

115.   Wiens, Roger C. "Radiometric Dating." *A Christian Perspective. The American Scientific Association*. (2002).

116.   Young, Davis A. *Christianity and the Age of the Earth*. Artisan Pub, 1988.

117.   Miller, Kenneth R. *Finding Darwin's God: A Scientist's Search for Common Ground Between*

God and Evolution. Cliff Street Books, 1999.

118. Ibid.

119. Wetherill, George W. "Discordant uranium-lead ages, I." *Eos, Transactions American Geophysical Union* 37.3 (1956): 320-326.

120. Kitagawa, Hiroyuki, and Johannes van der Plicht. "A 40,000-year varve chronology from Lake Suigetsu, Japan; extension of the (super 14) C calibration curve." Radiocarbon 40.1 (1998): 505-515.

121. http://www.asa3.org/ASA/resources/Wiens.html

122. Dalrymple, G. Brent. *The age of the Earth*. Stanford University Press, 1994.

123. http://chem.tufts.edu/science/geology/adam-eve_toast.htm

124. Snelling, Andrew A. 2005. Radiohalos in granites: Evidence for accelerated nuclear decay. Chapter 3 (pp. 101-208) in L. Vardiman, A., A. Snelling, and E.F. Chaffin (eds.) Radioisotopes and the Age of the Earth, Volume II: Results of a Young-Earth Creationist Research Initiative, Institute for Creation Research, El Cajon, California, 818.

125. DeYoung, Don. 2005. Thousands. Not Billions: Challenging an Icon of Evolution, Questioning the Age of the Earth. Master Books, Forest Green Arkansas, 190.

126. Peppe, D. J., and A. L. Deino. "Dating rocks and fossils using geologic methods." *Nature Education Knowledge, Cambridge* 4.10 (2013): 1.

CHAPTER NINE: SIMILARITIES

1.   Penny, David, and M. Hendy. "Estimating the reliability of evolutionary trees." *Molecular Biology and Evolution* 3.5 (1986): 403-417.

2.   Doyle, James A., and Peter K. Endress. "Morphological phylogenetic analysis of basal angiosperms: comparison and combination with molecular data." *International Journal of Plant Sciences* 161.S6 (2000): S121-S153.

3.   Fitch, Walter M., and Emanuel Margoliash. "Construction of phylogenetic trees."Science 155.3760 (1967): 279-284.

4.   Gilad, Yoav, et al. "Human specific loss of olfactory receptor genes." *Proceedings of the National Academy of Sciences* 100.6 (2003): 3324-3327.

5.   Kurdyukov, Sergey G., et al. "Full-sized HERV-K (HML-2) human endogenous retroviral LTR sequences on human chromosome 21: map locations and evolutionary history." *Gene* 273.1 (2001): 51-61.

6.   Lebedev, Yuri B., et al. "Differences in HERV-K LTR insertions in orthologous loci of humans and great apes." *Gene* 247.1 (2000): 265-277.

7.   Takezaki, Naoko, and Masatoshi Nei. "Genetic distances and reconstruction of phylogenetic trees from microsatellite DNA." *Genetics* 144.1 (1996): 389-399.

8.   Penny, David, and M. Hendy. "Estimating the reliability of evolutionary trees." *Molecular Biology and Evolution* 3.5 (1986): 403-417.

9.   Diogo, R., et al. "From fish to modern humans—comparative anatomy, homologies and evolution of the pectoral and forelimb musculature." *Journal of Anatomy* 214.5 (2009): 694-716.

10. Darwin, Charles. "The origin of species by means of natural selection: or, the preservation of favored races in the struggle for life." (2009).

11. Diogo, R., et al. "From fish to modern humans—comparative anatomy, homologies and evolution of the pectoral and forelimb musculature." *Journal of Anatomy* 214.5 (2009): 694-716.

12. Shubin, Neil H., and Pere Alberch. "A morphogenetic approach to the origin and basic organization of the tetrapod limb." *Evolutionary biology*. Springer US, 1986. 319-387.

13. Hall, Brian; Halgrimmson, Benedikt. *Strickberger's Evolution*. Jones and Bartlett Publishers, 2007.

14. Ibid.

15. Diogo, R., et al. "From fish to modern humans—comparative anatomy, homologies and evolution of the pectoral and forelimb musculature." *Journal of Anatomy* 214.5 (2009):

694-716.

16.   Shubin, Neil H., and Pere Alberch. "A morphogenetic approach to the origin and basic organization of the tetrapod limb." *Evolutionary biology*. Springer US, 1986. 319-387.

17.   Wong, J. "Coevolution theory of the genetic code at age thirty." *BioEssays* 27.4 (2005): 416-425.

18.   Wong, J. Tze-Fei. "The evolution of a universal genetic code." *Proceedings of the National Academy of Sciences* 73.7 (1976): 2336-2340

19.   Hinegardner, Ralph T., and Joseph Engelberg. "Rationale for a universal genetic code." *Science* 142.3595 (1963): 1083-1085.

20.   Koonin, Eugene V., and Artem S. Novozhilov. "Origin and evolution of the genetic code: the universal enigma." *IUBMB life* 61.2 (2009): 99-111.

21.   Ibid.

22.   Wong, J. "Coevolution theory of the genetic code at age thirty." *BioEssays* 27.4 (2005): 416-425.

23.   Wong, J. Tze-Fei. "The evolution of a universal genetic code." *Proceedings of the National Academy of Sciences* 73.7 (1976): 2336-2340.

24.   Hinegardner, Ralph T., and Joseph Engelberg. "Rationale for a universal genetic code." *Science* 142.3595 (1963): 1083-1085.

25.   Barton, N. H., et al. *Evolution*. Cold Spring Harbor Laboratory Press, 2007.

26.   Ibid.

27.   Ibid.

28.   Hall, Brian; Halgrimmson, Benedikt. *Strickberger's Evolution*. Jones and Bartlett Publishers, 2007.

29.   Koonin EV (2005). "Orthologs, paralogs, and evolutionary genomics". *Annual Review of Genetics* 39: 309–38.

30.   Womack, J. E., and Y. D. Moll, 1986. Gene map of the cow: Conservation of linkage with mouse and man. *J. Hered.*, 77,2-7.

31.   Buchberg, A. M., et al. "A comprehensive genetic map of murine chromosome 11 reveals extensive linkage conservation between mouse and human." *Genetics* 122.1 (1989): 153-161.

32.   Collins, Francis S. *The language of God: A scientist presents evidence for belief*. No. 111. Simon and Schuster, 2006.

33.   https://ghr.nlm.nih.gov/chromosome/17

34.   Collins, Francis S. *The language of God: A scientist presents evidence for belief*. No. 111. Simon and Schuster, 2006.

35.   Koonin EV (2005). "Orthologs, paralogs, and evolutionary genomics". *Annual Review of Genetics* 39: 309–38.

36.   Hall, Brian; Halgrimmson, Benedikt. *Strickberger's Evolution*. Jones and Bartlett Publishers, 2007.

37.   Douzery, Emmanuel JP, et al. "The timing of eukaryotic evolution: does a relaxed molecular clock reconcile proteins and fossils?." *Proceedings of the National Academy of Sciences of the United States of America* 101.43 (2004): 15386-15391.

38.   Kachroo, Aashiq H., et al. "Systematic humanization of yeast genes reveals conserved functions and genetic modularity." *Science* 348.6237 (2015): 921-925.

39.   http://eugenes.org/all/hgsummary.html

40.   Ibid.

41.   Ibid.

42.   Elsik, Christine G., Ross L. Tellam, and Kim C. Worley. "The genome sequence of taurine cattle: a window to ruminant biology and evolution." *Science* 324.5926 (2009): 522-528.

43.   Pontius, Joan U., et al. "Initial sequence and comparative analysis of the cat genome." *Genome research* 17.11 (2007): 1675-1689.

44.   Sequencing, The Chimpanzee, and Analysis Consortium. "Initial sequence of the

chimpanzee genome and comparison with the human genome." *Nature* 437.7055 (2005): 69-87.

45. Varki, Ajit, and David L. Nelson. "Genomic comparisons of humans and chimpanzees." *Annual Review of Anthropology* 36.1 (2007): 191.

46. Britten, Roy J. "Divergence between samples of chimpanzee and human DNA sequences is 5%, counting indels." *Proceedings of the National Academy of Sciences* 99.21 (2002): 13633-13635.

47. Wetterbom, Anna, et al. "Comparative genomic analysis of human and chimpanzee indicates a key role for indels in primate evolution." *Journal of molecular evolution* 63.5 (2006): 682-690.

48. https://www.genome.gov/15515096

49. Wildman, Derek E., et al. "Implications of natural selection in shaping 99.4% nonsynonymous DNA identity between humans and chimpanzees: enlarging genus Homo." *Proceedings of the national Academy of Sciences* 100.12 (2003): 7181-7188.

50. Chen, F.C.; Li, W.H. (2001). "Genomic Divergences between Humans and Other Hominoids and the Effective Population Size of the Common Ancestor of Humans and Chimpanzees". *American Journal of Human Genetics* 68 (2): 444–56.

51. Cooper, G.M.; Brudno, M.; Green, E.D.; Batzoglou, S.; Sidow, A. (2003). "Quantitative Estimates of Sequence Divergence for Comparative Analyses of Mammalian Genomes". *Genome Res.* 13 (5): 813–20.

52. Spaulding, Michelle, Maureen A. O'Leary, and John Gatesy. "Relationships of Cetacea (Artiodactyla) among mammals: increased taxon sampling alters interpretations of key fossils and character evolution." *Plos one* 4.9 (2009): e7062.

53. Shimamura, Mitsuru, et al. "Molecular evidence from retroposons that whales form a clade within even-toed ungulates." *Nature* 388.6643 (1997): 666-670.

54. Arnason, Ulfur, et al. "The mitochondrial genome of the sperm whale and a new molecular reference for estimating eutherian divergence dates." *Journal of Molecular Evolution* 50.6 (2000): 569-578).

55. Yim, Hyung-Soon, et al. "Minke whale genome and aquatic adaptation in cetaceans." *Nature genetics* 46.1 (2014): 88-92.

56. Yunis, Jorge J., and Ora Prakash. "The origin of man: a chromosomal pictorial legacy." *Science* 215.4539 (1982): 1525-1530.

57. Sequencing, The Chimpanzee, and Analysis Consortium. "Initial sequence of the chimpanzee genome and comparison with the human genome." *Nature* 437.7055 (2005): 69-87.

58. Fan, Yuxin, et al. "Genomic structure and evolution of the ancestral chromosome fusion site in 2q13–2q14. 1 and paralogous regions on other human chromosomes." *Genome research* 12.11 (2002): 1651-1662.

59. Ibid.

60. Yunis, Jorge J., and Ora Prakash. "The origin of man: a chromosomal pictorial legacy." *Science* 215.4539 (1982): 1525-1530.

61. http://www.pbs.org/wgbh/evolution/library/07/3/l_073_47.html

62. Podlaha, Ondrej; and Zhang, Jianzhi (November 2010) Pseudogenes and Their Evolution. In: Encyclopedia of Life Sciences (ELS). John Wiley & Sons, Ltd: Chichester. DOI: 10.1002/9780470015902.a0005118.pub2

63. Harrow, Jennifer, et al. "GENCODE: the reference human genome annotation for The ENCODE Project." *Genome research* 22.9 (2012): 1760-1774.

64. Podlaha, Ondrej; and Zhang, Jianzhi (November 2010) Pseudogenes and Their Evolution. In: Encyclopedia of Life Sciences (ELS). John Wiley & Sons, Ltd: Chichester. DOI: 10.1002/9780470015902.a0005118.pub2

65. Pei, Baikang, et al. "The GENCODE pseudogene resource." *Genome Biol* 13.9 (2012): R51.

66. Ibid.

67. Brawand, David, Walter Wahli, and Henrik Kaessmann. "Loss of egg yolk genes in mammals and the origin of lactation and placentation." *PLoS Biol* 6.3 (2008): e63.

68. Zambidis, Elias T., et al. "Hematopoietic differentiation of human embryonic stem cells progresses through sequential hematoendothelial, primitive, and definitive stages resembling human yolk sac development." *Blood* 106.3 (2005): 860-870.

69. Freyer C, Zeller U, Renfree MB (2007) Placental function in two distantly related marsupials. Placenta 28: 249–257.

70. Hughes RL, Hall LS (1998) Early development and embryology of the platypus. Philos Trans R Soc Lond B Biol Sci 353: 1101–1114.

71. Brawand, David, Walter Wahli, and Henrik Kaessmann. "Loss of egg yolk genes in mammals and the origin of lactation and placentation." *PLoS Biol* 6.3 (2008): e63.

72. Ibid.

73. Ibid.

74. Drouin, Guy, Jean-Rémi Godin, and Benoît Pagé. "The genetics of vitamin C loss in vertebrates." *Current genomics* 12.5 (2011): 371.

75. Hillier, LaDeana W., et al. "Sequence and comparative analysis of the chicken genome provide unique perspectives on vertebrate evolution." *Nature* 432.7018 (2004): 695-716.

76. Glusman, Gustavo, et al. "The complete human olfactory subgenome." *Genome research* 11.5 (2001): 685-702.

77. Wang, Wei, et al. "Activity of α-and θ-defensins against primary isolates of HIV-1." *The Journal of Immunology* 173.1 (2004): 515-520.

78. Kawaguchi, H., C. O'hUigin, and J. Klein. "Evolutionary origin of mutations in the primate cytochrome P450c21 gene." *American journal of human genetics* 50.4 (1992): 766.

79. Ibid; note: humans also have 2 additional mutations in this pseudogene

80. Nachman, Michael W., and Susan L. Crowell. "Estimate of the mutation rate per nucleotide in humans." *Genetics* 156.1 (2000): 297-304.

81. Chen, Feng-Chi, and Wen-Hsiung Li. "Genomic divergences between humans and other hominoids and the effective population size of the common ancestor of humans and chimpanzees." *The American Journal of Human Genetics* 68.2 (2001): 444-456.

82. Gilad, Yoav, et al. "Human specific loss of olfactory receptor genes." *Proceedings of the National Academy of Sciences* 100.6 (2003): 3324-3327.

83. Ibid.

84. Polavarapu, Nalini, Nathan J. Bowen, and John F. McDonald. "Identification, characterization and comparative genomics of chimpanzee endogenous retroviruses." *Genome biology* 7.6 (2006): R51.

85. Ibid.

86. Lander, Eric S., et al. "Initial sequencing and analysis of the human genome." *Nature* 409.6822 (2001): 860-921.

87. Sequencing, The Chimpanzee, and Analysis Consortium. "Initial sequence of the chimpanzee genome and comparison with the human genome." *Nature* 437.7055 (2005): 69-87.

88. Polavarapu, Nalini, Nathan J. Bowen, and John F. McDonald. "Identification, characterization and comparative genomics of chimpanzee endogenous retroviruses." *Genome biology* 7.6 (2006): R51.

89. Johnson, Welkin E., and John M. Coffin. "Constructing primate phylogenies from ancient retrovirus sequences." *Proceedings of the National Academy of Sciences* 96.18 (1999): 10254-10260.

90. Kurdyukov, Sergey G., et al. "Full-sized HERV-K (HML-2) human endogenous retroviral LTR sequences on human chromosome 21: map locations and evolutionary history." *Gene* 273.1 (2001): 51-61.

91. Lebedev, Yuri B., et al. "Differences in HERV-K LTR insertions in orthologous loci of humans and great apes." *Gene* 247.1 (2000): 265-277.

92. Johnson, Welkin E., and John M. Coffin. "Constructing primate phylogenies from

ancient retrovirus sequences." *Proceedings of the National Academy of Sciences* 96.18 (1999): 10254-10260.

93. Wang, Ting, et al. "Species-specific endogenous retroviruses shape the transcriptional network of the human tumor suppressor protein p53."*Proceedings of the National Academy of Sciences* 104.47 (2007): 18613-18618.

94. Belshaw, Robert, et al. "Long-term reinfection of the human genome by endogenous retroviruses." *Proceedings of the National Academy of Sciences of the United States of America* 101.14 (2004): 4894-4899.

95. Serrao, Erik, et al. "Key determinants of target DNA recognition by retroviral intasomes." *Retrovirology* 12.1 (2015): 1.

96. Desfarges, Sébastien, and Angela Ciuffi. "Retroviral integration site selection." *Viruses* 2.1 (2010): 111-130.

97. Ibid.

98. Serrao, Erik, et al. "Key determinants of target DNA recognition by retroviral intasomes." *Retrovirology* 12.1 (2015): 1.

99. Ibid.

100. Desfarges, Sébastien, and Angela Ciuffi. "Retroviral integration site selection." *Viruses* 2.1 (2010): 111-130.

101. Ibid.

102. Serrao, Erik, et al. "Key determinants of target DNA recognition by retroviral intasomes." *Retrovirology* 12.1 (2015): 1.

103. Johnson, Welkin E., and John M. Coffin. "Constructing primate phylogenies from ancient retrovirus sequences." *Proceedings of the National Academy of Sciences* 96.18 (1999): 10254-10260.

CHAPTER TEN: LEFT BEHIND

1.   Spaulding, Michelle, Maureen A. O'Leary, and John Gatesy. "Relationships of Cetacea (Artiodactyla) among mammals: increased taxon sampling alters interpretations of key fossils and character evolution." *Plos one* 4.9 (2009): e7062.

2.   Shimamura, Mitsuru, et al. "Molecular evidence from retroposons that whales form a clade within even-toed ungulates." *Nature* 388.6643 (1997): 666-670.

3.   Arnason, Ulfur, et al. "The mitochondrial genome of the sperm whale and a new molecular reference for estimating eutherian divergence dates." *Journal of Molecular Evolution* 50.6 (2000): 569-578).

4.   Yim, Hyung-Soon, et al. "Minke whale genome and aquatic adaptation in cetaceans." *Nature genetics* 46.1 (2014): 88-92.

5.   Hall, Brian K. "Developmental mechanisms underlying the formation of atavisms." *Biological Reviews* 59.1 (1984): 89-122.

6.   Simões-Lopes, Paulo C., and Carolina S. Gutstein. "Notes on the anatomy, positioning and homology of the pelvic bones in small cetaceans (Cetacea, Delphinidae, Pontoporiidae)." *Latin American Journal of Aquatic Mammals*3.2 (2004): 157-162.

7.   http://bergenmuseum.uib.no/fagsider/osteologi/hvaler/e_bekken.htm

8.   Bejder, Lars, and Brian K. Hall. "Limbs in whales and limblessness in other vertebrates: mechanisms of evolutionary and developmental transformation and loss." *Evolution & development* 4.6 (2002): 445-458.

9.   Cohn, Martin J., and Cheryll Tickle. "Developmental basis of limblessness and axial patterning in snakes." *Nature* 399.6735 (1999): 474-479.

10. Nehm, Ross H., and Irvin Sam Schonfeld. "The future of natural selection knowledge measurement: a reply to Anderson et al.(2010)." *Journal of Research in Science Teaching* 47.3 (2010): 358-362.

11. Elipot, Yannick, et al. "Evolutionary shift from fighting to foraging in blind cavefish through changes in the serotonin network." *Current Biology* 23.1 (2013): 1-10.

12. Is Mutation a Factor in the Production of Vestigial Wings among Insects? Charles T.

Brues Journal of the New York Entomological Society Vol. 16, No. 1 (Mar., 1908), 45-52.

13. Le Duc, Diana, et al. "Kiwi genome provides insights into evolution of a nocturnal lifestyle." *Genome biology* 16.1 (2015): 1-15.

14. Torkamani, N., et al. "Destruction of the arrector pili muscle and fat infiltration in androgenic alopecia." *British Journal of Dermatology* 170.6 (2014): 1291-1298.

15. Reflexes and other motor activities in newborn infants: a report of 125 cases as a preliminary study of infant behavior" published in the *Bull. Neurol. Inst. New York*, 1932, Vol. 2, 1–56.

16. Friedman, Jay W. "The prophylactic extraction of third molars: a public health hazard." *American journal of public health* 97.9 (2007): 1554.

17. Rozkovcová, E; Marková, M; Dolejší, J (1999). "Studies on agenesis of third molars amongst populations of different origin". *Sbornik lekarsky* 100 (2): 71–84.

18. Newcomb, R. D. et al. 1997. A single amino acid substitution converts a carboxylesterase to an organophosporus hydrolase and confers insecticide resistance on a blowfly. *Proceedings of the National Academy of Science USA* 94: 7464-7468.

19. Hall, Brian; Halgrimmson, Benedikt. *Strickberger's Evolution*. Jones and Bartlett Publishers, 2007.

20. Conrad, Donald F., et al. "Variation in genome-wide mutation rates within and between human families."*Nature* 201.1 (2011).

21. Xing, Jinchuan, et al. "Mobile elements create structural variation: analysis of a complete human genome."*Genome research* 19.9 (2009): 1516-1526.

22. Keeling, Patrick J., and Jeffrey D. Palmer. "Horizontal gene transfer in eukaryotic evolution." *Nature Reviews Genetics* 9.8 (2008): 605-618.

23. Peeters, Nemo, and Ian Small. "Dual targeting to mitochondria and chloroplasts." *Biochimica et Biophysica Acta (BBA)-Molecular Cell Research* 1541.1 (2001): 54-63.

24. Kent, W. James, et al. "Evolution's cauldron: duplication, deletion, and rearrangement in the mouse and human genomes." *Proceedings of the National Academy of Sciences* 100.20 (2003): 11484-11489.

25. Otto, Sarah P. "The evolutionary consequences of polyploidy." *Cell* 131.3 (2007): 452-462.

26. Desai, Michael M., and Daniel S. Fisher. "Beneficial mutation–selection balance and the effect of linkage on positive selection." *Genetics* 176.3 (2007): 1759-1798.

27. Ibid.

28. Ibid.

29. Perfeito, Lília, et al. "Adaptive mutations in bacteria: high rate and small effects." *Science* 317.5839 (2007): 813-815.

30. Newcomb, R. D. et al. 1997. A single amino acid substitution converts a carboxylesterase to an organophosporus hydrolase and confers insecticide resistance on a blowfly. *Proceedings of the National Academy of Science USA* 94: 7464-7468.

31. Gerrish, Philip J., and Richard E. Lenski. "The fate of competing beneficial mutations in an asexual population." *Genetica* 102 (1998): 127-144.

32. Ferenci, T. "The spread of a beneficial mutation in experimental bacterial populations: the influence of the environment and genotype on the fixation of rpoS mutations." *Heredity* 100.5 (2008): 446-452.

33. Ibid.

34. Enard, Wolfgang, et al. "Molecular evolution of FOXP2, a gene involved in speech and language." *Nature* 418.6900 (2002): 869-872.

35. Preuss, Todd M. "Human brain evolution: from gene discovery to phenotype discovery." *Proceedings of the National Academy of Sciences* 109.Supplement 1 (2012): 10709-10716.

36. Beja-Pereira, Albano, et al. "Gene-culture coevolution between cattle milk protein genes and human lactase genes."*Nature genetics* 35.4 (2003): 311-313.

37. Ibid.

38. Arrese, Catherine A., et al. "Cone topography and spectral sensitivity in two potentially trichromatic marsupials, the quokka (Setonix brachyurus) and quenda (Isoodon obesulus)." *Proceedings of the Royal Society of London B: Biological Sciences* 272.1565 (2005): 791-796.

39. Surridge, Alison K., Daniel Osorio, and Nicholas I. Mundy. "Evolution and selection of trichromatic vision in primates." *Trends in Ecology & Evolution*18.4 (2003): 198-205.

40. Tomić, Nenad, and Victor Benno Meyer-Rochow. "Atavisms: medical, genetic, and evolutionary implications." *Perspectives in biology and medicine* 54.3 (2011): 332-353.

41. Zhang, Guojie, et al. "Comparative genomics reveals insights into avian genome evolution and adaptation." *Science* 346.6215 (2014): 1311-1320.

42. Harris, Matthew P., et al. "The development of archosaurian first-generation teeth in a chicken mutant." *Current Biology* 16.4 (2006): 371-377.

43. Tyson, R.; Graham, J. P.; Colahan, P. T.; Berry, C. R. (2004). "Skeletal atavism in a miniature horse".*Veterinary radiology & ultrasound: the official journal of the American College of Veterinary Radiology and the International Veterinary Radiology Association* 45 (4): 315–317.

44. Hall, Brian K. "Developmental mechanisms underlying the formation of atavisms." *Biological Reviews* 59.1 (1984): 89-122.

45. Dao, Anh H., and Martin G. Netsky. "Human tails and pseudotails." *Human pathology* 15.5 (1984): 449-453.

46. Shad, Jimmy, and Rakesh Biswas. "An infant with caudal appendage." *BMJ case reports* 2012 (2012): bcr1120115160.

47. Bar-Maor, J. A., K. M. Kesner, and J. K. Kaftori. "Human tails." *Journal of Bone & Joint Surgery, British Volume* 62.4 (1980): 508-510

48. Ibid.

49. Parsons, Robert W. "Human tails."*Plastic and Reconstructive Surgery* 25.6 (1960): 618-621.

50. Shad, Jimmy, and Rakesh Biswas. "An infant with caudal appendage." *BMJ case reports* 2012 (2012): bcr1120115160.

51. Dao, Anh H., and Martin G. Netsky. "Human tails and pseudotails." *Human pathology* 15.5 (1984): 449-453.

52. Bejder, Lars, and Brian K. Hall. "Limbs in whales and limblessness in other vertebrates: mechanisms of evolutionary and developmental transformation and loss."*Evolution & development* 4.6 (2002): 445-458.

53. Hall, Brian K. "Developmental mechanisms underlying the formation of atavisms." *Biological Reviews* 59.1 (1984): 89-122.

54. Gingerich, Philip D., B. Holly Smith, and Elwyn L. Simons. "Hind limbs of Eocene Basilosaurus: evidence of feet in whales."*Science* 249.13 (1990): 154-7.

55. Gingerich, Philip D., et al. "Origin of whales from early artiodactyls: hands and feet of Eocene Protocetidae from Pakistan."*Science* 293.5538 (2001): 2239-2242.

56. Bejder, Lars, and Brian K. Hall. "Limbs in whales and limblessness in other vertebrates: mechanisms of evolutionary and developmental transformation and loss."*Evolution & developmentn* 4.6 (2002): 445-458.

57. Hall, Brian K. "Developmental mechanisms underlying the formation of atavisms." *Biological Reviews* 59.1 (1984): 89-122.

58. Andrews, Roy Chapman. *A remarkable case of external hind limbs in a humpback whale*. By order of the Trustees of The American Museum of Natural History, 1921.

59. Ibid.

60. Ohsumi, Seiji, and Hidehiro Kato. "A bottlenose dolphin (Tursiops truncatus) with fin-shaped hind appendages." *Marine mammal science* 24.3 (2008): 743-745.

61. Ibid.

CHAPTER TWELVE: FOSSILS

1. Hall, Brian; Halgrimmson, Benedikt. *Strickberger's Evolution*. Jones and Bartlett

Publishers, 2007.

2.   Allwood, Abigail C., et al. "Stromatolite reef from the Early Archaean era of Australia." *Nature* 441.7094 (2006): 714-718.

3.   Barfod, Gry H., et al. "New Lu–Hf and Pb–Pb age constraints on the earliest animal fossils."*Earth and Planetary Science Letters* 201.1 (2002): 203-212.

4.   Brown, Kathryn S., 1999. Deep Green rewrites evolutionary history of plants. *Science* 285: 990-991.

5.   Lawton-Rauh A.; Alvarez-Buylla, ER; Purugganan, MD (2000). "Molecular evolution of flower development". *Trends in Ecology and Evolution* 15 (4): 144–149.

6.   http://creation.com/Archaeopteryx

7.   http://www.icr.org/fossils-stasis

8.   Prothero, Donald. "What missing link?." *New Scientist* 197.2645 (2008): 35-41. http://www.donaldprothero.com/files/92313517.pdf

9.   Ahlberg, Per Erik, and Jennifer A. Clack. "Palaeontology: a firm step from water to land." *Nature* 440.7085 (2006): 747-749.

10.   MacFadden, Bruce J. "Fossil horses—evidence for evolution." *Science*307.5716 (2005): 1728-1730.

11.   Gingerich, Philip D., et al. "Origin of whales from early artiodactyls: hands and feet of Eocene Protocetidae from Pakistan." *Science* 293.5538 (2001): 2239-2242.

12.   Norell, M. A. and J. A. Clarke. 2001. Fossil that fills a critical gap in avian evolution. *Nature* 409: 181-184.

13.   White, Tim D., et al. "Ardipithecus ramidus and the paleobiology of early hominids." *science* 326.5949 (2009): 64-86.

14.   Ahlberg, Per Erik, and Jennifer A. Clack. "Palaeontology: a firm step from water to land." *Nature* 440.7085 (2006): 747-749.

15.   Clack, Jennifer A. "The Fish–Tetrapod Transition: New Fossils and Interpretations." *Evolution: Education and Outreach* 2.2 (2009): 213-223.

16.   Brazeau, M.D.; Ahlberg, P.E. (2006). "Tetrapod-like middle ear architecture in a Devonian fish". *Nature* 439 (7074): 318–321.

17.   Carroll, R. (1995). "Between fish and amphibians".*Nature* 373 (6513): 389–390.

18.   Shubin, Neil H., Edward B. Daeschler, and Farish A. Jenkins. "The pectoral fin of Tiktaalik roseae and the origin of the tetrapod limb." *Nature* 440.7085 (2006): 764-771.

19.   Coates, M. I. and J. A. Clack, 1991. Fish-like gills and breathing in the earliest known tetrapod. *Nature* 352: 234-236.

20.   Ibid.

21.   Ahlberg, Per Erik, Jennifer A. Clack, and Henning Blom. "The axial skeleton of the Devonian tetrapod Ichthyostega." *Nature* 437.7055 (2005): 137-140.

22.   Coates, M. I., and J. A. Clack. "Polydactyly in the earliest known tetrapod limbs." *Nature* 347.6288 (1990): 66-69.

23.   Ahlberg, Per Erik, Jennifer A. Clack, and Henning Blom. "The axial skeleton of the Devonian tetrapod Ichthyostega." *Nature* 437.7055 (2005): 137-140.

24.   MacFadden, Bruce J. *Fossil horses: systematics, paleobiology, and evolution of the family Equidae.* Cambridge University Press, 1994

25.   MacFadden, Bruce J. "Fossil horses—evidence for evolution." *Science* 307.5716 (2005): 1728-1730.

26.   Groves, Colin P., and Oliver A. Ryder. "Systematics and phylogeny of the horse." *The genetics of the horse* (2000): 1-24.

27.   Prothero, Donald R., and Robert M. Schoch, eds.*The evolution of perissodactyls.* New York: Clarendon Press, 1989.

28.   Vaughan, Terry A., James M. Ryan, and Nicholas J. Czaplewski.*Mammalogy.* Jones & Bartlett Publishers, 2013.

29.   http://www.flmnh.ufl.edu/vertpaleo/fhc/firstCM.htm

30.   http://chem.tufts.edu/science/evolution/horseevolution.htm

31. Hall, Brian; Halgrimmson, Benedikt. *Strickberger's Evolution*. Jones and Bartlett Publishers, 2007.

32. Vaughan, Terry A., James M. Ryan, and Nicholas J. Czaplewski.*Mammalogy*. Jones & Bartlett Publishers, 2013.

33. Ibid.

34. MacFadden, Bruce J. "Fossil horses—evidence for evolution." *Science* 307.5716 (2005): 1728-1730.

35. Vaughan, Terry A., James M. Ryan, and Nicholas J. Czaplewski.*Mammalogy*. Jones & Bartlett Publishers, 2013.

36. http://www.flmnh.ufl.edu/vertpaleo/fhc/firstCM.htm

37. Ibid.

38. http://chem.tufts.edu/science/evolution/horseevolution.htm

39. Ibid.

40. http://www.flmnh.ufl.edu/vertpaleo/fhc/firstCM.htm

41. Woodburne, Michael O. "Chapter 16: Craniodental Analysis of Merychippus insignis and Cormohipparion goorisi (Mammalia, Equidae), Barstovian, North America."*Bulletin of the American Museum of Natural History* (2003): 397-468.

42. http://chem.tufts.edu/science/evolution/horseevolution.htm

43. http://www.flmnh.ufl.edu/vertpaleo/fhc/firstCM.htm

44. fossilworks.org

45. Gingerich, Philip D., B. Holly Smith, and Elwyn L. Simons. "Hind limbs of Eocene Basilosaurus: evidence of feet in whales."*Science* 249.13 (1990): 154-7.

46. Gingerich, Philip D., et al. "Origin of whales from early artiodactyls: hands and feet of Eocene Protocetidae from Pakistan."*Science* 293.5538 (2001): 2239-2242.

47. Bejder, Lars, and Brian K. Hall. "Limbs in whales and limblessness in other vertebrates: mechanisms of evolutionary and developmental transformation and loss."*Evolution & developmentn* 4.6 (2002): 445-458.

48. Gingerich, Philip D., and Donald E. Russell. *Pakicetus inachus, a new archaeocete (Mammalia, Cetacea) from the early-middle Eocene Kuldana Formation of Kohat (Pakistan)*. No. 56 UNI. Museum of Paleontology, University of Michigan, 1981.

49. Thewissen, J.G.M.; Hussain, S.T. (1993). "Origin Of Underwater Hearing In Whales". *Nature* 361 (6411): 444–445.

50. Thewissen, Johannes GM, et al. "Skeletons of terrestrial cetaceans and the relationship of whales to artiodactyls." *Nature* 413.6853 (2001): 277-281.

51. Sutera, Raymond. "The origin of whales and the power of independent evidence." *Natl Cent Sci Educ* 20.5 (2000): 33-41.

52. Newsome, Seth D., Mark T. Clementz, and Paul L. Koch. "Using stable isotope biogeochemistry to study marine mammal ecology."*Marine Mammal Science* 26.3 (2010): 509-572.

53. http://evolution.berkeley.edu/evolibrary/article/evograms_03

54. Sutera, Raymond. "The origin of whales and the power of independent evidence." *Natl Cent Sci Educ* 20.5 (2000): 33-41.

55. Bejder, Lars, and Brian K. Hall. "Limbs in whales and limblessness in other vertebrates: mechanisms of evolutionary and developmental transformation and loss."*Evolution & development* 4.6 (2002): 445-458.

56. Sutera, Raymond. "The origin of whales and the power of independent evidence." *Natl Cent Sci Educ* 20.5 (2000): 33-41.

57. Bejder, Lars, and Brian K. Hall. "Limbs in whales and limblessness in other vertebrates: mechanisms of evolutionary and developmental transformation and loss."*Evolution & development* 4.6 (2002): 445-458.

58. Berta, Annalisa, Eric G. Ekdale, and Ted W. Cranford. "Review of the cetacean nose: form, function, and evolution." *The Anatomical Record*297.11 (2014): 2205-2215.

59. Gingerich, Philip D., et al. "Origin of whales from early artiodactyls: hands and feet of

Eocene Protocetidae from Pakistan."*Science* 293.5538 (2001): 2239-2242.

60. Ibid.

61. Graur, Dan, and Desmond G. Higgins. "Molecular evidence for the inclusion of cetaceans within the order Artiodactyla."*Molecular Biology and Evolution*11.3 (1994): 357-364.

62. Shimamura, Mitsuru, et al. "Molecular evidence from retroposons that whales form a clade within even-toed ungulates." *Nature* 388.6643 (1997): 666-670.

63. Gingerich, Philip D., et al. "Origin of whales from early artiodactyls: hands and feet of Eocene Protocetidae from Pakistan."*Science* 293.5538 (2001): 2239-2242.

64. Spaulding, Michelle, Maureen A. O'Leary, and John Gatesy. "Relationships of Cetacea (Artiodactyla) among mammals: increased taxon sampling alters interpretations of key fossils and character evolution." *Plos one* 4.9 (2009): e7062.

65. Yim, Hyung-Soon, et al. "Minke whale genome and aquatic adaptation in cetaceans." *Nature genetics* 46.1 (2014): 88-92.

66. Arnason, Ulfur, et al. "The mitochondrial genome of the sperm whale and a new molecular reference for estimating eutherian divergence dates." *Journal of Molecular Evolution* 50.6 (2000): 569-578.

67. Lee, Michael SY, and Trevor H. Worthy. "Likelihood reinstates Archaeopteryx as a primitive bird." *Biology letters* 8.2 (2012): 299-303.

68. Foth, Christian, Helmut Tischlinger, and Oliver WM Rauhut. "New specimen of Archaeopteryx provides insights into the evolution of pennaceous feathers." *Nature* 511.7507 (2014): 79-82.

69. http://www.ucmp.berkeley.edu/diapsids/birds/archaeopteryx.html

70. Gill, Frank B. *Ornithology*. W. H. Freeman, 2006.

71. Ibid.

72. Gauthier, Jacques. "Saurischian monophyly and the origin of birds." *Memoirs of the California Academy of Sciences* 8.1-55 (1986).

73. Hou, Lianhai, et al. "Early adaptive radiation of birds: evidence from fossils from northeastern China." *Science* 274.5290 (1996): 1164-1167.

74. http://www.ucmp.berkeley.edu/diapsids/birds/archaeopteryx.html

75. Gregg, K., et al. "A comparison of genomic coding sequences for feather and scale keratins: structural and evolutionary implications." *The EMBO journal* 3.1 (1984): 175.

76. http://tasc-creationscience.org/content/what-was-archaeopteryx

77. https://www.icr.org/article/321/

78. Alonso, Patricio Domínguez, et al. "The avian nature of the brain and inner ear of Archaeopteryx." *Nature* 430.7000 (2004): 666-669.

79. Ibid.

80. Gill, Frank B. *Ornithology*. W. H. Freeman, 2006.

81. Norell, M. A. and J. A. Clarke. 2001. Fossil that fills a critical gap in avian evolution. *Nature* 409: 181-184.

82. Chiappe, L. M. 2002. Basal bird phylogeny. In: Chiappe and Witmer, pp. 448-472.

83. Langergraber, Kevin E., et al. "Generation times in wild chimpanzees and gorillas suggest earlier divergence times in great ape and human evolution."*Proceedings of the National Academy of Sciences* 109.39 (2012): 15716-15721.

84. fossilworks.org

85. http://humanorigins.si.edu/evidence/human-fossils

86. Lovejoy, C. Owen. "Evolution of human walking." *Sci Am* 259.5 (1988): 118-25.

87. Russo, Gabrielle A., and E. Christopher Kirk. "Foramen magnum position in bipedal mammals." *Journal of human evolution* 65.5 (2013): 656-670.

88. Ibid.

89. Pontzer, Herman. "Overview of hominin evolution."*Nature Education Knowledge* 3.10 (2012): 8.

90. Langergraber, Kevin E., et al. "Generation times in wild chimpanzees and gorillas

suggest earlier divergence times in great ape and human evolution." *Proceedings of the National Academy of Sciences* 109.39 (2012): 15716-15721.

91. Zollikofer, Christoph PE, et al. "Virtual cranial reconstruction of Sahelanthropus tchadensis." *Nature* 434.7034 (2005): 755-759.

92. Su, D. F. The Earliest Hominins: Sahelanthropis, Orrorin, and Ardipithecus (2013) *Nature Education Knowledge* 4(4):11.

93. Barton, N. H., et al. *Evolution.* Cold Spring Harbor Laboratory Press, 2007, 731.

94. Brunet, Michel, et al. "New material of the earliest hominid from the Upper Miocene of Chad." *Nature* 434.7034 (2005): 752-755.

95. Zollikofer, Christoph PE, et al. "Virtual cranial reconstruction of Sahelanthropus tchadensis." *Nature* 434.7034 (2005): 755-759.

96. Su, D. F. The Earliest Hominins: Sahelanthropis, Orrorin, and Ardipithecus (2013) *Nature Education Knowledge* 4(4):11.

97. Pickford, Martin, et al. "Bipedalism in Orrorin tugenensis revealed by its femora." *Comptes Rendus Palevol* 1.4 (2002): 191-203.

98. Pontzer, Herman. "Overview of hominin evolution." *Nature Education Knowledge* 3.10 (2012): 8.

99. White, Tim D., et al. "Ardipithecus ramidus and the paleobiology of early hominids." *science* 326.5949 (2009): 64-86.

100. Ibid.

101. Ibid.

102. Ibid.

103. Ibid.

104. Ward, Carol V. "Interpreting the posture and locomotion of Australopithecus afarensis: where do we stand?." *American journal of physical anthropology* 119.S35 (2002): 185-215.

105. Harcourt-Smith, William EH, and Leslie C. Aiello. "Fossils, feet and the evolution of human bipedal locomotion." *Journal of Anatomy* 204.5 (2004): 403-416.

106. Agnew, Neville, and Martha Demas. "Preserving the Laetoli footprints." *Scientific American* 279.3 (1998): 26-37.

107. Pontzer, Herman. "Overview of hominin evolution." *Nature Education Knowledge* 3.10 (2012): 8.

108. De Miguel, Carmen, and Maciej Henneberg. "Variation in hominid brain size: how much is due to method?." *HOMO-Journal of Comparative Human Biology* 52.1 (2001): 3-58.

109. Pontzer, Herman. "Overview of hominin evolution." *Nature Education Knowledge* 3.10 (2012): 8.

110. Hall, Brian; Halgrimmson, Benedikt. *Strickberger's Evolution.* Jones and Bartlett Publishers, 2007.

111. Ibid.

112. Tobias, Phillip V. "The brain of Homo habilis: A new level of organization in cerebral evolution." *Journal of Human Evolution* 16.7 (1987): 741-761.

113. Johanson, Donald C., et al. "New partial skeleton of Homo habilis from Olduvai Gorge, Tanzania." *Nature* 327.6119 (1987): 205-209.

114. Pontzer, Herman. "Overview of hominin evolution." *Nature Education Knowledge* 3.10 (2012): 8.

115. Antón, Susan C. "Natural history of Homo erectus." *American journal of physical anthropology* 122.S37 (2003): 126-170.

116. Ibid.

117. Leakey, Richard E., and Roger Lewin. *Origins: What new discoveries reveal about the emergence of our species and its possible future.* Macdonald and Jane's, 1977.

118. Franciscus, Robert G., and Erik Trinkaus. "Nasal morphology and the emergence of Homo erectus." *American Journal of Physical Anthropology* 75.4 (1988): 517-527.

119. Pontzer, Herman. "Overview of hominin evolution." *Nature Education Knowledge* 3.10 (2012): 8.

120. Leakey, Richard E., and Roger Lewin. *Origins: What new discoveries reveal about the emergence of our species and its possible future.* Macdonald and Jane's, 1977.

121. White, Tim D., et al. "Pleistocene homo sapiens from middle awash, ethiopia." *Nature* 423.6941 (2003): 742-747.

122. Henneberg, Maciej. "Decrease of human skull size in the Holocene." *Human biology* (1988): 395-405.

123. http://humanorigins.si.edu/evidence/dating

124. http://www.talkorigins.org/faqs/homs/compare.html

125. Friedman, Matt, and Michael I. Coates. "A newly recognized fossil coelacanth highlights the early morphological diversification of the clade."*Proceedings of the Royal Society of London B: Biological Sciences*273.1583 (2006): 245-250.

126. Friedman, Matt, Michael I. Coates, and Philip Anderson. "First discovery of a primitive coelacanth fin fills a major gap in the evolution of lobed fins and limbs." *Evolution & development* 9.4 (2007): 329-337.

127. Valentine, James W., David Jablonski, and Douglas H. Erwin. "Fossils, molecules and embryos: new perspectives on the Cambrian explosion."*Development* 126.5 (1999): 851-859.

128. El Albani, Abderrazak, et al. "Large colonial organisms with coordinated growth in oxygenated environments 2.1 |thinsp| Gyr ago." *Nature* 466.7302 (2010): 100-104.

129. Han, Tsu-Ming, and Bruce Runnegar. "Megascopic eukaryotic algae from the 2.1-billion-year-old Negaunee Iron-Formation, Michigan." *Science* 257.5067 (1992): 232-235.

130. Valentine, James W., David Jablonski, and Douglas H. Erwin. "Fossils, molecules and embryos: new perspectives on the Cambrian explosion."*Development* 126.5 (1999): 851-859.

131. Meert, Joseph G., and Bruce S. Lieberman. "The Neoproterozoic assembly of Gondwana and its relationship to the Ediacaran–Cambrian radiation."*Gondwana Research* 14.1 (2008): 5-21.

132. Seilacher, Adolf, Dmitri Grazhdankin, and Anton Legouta. "Ediacaran biota: the dawn of animal life in the shadow of giant protists." *Paleontological Research* 7.1 (2003): 43-54.

133. Ibid.

134. Wang, D. Y.-C., S. Kumar and S. B. Hedges, 1999. Divergence time estimates for the early history of animal phyla and the origin of plants, animals and fungi. Proceedings of the Royal Society of London, Series B, Biological Sciences 266: 163-71.

135. Peterson, Kevin J., et al. "The Ediacaran emergence of bilaterians: congruence between the genetic and the geological fossil records."*Philosophical Transactions of the Royal Society of London B: Biological Sciences* 363.1496 (2008): 1435-1443.

136. Li, Chia-Wei, Jun-Yuan Chen, and Tzu-En Hua. "Precambrian sponges with cellular structures." *Science* 279.5352 (1998): 879-882

137. Meert, Joseph G., and Bruce S. Lieberman. "The Neoproterozoic assembly of Gondwana and its relationship to the Ediacaran–Cambrian radiation."*Gondwana Research* 14.1 (2008): 5-21.

138. Valentine, James W., David Jablonski, and Douglas H. Erwin. "Fossils, molecules and embryos: new perspectives on the Cambrian explosion."*Development* 126.5 (1999): 851-859.

139. Narbonne, Guy M. "The Ediacara biota: Neoproterozoic origin of animals and their ecosystems." Annu. Rev. Earth Planet. Sci. 33 (2005): 421-442.

140. Ibid.

141. Narbonne, Guy M., and James G. Gehling. "Life after snowball: the oldest complex Ediacaran fossils." *Geology* 31.1 (2003): 27-30.

142. Taylor, P.D.; Berning, B.; Wilson, M.A. (2013). "Reinterpretation of the Cambrian 'bryozoan'*Pywackia* as an octocoral". *Journal of Paleontology* 87(6): 984–990.

143. Valentine, James W. *On the origin of phyla.* University of Chicago Press, 2004.

144. Note that some classification schemes have only 10 phyla of plants.

145. Wellman, Charles H.; Osterloff, Peter L.; Mohiuddin, Uzma (2003). "Fragments of the earliest land plants". Nature 425: 282–285.

146. Brown, Kathryn S., 1999. Deep Green rewrites evolutionary history of plants. Science 285: 990-991.

147. Lawton-Rauh A.; Alvarez-Buylla, ER; Purugganan, MD (2000). "Molecular evolution of flower development". *Trends in Ecology and Evolution* 15 (4): 144–149.

148. Smith, Martin R. "Cord-forming Palaeozoic fungi in terrestrial assemblages."*Botanical Journal of the Linnean Society* (2016).

149. Hall, Brian; Halgrimmson, Benedikt. *Strickberger's Evolution.* Jones and Bartlett Publishers, 2007.

150. Valentine, James W., David Jablonski, and Douglas H. Erwin. "Fossils, molecules and embryos: new perspectives on the Cambrian explosion."*Development* 126.5 (1999): 851-859.

151. Budd, Graham E. "At the origin of animals: the revolutionary Cambrian fossil record." *Current genomics* 14.6 (2013): 344.

152. Erwin, Douglas H., et al. "The Cambrian conundrum: early divergence and later ecological success in the early history of animals." *Science* 334.6059 (2011): 1091-1097.

153. Philippe, Hervé, Anne Chenuil, and André Adoutte. "Can the Cambrian explosion be inferred through molecular phylogeny?." *Development*1994.Supplement (1994): 15-25.

154. Kouchinsky, A., Bengtson, S., Runnegar, B. N., Skovsted, C. B., Steiner, M. & Vendrasco, M. J. 2012. Chronology of early Cambrian biomineralization. Geological Magazine, 149, 221–251.

155. Budd, Graham E. "At the origin of animals: the revolutionary Cambrian fossil record." *Current genomics* 14.6 (2013): 344.

156. Abouheif, Ehab, Rafael Zardoya, and Axel Meyer. "Limitations of metazoan 18S rRNA sequence data: implications for reconstructing a phylogeny of the animal kingdom and inferring the reality of the Cambrian explosion." *Journal of Molecular Evolution* 47.4 (1998): 394-405.

157. Valentine, James W., David Jablonski, and Douglas H. Erwin. "Fossils, molecules and embryos: new perspectives on the Cambrian explosion."*Development* 126.5 (1999): 851-859.

158. Goodman, Corey S., and Bridget C. Coughlin. "The evolution of evo-devo biology."*Proceedings of the National Academy of Sciences* 97.9 (2000): 4424-4425.

159. Morris, Simon Conway. "The Cambrian "explosion": slow-fuse or megatonnage?." *Proceedings of the National Academy of Sciences* 97.9 (2000): 4426-4429.

160. Liu, Jianni, et al. "A large xenusiid lobopod with complex appendages from the Lower Cambrian Chengjiang Lagerstatte." Ac-ta Palaeontologica Polonica51.2 (2006): 215.

161. Prothero, Donald. "What missing link?." *New Scientist* 197.2645 (2008): 35-41.

162. Hall, Brian; Halgrimmson, Benedikt. *Strickberger's Evolution.* Jones and Bartlett Publishers, 2007.

163. Singer, Ronald, ed. *Encyclopedia of Paleontology: MZ.* Fitzroy Dearborn Publishers, 1999.

164. Ibid.

165. Hall, Brian; Halgrimmson, Benedikt. *Strickberger's Evolution.* Jones and Bartlett Publishers, 2007.

166. Ibid.

167. Ayala, F. (2005). "The Structure of Evolutionary Theory" . *Theology and Science* 3 (1): 104.

168. Domning, Daryl P. "The earliest known fully quadrupedal sirenian." *Nature*413.6856 (2001): 625-627.

169. Lee, Michael SY, Gorden L. Bell, and Michael W. Caldwell. "The origin of snake feeding." *Nature* 400.6745 (1999): 655-659.

170. Rieppel, Olivier, et al. "The anatomy and relationships of Haasiophis terrasanctus, a fossil snake by well-developed hind limbs from the Mid-Cretaceous of the Middle East." *Journal of Paleontology* 77.03 (2003): 536-558.

171. Pearson, Paul Nicholas, N. J. Shackleton, and M. A. Hall. "Stable isotopic evidence for the sympatric divergence of Globigerinoides trilobus and Orbulina universa (planktonic foraminifera)." *Journal of the Geological Society* 154.2 (1997): 295-302.

172. Cronin, Thomas M., and Cynthia E. Schneider. "Climatic influences on species: evidence from the fossil record." *Trends in ecology & evolution* 5.9 (1990): 275-279.

CHAPTER TWELVE: DOUBTS MISPLACED

1. Coyne, Jerry A. *Why evolution is true.* Penguin, 2009.

2. Darwin, Charles. "The origin of species by means of natural selection: or, the preservation of favored races in the struggle for life." (2009).

3. While there are no true native members of Cactacea (true cactus) outside the Americas, there are look-alikes from the family Euphorbaceae abroad that superficially resemble cactus but are not true cactus.

4. Chuk, M. "Invasive cacti–a threat to the rangelands of Australia."*Proceedings of the 16th Biennial Conference of the Australian Rangeland Society, Perth, Bourke. Perth, Australia: Australian Rangeland Society http://www. austrangesoc. com. au/site/conference_papers. php. AccessedAugust.* Vol. 1. 2010.

5. Mittermeier, Russell A., et al. "Lemur diversity in Madagascar." *International Journal of Primatology* 29.6 (2008): 1607-1656.

6. Note that bats, seals and sea lions are placental mammals that occur in Australia and some other islands, but of course being flying and swimming creatures respectively this is not a surprise. Dingoes are not native to Australia and were brought approximately 3,500 years ago by humans (Johnson, C. N., and S. Wroe. "Causes of extinction of vertebrates during the Holocene of mainland Australia: arrival of the dingo, or human impact?." *The Holocene* 13.6 (2003): 941-948).

7. Note that native freshwater fish occasionally inhabit islands but they are diadromous species which cycle between the ocean and freshwater depending on lifecycle stage. This does not pose a challenge to evolution but on the contrary demonstrates microevolutionary change. For more information see: http://dlnr.hawaii.gov/dar/habitat/streams/native-animals/

8. John Measey, G., et al. "Freshwater paths across the ocean: molecular phylogeny of the frog Ptychadena newtoni gives insights into amphibian colonization of oceanic islands." *Journal of Biogeography* 34.1 (2007): 7-20.

9. Kraus, Fred, et al. "Eleutherodactylus Frog introduction to Hawaii."*Herpetological Review* 30.1 (1999): 21-25.

10. Fitzsimons, James, et al. *Into oblivion? The disappearing native mammals of northern Australia.* The Nature Conservancy, 2010; Note that dingoes and shrews are not native to Australia.

11. Vaughan, Terry A., James M. Ryan, and Nicholas J. Czaplewski.*Mammalogy.* Jones & Bartlett Publishers, 2013.

12. Tyndale-Biscoe, Hugh. "Life of marsupials." 2005, 55.

13. Vaughan, Terry A., James M. Ryan, and Nicholas J. Czaplewski.*Mammalogy.* Jones & Bartlett Publishers, 2013.

14. Ali, Jason R., and Jonathan C. Aitchison. "Gondwana to Asia: plate tectonics, paleogeography and the biological connectivity of the Indian sub-continent from the Middle Jurassic through latest Eocene (166–35 Ma)."*Earth-Science Reviews* 88.3 (2008): 145-166.

15. Woodburne, Michael O., and Judd A. Case. "Dispersal, vicariance, and the Late Cretaceous to early Tertiary land mammal biogeography from South America to Australia." *Journal of Mammalian Evolution* 3.2 (1996): 121-161.

16. Vaughan, Terry A., James M. Ryan, and Nicholas J. Czaplewski.*Mammalogy.* Jones & Bartlett Publishers, 2013.

17. Barnett, C. H., and J. R. Napier. "The form and mobility of the fibula in metatherian

mammals."*Journal of anatomy* 87.Pt 2 (1953): 207.

18. Woodburne, Michael O., and William J. Zinsmeister. "Fossil land mammal from Antarctica."*Science* 218.4569 (1982): 284-286.

19. Marenssi, S. A., et al. "Eocene land mammals from Seymour Island, Antarctica: palaeobiogeographical implications." *Antarctic Science* 6.01 (1994): 3-15.

20. Gerlach, Justin, Catharine Muir, and Matthew D. Richmond. "The first substantiated case of trans-oceanic tortoise dispersal."*Journal of Natural History* 40.41-43 (2006): 2403-2408.

21. Censky, Ellen J., Karim Hodge, and Judy Dudley. "Over-water dispersal of lizards due to hurricanes."*Nature* 395.6702 (1998): 556-556.

22. Dawson, William R., George A. Bartholomew, and Albert F. Bennett. "A reappraisal of the aquatic specializations of the Galapagos marine iguana (Amblyrhynchus cristatus)." *Evolution* (1977): 891-897.

23. Caccone, Adalgisa, et al. "Origin and evolutionary relationships of giant Galápagos tortoises."*Proceedings of the National Academy of Sciences* 96.23 (1999): 13223-13228.

24. Darwin, Charles. "The origin of species by means of natural selection: or, the preservation of favored races in the struggle for life." (2009).

25. Hendry, Andrew P., and Michael T. Kinnison. "Perspective: the pace of modern life: measuring rates of contemporary microevolution."*Evolution*(1999): 1637-1653.

26. Davies, Julian, and Dorothy Davies. "Origins and evolution of antibiotic resistance." *Microbiology and Molecular Biology Reviews* 74.3 (2010): 417-433.

27. Roush, Richard, and Bruce E. Tabashnik, eds. *Pesticide resistance in arthropods*. Springer Science & Business Media, 2012.

28. Romero, Alvaro, et al. "Insecticide resistance in the bed bug: a factor in the pest's sudden resurgence?."*Journal of medical entomology* 44.2 (2007): 175-178.

29. Newcomb, R. D. et al. 1997. A single amino acid substitution converts a carboxylesterase to an organophosporus hydrolase and confers insecticide resistance on a blowfly. *Proceedings of the National Academy of Science USA* 94: 7464-7468.

30. Darwin, Charles. "The origin of species by means of natural selection: or, the preservation of favored races in the struggle for life." (2009).

31. Hart, Adam G.; Stafford, Richard; Smith, Angela L.; Goodenough, Anne E. (2010). "Evidence for contemporary evolution during Darwin's lifetime". *Current Biology* 20 (3): R95.

32. Grant, B. S., and L. L. Wiseman. "Recent history of melanism in American peppered moths." *Journal of Heredity* 93.2 (2002): 86-90.

33. Lizards Rapidly Evolve After Introduction to Island, kimberly johnson natgeo apr 21 2008. http://news.nationalgeographic.com/news/2008/04/080421-lizard-evolution.html

34. Herrel, Anthony, et al. "Rapid large-scale evolutionary divergence in morphology and performance associated with exploitation of a different dietary resource." *Proceedings of the National Academy of Sciences* 105.12 (2008): 4792-4795.

35. Ibid.

36. Ibid.

37. Note that while this is essentially true, a fuller picture is somewhat more nuanced. For a more in depth discussion see: Carroll, Sean B. "The big picture."*Nature* 409.6821 (2001): 669-669; Erwin, Douglas H. "Macroevolution is more than repeated rounds of microevolution." *Evolution & development* 2.2 (2000): 78-84.

38. Note that biological restraints such as stabilizing selection, morphogenetic, physical, and phyletic constraint can make populations resistant to evolutionary change but not impervious to it.

39. Of course there are other factors at play in addition to microevolution (see note 37), but the point remains that macroevolution is comprised at least in part (if not wholly) of many microevolutionary changes.

40.   Gould, Niles Eldredge-Stephen Jay. "Punctuated equilibria: an alternative to phyletic gradualism." (1972): 82-115.

41.   Ayala, F. (2005). "The Structure of Evolutionary Theory" . *Theology and Science* 3 (1): 104.

42.   Gould, S. J. (1981). "Evolution as Fact and Theory," *Discover* 2 (May): 34-37.

43.   Ibid.

44.   Dawkins, Richard. *The blind watchmaker: Why the evidence of evolution reveals a universe without design.* WW Norton & Company, 1986.

45.   Behe, Michael J. *Darwin's black box: The biochemical challenge to evolution.* Simon and Schuster, 1996.

46.   Ibid, 40.

47.   http://ncse.com/files/pub/legal/kitzmiller/highlights/2005-12-20_Kitzmiller_decision.pdf

48.   Ibid.

49.   Ibid.

50.   Doolittle, Russell F., Yong Jiang, and Justin Nand. "Genomic evidence for a simpler clotting scheme in jawless vertebrates." *Journal of molecular evolution* 66.2 (2008): 185-196.

51.   Hartenstein, Volker. "Blood cells and blood cell development in the animal kingdom." *Annu. Rev. Cell Dev. Biol.* 22 (2006): 677-712.

52.   Ponczek, Michal B., David Gailani, and Russell F. Doolittle. "Evolution of the contact phase of vertebrate blood coagulation." *Journal of Thrombosis and Haemostasis* 6.11 (2008): 1876-1883.

53.   Behe, Michael J. *Darwin's black box: The biochemical challenge to evolution.* Simon and Schuster, 1996, 72.

54.   Miller, Kenneth R. *Finding Darwin's God: A Scientist's Search for Common Ground Between God and Evolution.* Cliff Street Books, 1999, 140.

55.   Musgrave, Ian. "The evolution of the bacterial flagellum." *Why Intelligent Design fails. A scientific critique of the new creationism. Rutgers University Press* (2004): 72-84.

56.   Pallen, Mark J., and Nicholas J. Matzke. "From The Origin of Species to the origin of bacterial flagella." *Nature Reviews Microbiology* 4.1 (2006): 784-790.

57.   Mitchell, David R. "The evolution of eukaryotic cilia and flagella as motile and sensory organelles." *Eukaryotic Membranes and Cytoskeleton.* Springer New York, 2007. 130-140.

58.   Miller, Kenneth R. *Finding Darwin's God: A Scientist's Search for Common Ground Between God and Evolution.* Cliff Street Books, 1999, 164.

59.   Dembski, William A. *Intelligent Design.* InterVarsity Press, 1999, 47.

60.   Elsberry, Wesley, and Jeffrey Shallit. "Information theory, evolutionary computation, and Dembski's "complex specified information"." *Synthese* 178.2 (2011): 237-270.

61.   Rosenhouse, Jason. "How anti-evolutionists abuse mathematics." *The Mathematical Intelligencer* 23.4 (2001): 3-8.

62.   Martin Nowak (2005). Time Magazine, 15 August 2005, 32.

63.   Yedid, Gabriel, and Graham Bell. "Macroevolution simulated with autonomously replicating computer programs." *Nature* 420.6917 (2002): 810-812.

64.   Evolutionary algorithms now surpass human designers New Scientist, 28 July 2007.

65.   Barton, N. H., et al. *Evolution.* Cold Spring Harbor Laboratory Press, 2007.

66.   Newcomb, R. D. et al. 1997. A single amino acid substitution converts a carboxylesterase to an organophosporus hydrolase and confers insecticide resistance on a blowfly. *Proceedings of the National Academy of Science USA* 94: 7464-7468.

67.   Hall, Barry G. "Evolution of a regulated operon in the laboratory." *Genetics* 101.3-4 (1982): 335-344.

68.   Herrel, Anthony, et al. "Rapid large-scale evolutionary divergence in morphology and performance associated with exploitation of a different dietary resource." *Proceedings of the National Academy of Sciences* 105.12 (2008): 4792-4795.

69.   Lizards Rapidly Evolve After Introduction to Island, kimberly johnson natgeo apr 21 2008   http://news.nationalgeographic.com/news/2008/04/080421-lizard-

evolution.html

70. Kinoshita, Shinichi, et al. "Utilization of a Cyclic Dimer and Linear Oligomers of ε-Aminocaproic Acid by Achrornobacter guttatus KI 72."*Agricultural and Biological Chemistry* 39.6 (1975): 1219-1223.

71. Dembski, William A. *Intelligent Design*. InterVarsity Press, 1999.

72. Dembski, William A., 2002. *No Free Lunch*, Lanham, MD: Rowman & Littlefield.

73. Schopf, J. William. "Fossil evidence of Archaean life."*Philosophical Transactions of the Royal Society of London B: Biological Sciences*361.1470 (2006): 869-885.

74. Schopf, J. William, et al. "Evidence of Archean life: stromatolites and microfossils."*Precambrian Research* 158.3 (2007): 141-155.

75. Wacey, David, et al. "Microfossils of sulphur-metabolizing cells in 3.4-billion-year-old rocks of Western Australia."*Nature Geoscience* 4.10 (2011): 698-702.

76. Miller, Stanley L. "A production of amino acids under possible primitive earth conditions."*Science* 117.3046 (1953): 528-529.

77. Parker, Eric T., et al. "Primordial synthesis of amines and amino acids in a 1958 Miller H2S-rich spark discharge experiment."*Proceedings of the National Academy of Sciences* 108.14 (2011): 5526-5531.

78. Cleaves, H. James, et al. "A reassessment of prebiotic organic synthesis in neutral planetary atmospheres."*Origins of Life and Evolution of Biospheres*38.2 (2008): 105-115.

79. Schlesinger, Gordon, and Stanley L. Miller. "Prebiotic synthesis in atmospheres containing CH4, CO, and CO2."*Journal of molecular evolution*19.5 (1983): 376-382.

80. Miller, S. L. "Which organic compounds could have occurred on the prebiotic earth?."*Cold Spring Harbor Symposia on Quantitative Biology*. Vol. 52. Cold Spring Harbor Laboratory Press, 1987.

81. Schmitt-Kopplin, Philippe, et al. "High molecular diversity of extraterrestrial organic matter in Murchison meteorite revealed 40 years after its fall."*Proceedings of the National Academy of Sciences* 107.7 (2010): 2763-2768.

82. Robertson, Michael P., and Gerald F. Joyce. "The origins of the RNA world."*Cold Spring Harbor perspectives in biology* 4.5 (2012): a003608.

83. Orgel, Leslie E. "Some consequences of the RNA world hypothesis."*Origins of Life and Evolution of the Biosphere* 33.2 (2003): 211-218.

84. Spiegelman, S., et al. "The synthesis of a self-propagating and infectious nucleic acid with a purified enzyme."*Proceedings of the National Academy of Sciences* 54.3 (1965): 919-927.

85. Dzieciol, Alicja J., and Stephen Mann. "Designs for life: protocell models in the laboratory."*Chemical Society reviews* 41.1 (2012): 79-85.

86. Strobel, Lee. *The case for a Creator: A journalist investigates scientific evidence that points toward God*. Zondervan, 2004, 229.

CHAPTER THIRTEEN: COMFORT IN THE END

1. Inspired by a Ravi Zacharias message. http://rzim.org/just-thinking/lessons-from-war-in-a-battle-of-ideas

2. Augustine, Saint. *The literal meaning of Genesis*. No. 41. Newman Press, 1982.

IMAGE CREDITS

Cover image from: Pbuergler, Richard Lydekker, and Brehms Tierleben (Wikimedia commons)
Johnny_Automatic (freestockphotos.biz)

Figure 7.1 from: NOAA (Wikimedia commons)

Figure 7.2 from: Sauramo, Matti. Studies on the Quaternary varve sediments in southern Finland. No. 60. Valtioneuvoston Kirjapaino, 1923. (Wikimedia commons)

Figures 7.3 and 8.4 USGS (Wikimedia commons)

Recommended Resources

Biologos.org
The Language of God – Francis Collins
What's so Great About Christianity? - Dinesh D'Souza
Evolution of Adam; Inspiration and Incarnation – Peter Enns
Finding Darwin's God – Kenneth Miller
The Lost World of Genesis One – John Walton

INDEX

Made in the USA
Middletown, DE
23 June 2017